PHYSICAL META.

PHYSICAL METALLURGY

PRINCIPLES AND PRACTICE

[Third Edition]

V. RAGHAVAN

Formerly Professor
Indian Institute of Technology Delhi

PHI Learning Private Limited

Delhi-110092

2016

₹ 250.00

PHYSICAL METALLURGY: Principles and Practice, Third Edition
V. Raghavan

ISBN-978-81-203-5170-7

Twenty-fifth Printing (Third Edition)   ⋯   ⋯   ⋯   **October, 2015**

Published by Asoke K. Ghosh, PHI Learning Private Limited, Rimjhim House, 111, Patparganj Industrial Estate, Delhi-110092 and Printed by Mohan Makhijani at Rekha Printers Private Limited, New Delhi-110020.

Contents

PREFACE

In the Third Edition, as an important update, a new chapter on 'Nanomaterials' (Chapter 8) has been added. Nanotechnology and nanomaterials cover many disciplines such as physical metallurgy, materials science, physics, chemistry, biology, mechanical and electrical engineering and medicine. This chapter of limited scope and length, discusses how and why the properties of conventional materials outlined in earlier chapters get modified in the nanorange. As may be needed, the teacher is free to include a brief account of the nanostate, when discussing individual properties of conventional materials from earlier chapters.

The author wishes to thank the editorial and production team of PHI Learning for their assistance and support in bringing out this edition.

V. RAGHAVAN

PREFACE TO THE FIRST EDITION

Physical Metallurgy deals with the relationship between structure and properties of metals and alloys. It forms a vital link in the processes of making, shaping and heat treating of metals. It thus interfaces with the other areas of metallurgy such as process metallurgy, mechanical metallurgy and engineering metallurgy. Voluminous books are available which deal with the fundamentals of this subject in a detailed and rigorous manner. In addition, there are books dealing with specific topics such as the structural aspect at an advanced level. At the other end, some books present just factual data on the properties and uses of various grades of steels and nonferrous alloys. There is thus a clear need for a book that gives a broad introduction to the subject dealing with the principles at a reasonable depth and at the same time discussing their relationship to practice. This book aims to do that.

All undergraduate students of engineering and metallurgy study phase diagrams, heat treatment principles, mechanical behaviour of alloys, corrosion phenomena, and properties and uses of specific engineering alloys. Undergraduate students of metallurgy have an introductory course on physical metallurgy in their early years. Students of engineering, specially mechanical and chemical engineering, study these topics in one course or the other—whether it be metallurgy, engineering materials or materials science and metallurgy. This book is intended for such students. In addition, the book is designed to be used by students doing self-study and preparing for the associate membership examinations of the Indian Institute of Metals (AMIIM), the Institution of Mechanical Engineers, the Institution of Engineers, etc. The simple style of the book should make it attractive to them.

The opening chapter covers the structural aspects with a discussion of the unit cells of metallic crystals, solid solutions, intermediate phases and structural imperfections. Equilibrium diagrams are introduced in the second chapter, with emphasis on the binary diagrams. Short sections on ternary systems and on experimental methods of determining phase diagrams are included. The major topics under phase changes are solidification, steel transformations and precipitation processes in nonferrous alloys. A separate chapter is devoted to the heat treatment of steels, with a detailed discussion of the concept of hardenability. The chapter on mechanical properties not only covers the basic concepts on deformation and strengthening mechanisms, but also deals with applications to creep, fatigue and fracture. Even though corrosion is a peripheral topic in physical metallurgy, in view of its importance, it is discussed in a separate chapter. The last chapter is totally devoted to practice, giving information on structure, treatment, properties and uses of individual alloys with their specifications, covering most types of steels and common nonferrous alloys.

The author wishes to thank his colleagues in the metallurgy group of the Department of Applied Mechanics for their assistance. Support received from IIT Delhi for preparing the manuscript and the diagrams is acknowledged. Encouragement from Dr. D.P. Antia, Shri C.V. Sundaram and Professor A.K. Seal of the Indian Institute of Metals is appreciated.

New Delhi   V. RAGHAVAN
July 20, 1983

PHYSICAL CONSTANTS

Avogadro's number	$N = 6.023 \times 10^{23}$ mol^{-1}
Boltzmann's constant	$k = 1.380 \times 10^{-23}$ J K^{-1}
	$= 8.614 \times 10^{-5}$ eV K^{-1}
Gas constant	$R = 8.314$ J mol^{-1} K^{-1}
Planck's constant	$h = 6.626 \times 10^{-34}$ J s
Electronic charge	$e = 1.602 \times 10^{-19}$ C
Electron rest mass	$m_0 = 9.109 \times 10^{-31}$ kg
Velocity of light	$c = 2.998 \times 10^{8}$ m s^{-1}
Bohr magneton (magnetic moment)	$\mu_B = 9.273 \times 10^{-24}$ A m^2
Permittivity of free space	$\varepsilon_0 = 8.854 \times 10^{-12}$ F m^{-1}
Permeability of free space	$\mu_0 = 4\pi \times 10^{-7}$ H m^{-1}
	$= 1.257 \times 10^{-6}$ H m^{-1}
Faraday's constant	$F = 96.49$ kC mol^{-1} (of electrons)
Atomic mass unit (amu)	$1/(10^3 N) = 1.660 \times 10^{-27}$ kg
Acceleration due to gravity	$g = 9.81$ m s^{-2}

CONVERSION FACTORS

1 inch	=	25.4 mm
1 nm	=	10^{-9} m
1 Å	=	10^{-10} m $= 0.1$ nm
1°	=	1/57.3 rad
T °C	=	$(T + 273.15)$ K
T °F	=	$5/9(T + 459.67)$ K
1 per °F	=	$9/5$ K^{-1}
1 kgf	=	9.81 N
1 lb	=	4.45 N
1 dyne	=	10^{-5} N
1 dyne/cm	=	10^{-3} N m^{-1}
1 atmosphere	=	0.101 325 MN m^{-2}
1 bar	=	10^{-1} MPa
1 psi	=	6.89 kN m^{-2}
1 ksi (10^3 psi)	=	6.89 MN m^{-2}
1 ton/sq.in.	=	15.46 MN m^{-2}
1 kgf/cm^2	=	98.1 kN m^{-2}
1 kgf/mm^2	=	9.81 MN m^{-2}
1 dyne/cm^2	=	0.1 N m^{-2}
1 torr (mm of Hg)	=	133.3 N m^{-2}
1 kgf/mm$^{3/2}$	=	0.310 MN m$^{-3/2}$
1 ksi $\sqrt{\text{in}}$	=	1.10 MN m$^{-3/2}$
1 eV	=	1.602×10^{-19} J
1 erg	=	10^{-7} J
1 calorie	=	4.18 J
1 eV/entity	=	96.49 kJ mol^{-1}
1 erg/cm	=	10^{-5} J m^{-1}
1 erg/cm^2	=	10^{-3} J m^{-2}
1 erg/cm^3	=	0.1 J m^{-3}
1 lb-in/in^2	=	175 J m^{-2}
1 lb/cu.in	=	27 680 kg m^{-3}
1 cm/cm^3	=	10^4 m m^{-3}

1 mole/cm^2/sec	=	10^4 mol m^{-2} s^{-1}
1 mole/cm^3	=	10^6 mol m^{-3}
1 cm^2/sec	=	10^{-4} m^2 s^{-1}
1 mA/cm^2	=	10 A m^{-2}
1 A hr	=	3.6 kC

Chapter 1

STRUCTURE OF METALS AND ALLOYS

Physical metallurgy deals with the relationship between structure and properties of metals and alloys. The structure is influenced significantly by the process adopted for metal extraction from the ores and subsequent fabrication. The properties of interest are mainly those demanded by engineers such as strength, ductility, toughness and corrosion resistance. Thus physical metallurgy interfaces with areas of process or chemical metallurgy, mechanical metallurgy and engineering metallurgy. It provides a vital link in making, shaping, treating and using metals and alloys. In this introductory textbook, the principles and the corresponding practice of physical metallurgy are outlined in simple terms, without going into a rigorous mathematical treatment of the structure-property relationships.

1.1 NATURE OF METALLIC BONDING

The atoms in a metal are held together by chemical bonds known as *metallic bonds*. The metallic bonding has certain unique characteristics as listed below:

 1. A metallic crystal can be visualized as an array of positive ions, with a common pool of electrons to which all the metal atoms have contributed their outermost electrons. The electrons in this pool have freedom to move through the crystal to any part and virtually in any direction. They are known as *free electrons*. The attractive force between the positive ions and the negatively-charged free electrons is what binds the metal atoms together in the crystal.

1

2. The free electrons carry both electric current and heat through the crystal. They are responsible for *the excellent electrical and thermal conductivity* of metals.

3. The bonds formed by the free electrons are *nondirectional*. There are no constraints about bond angles. An atom in a metallic crystal is bonded to as many neighbours as space permits. This provides considerable flexibility in the directions along which the metal atoms can be displaced during plastic deformation. This is mainly responsible for the unique properties of *high ductility and malleability* that metals possess. For example, gold can be drawn into extremely thin wires; aluminium can be rolled into foils less than 0.1 mm thick.

1.2 CRYSTAL STRUCTURES OF METALS

Approximately three-fourths of the elements in the periodic table are metals. More than two-thirds of them (more than 50) possess relatively simple crystal structures. Understanding these structures and their characteristics is a first step in the study of physical metallurgy.

Body centred cubic (BCC) crystal   The reference unit (called the space lattice) for this crystal is a cube, with lattice points at the eight corners and at the body centre, as shown in Fig. 1.1a. In the unit cell of the crystal, atoms are positioned one at each lattice point, i.e. at the eight corners and at the body centre of the cube, as shown in Fig. 1.1b. The corner atoms are shared by other neighbouring units. As eight units meet at any corner, the share of the unit under consideration for a corner atom is one-eighth, see Fig. 1.1c. The atom at the body centre belongs entirely to the unit.

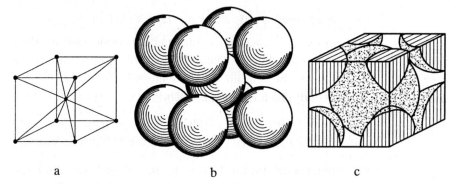

a   b   c

Figure 1.1   The body centred cubic crystal: (a) the BCC space lattice, (b) the unit cell of the BCC crystal, and (c) the sharing of corner atoms by the unit cell.

So, the *effective number* of atoms in the unit cell is

8 (corner atoms) × 1/8 + 1 (body centred atom) = 2

The body centred atom is touching all the corner atoms. Each corner atom in turn is touching eight body centred atoms of the neighbouring cells. The number of nearest neighbours to a given atom is called the *co-ordination number* Z. $Z = 8$ for the BCC crystal.

The distance between nearest atoms is used to define the radius r of the atom. For the BCC crystal, the centre-to-centre distance of nearest neighbours is clearly half of the body diagonal, $a\sqrt{3}/2$, where a is the length of the cube edge known as the *lattice parameter.* Noting from Fig. 1.1b that the nearest neighbours touch each other, we have

$$r = a\sqrt{3}/4$$

for the BCC crystal.

The *packing efficiency* (P.E.) of atoms in the unit cell is defined as

$$\text{P.E.} = \frac{\text{volume of atoms in the unit cell}}{\text{volume of the unit cell}}$$

$$= \frac{2 \times (4/3)\pi \, (a\sqrt{3}/4)^3}{a^3}$$

$$= 0.68$$

The *density* ρ of the crystal can be calculated as follows :

$$\rho = \frac{\text{mass of atoms in the unit cell}}{\text{volume of the unit cell}}$$

For example, for BCC iron at room temperature,

lattice parameter a = 2.87 Å (2.87 × 10^{-10} m)

mass of the Fe atom = 55.85 atomic mass units (amu)

$$1 \text{ amu} = 1.66 \times 10^{-27} \text{ kg}$$

$$\rho_{Fe} = \frac{2 \times 55.85 \times 1.66 \times 10^{-27}}{(2.87 \times 10^{-10})^3}$$

$$= 7840 \text{ kg m}^{-3} = 7.84 \text{ g/cm}^3$$

Typical examples of metals which form BCC crystals are given below.

Metal	Cr	Fe	K	Li	Mo	Na	Nb	Ta	V	W
Lattice parameter, Å	2.88	2.87	5.25	3.51	3.15	4.29	3.30	3.30	3.03	3.16

Face centred cubic (FCC) crystal The face centred cubic space lattice is shown in Fig. 1.2a. In the FCC crystal, there are eight atoms at the eight corners of the cube, with six more atoms located at the six face centres, Fig. 1.2b. A face centred atom is shared by two neighbouring unit cells, for which that face is common, as can be seen from Fig. 1.2c. The effective number of atoms in the FCC unit cell is

8 (corner atoms) × 1/8 + 6 (face centred atoms) × 1/2 = 4

In the FCC crystal, each atom is in contact with twelve neighbours. For example, the face centred atom of the front face in Fig. 1.2b is in contact with the four corner atoms on that face and the four face-centred atoms just behind it (on the top, the bottom and the two side faces of the unit cell). In addition, it is also in contact with four face-centred atoms of the unit cell in front of it (not seen in Fig. 1.2). So the coordination number of the FCC crystal $Z = 12$.

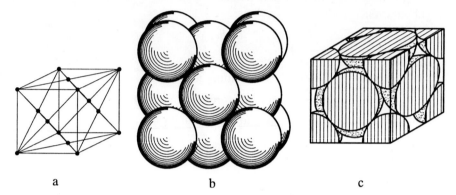

a   b   c

Figure 1.2 The face centred cubic crystal: (a) the FCC space lattice, (b) the unit cell of the FCC crystal, and (c) the sharing of atoms by the unit cell.

The distance between nearest neighbours is half of the face diagonal, $a\sqrt{2}/2$. The radius of the atom is $r = a\sqrt{2}/4$ for the FCC crystal.

The packing efficiency can be shown to be 0.74. Examples of metals forming the FCC crystal are listed below.

Metal	Ag	Al	Au	Cu	Fe(912-1394°C)	Ni	Pb	Pt
Lattice parameter, Å	4.09	4.05	4.08	3.61	3.65	3.52	4.95	3.92

Note that iron possesses more than one crystal form. It is BCC at low temperatures, changes over to the FCC at 912°C and back again to BCC at 1394°C. This phenomenon is called *polymorphism.*

Hexagonal close packed (HCP) crystal The hexagonal space lattice is shown in Fig. 1.3a. The atom arrangements within the HCP unit cell are shown in Fig. 1.3b. There are six atoms at the six corners of the two hexagonal faces and one each at their face centres. There are three atoms in the middle layer (where there are no lattice points). Each corner of the hexagonal prism is shared by six other prisms and the top and the bottom hexagonal faces are shared by two cells, Fig. 1.3c. The effective number of atoms in the HCP unit cell is

12 (corner atoms) × 1/6 + 2 (face centred atoms) × 1/2 +
3 (middle layer atoms within the cell)* = 6.

*Thin slices of the three middle-layer atoms fall outside the unit cell, but these are exactly compensated by three thin slices of outside atoms falling within the unit cell.

As in the FCC crystal, each atom here is in contact with twelve nearest neighbours. For example, referring to Fig. 1.3b, the central atom on the top hexagonal face touches the six surrounding atoms on the same face, three in the middle layer and three in the plane above (not shown), yielding $Z = 12$.

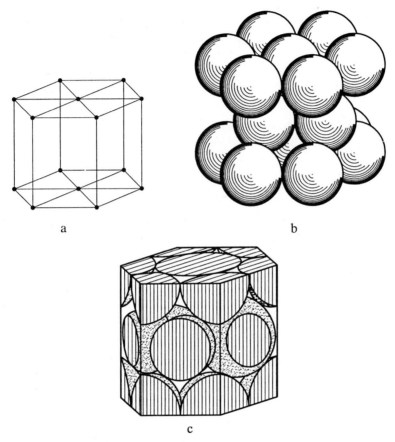

Figure 1.3 The hexagonal close packed crystal: (a) the hexagonal space lattice, (b) the HCP unit cell, and (c) the sharing of atoms by the unit cell.

The distance between nearest neighbours is the side of the hexagon a. So, $r = a/2$ for the HCP crystal.

The height of the prism gives the second lattice parameter c. The ideal packing efficiency can be shown to be the same as for the FCC crystal (0.74). Typical examples of HCP crystals and their lattice parameters are listed below.

Metal	Be	Cd	Mg	Ti (below 882°C)	Zn	Zr
a, Å	2.29	2.98	3.21	2.95	2.66	3.23
c, Å	3.58	5.62	5.21	4.68	4.95	5.15
c/a	1.56	1.89	1.62	1.59	1.86	1.59

Other less-commonly occurring metallic crystal structures include the tetragonal, the orthorhombic and the rhombohedral crystals. In the tetragonal cell, two sides of the unit cell are equal, but the third side is of a different length. In the orthorhombic unit cell, all the three sides are of different lengths. The angles between the axes in these two unit cells are the same as in the cubic crystal (90°). In the rhombohedral cell, the three axes are of the same length and the angles between axes are equal to one another, but not 90°.

Geometry of close packing   For a fuller understanding of the FCC and HCP crystalline arrangements, we need to examine the geometry of close packing (meaning closest packing). Figure 1.4a shows a close packed plane A of equal-sized spheres. The spheres cannot be put any closer than they are in Fig. 1.4a. In building a three-dimensional structure, another close packed plane can be placed over the first, such that its spheres fit into the triangular cavities between the spheres of the first layer. There are two sets of such cavities, designated B and C in Fig. 1.4a. The second plane of atoms, Fig. 1.4b or c, can rest vertically over either the B positions or the C positions. If we assume that they rest over B positions, then the third close packed plane can be stacked on the second in two ways. The atoms of the third plane can be vertically over the C positions or alternatively over the first-plane atoms, i.e. over A positions. These two arrangements are designated *ABC* and *ABA* stackings respectively.

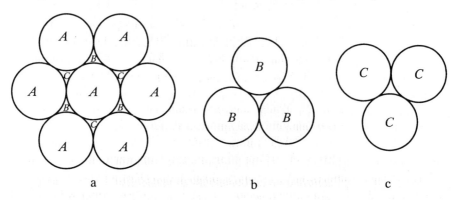

a   b   c

Figure 1.4   The geometry of close packing.

The FCC crystal is a stacking of close packed planes in the sequence ... *ABCABC*.... In Fig. 1.5, the correspondence between the ...*ABCABC*... stacking and the atoms of the unit cell is shown. This figure should be compared with Fig. 1.2b, where the atoms are drawn to their correct sizes. The close packed planes are inclined at an angle to the cube faces and are known as *octahedral planes*.

The HCP crystal is a stacking of close packed planes in the sequence ...*ABABA*.... Referring to Fig. 1.3b, if we call the close packed plane corresponding to the bottom hexagonal face A, it is easily seen that the atoms of the top hexagonal layer are vertically over those of the bottom layer and are, therefore, to be designated also as *A*. The three atoms in the middle fit into the triangular cavities between the top and the bottom layers and are *B* plane atoms. The *C* positions are not used in this stacking.

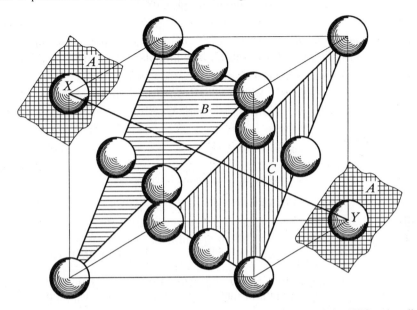

Figure 1.5 The correspondence between ...*ABCA*... stacking and the FCC unit cell. The body diagonal *XY* is perpendicular to the close packed planes.

The ideal *c/a* ratio of HCP stacking is 1.633. The ratios in real crystals, however, vary significantly from the ideal value, see table on page 5.

Miller indices   The method devised by Miller is widely used to denote directions and planes in crystals. Let the vector **r** in Fig. 1.6a represent a direction in a crystal (not cubic in this case). To find the Miller indices of this direction, the components of the vector along the three axes are determined as multiples of the unit vector corresponding to each direction.

The vector **r** has a component of 2 along the **a**-axis, 1 along **b** and 1 along **c**. Note that the absolute magnitudes of the components along **b** and **c** are not the same, but they are unity, when expressed as multiples of the corresponding unit vectors. The Miller indices of this direction is given by [211], where the square brackets stand for a direction. If there is a negative component, it is denoted by a bar placed on top of the appropriate number.

In cubic crystals, it is convenient to have a notation to specify a *family of directions*. The family is denoted by pointed brackets, e.g. <211> stands for [211], [21$\bar{1}$], [121], [11$\bar{2}$], [121], etc. giving all combinations of the indices both positive and negative. The cube edges in the unit cell are represented by <100>, the face diagonals by <110> and the body diagonals by <111>.

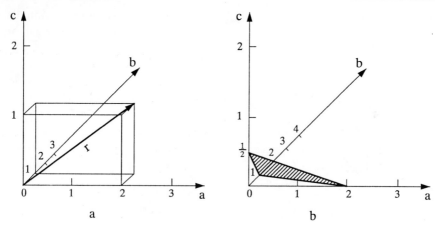

Figure 1.6 The Miller indices of (a) a crystal direction and (b) a crystal plane.

For determining the Miller indices of a plane in a crystal, the following procedure is used. Referring to Fig. 1.6b, the steps are :

1. Find the *intercepts* of the plane on the three coordinate axes   2   1   ½
2. Take reciprocals   ½   1   2
3. Convert into smallest integers in the same ratio   1   2   4
4. Enclose in parentheses   (124)

A family of planes is denoted by curly brackets { }. For example, the faces of a cube are denoted by {100}. The octahedral planes in Fig. 1.5 are {111}.

Example ────────────────────────────────

1. Draw a close packed plane within the unit cell of an FCC crystal and give its Miller indices.

2. Mark the close packed directions that lie on this plane and give their Miller indices.

3. Draw a (110) plane within the same unit cell and find the line of intersection of the two planes.

Solution

1. Referring to Fig. 1.5, the close packed planes in the FCC crystal are of the {111} type. Using D as the origin in Fig. 1.7, the Miller indices of the plane sketched is $(\bar{1}\,\bar{1}\,1)$.

2. The atoms are touching one another along the face diagonals of an FCC crystal. There are three face diagonals that lie on the above plane, corresponding to the three close packed directions. Their Miller indices are :

    Taking origin   at A, $\mathbf{AB} = [011]$

                      at B, $\mathbf{BC} = [\bar{1}\,0\,\bar{1}]$

                      at C, $\mathbf{CA} = [1\,\bar{1}\,0]$

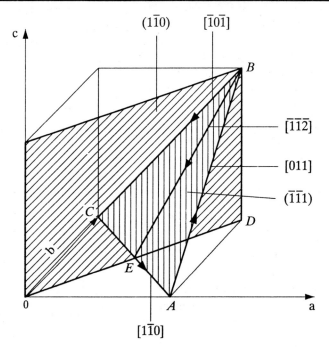

Figure 1.7 Planes and directions within the cubic unit cell.

3. Taking C as the origin, the $(1\bar{1}0)$ plane is drawn. The line of intersection of the two planes is BE.

Taking origin at B, $\mathbf{BE} = [\bar{1}\,\bar{1}\,\bar{2}]$

Note: As the choice of origin is arbitrary, it is chosen such that the directions start from the origin and the planes make intercepts on the three axes within the unit cell.

Miller-Bravais indices For hexagonal crystals, a four-digit notation *hkil*, known as Miller-Bravais indices, is used. The use of such a notation enables crystallographically equivalent planes or directions in a hexagonal crystal to be denoted by the same set of indices. Three of the axes $\mathbf{a}_1$, $\mathbf{a}_2$ and $\mathbf{a}_3$ are coplanar and lie on the basal plane of the hexagonal prism, Fig. 1.3, with a 120° angle between them. The fourth axis is the $\mathbf{c}$ axis perpendicular to the basal plane.

The determination of the Miller-Bravais indices is illustrated in Fig. 1.8 for the two examples given below. The indices of a prismatic plane (one of the vertical faces of the prism) is of the type $(10\bar{1}0)$. It makes an intercept of 1 and -1 along $\mathbf{a}_1$ and $\mathbf{a}_3$ axes respectively and is parallel to the $\mathbf{a}_2$ and $\mathbf{c}$ axes. Note that the use of three coplanar vectors results in the condition that $h + k = -i$.

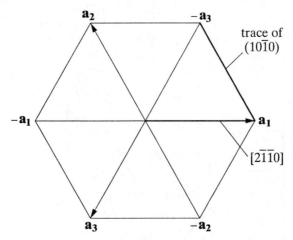

Figure 1.8 The Miller-Bravais indices for hexagonal crystals.

The indices of a direction that lie along one of the three **a** axes (parallel to a side of the hexagonal face) are of the type $[2\,\bar{1}\,\bar{1}\,0]$. For this example, the direction is parallel to the $\mathbf{a}_1$ axis and is resolved into components along $\mathbf{a}_2$ and $\mathbf{a}_3$. Each of these components being –1, the value of the first index corresponding to the $\mathbf{a}_1$ axis can be obtained as $-(-1-1) = 2$ from the condition that $h + k = -i$. This yields $[2\,\bar{1}\,\bar{1}\,0]$.

1.3 STRUCTURE OF ALLOYS

Types of solid solutions When two metals are melted together and crystallized, a single crystal structure may form. In the unit cell of this crystal, both the metal atoms are present in proportion to their concentration. This structure is known as a *solid solution*.

Figure 1.9 illustrates three types of solid solutions. Figure 1.9a is a *random substitutional* solid solution. Here the solute atoms (shown shaded) have substituted randomly for the parent atoms (not shaded) on their sites. Figure 1.9b shows an *ordered* (substitutional) solid solution. Here, the solute and the solvent atoms are arranged in a regular fashion on the atomic sites. Perfect order is possible, only when the two metals are mixed in some fixed proportion like 1:1, 3:1, etc.

Figure 1.9c shows an *interstitial* solid solution. Here, the solute atoms are much smaller than the parent atoms and have occupied randomly the interstitial voids between parent atoms. In the FCC unit cell, one set of interstitial voids is located at the mid-points of the cube edges, $(0, 0, \frac{1}{2})$, $(0, \frac{1}{2}, 0)$, $(\frac{1}{2}, 0, 0)$ etc. and at the body centre $(\frac{1}{2}, \frac{1}{2}, \frac{1}{2})$. These voids are called *octahedral voids*. The size of the atom that can fit into an octahedral void without distortion is $0.414r$, where r is the radius of the parent atoms that surround the void. Smaller tetrahedral voids are located on the body diagonals at (¼, ¼, ¼), (¾, ¾, ¾) and other equivalent positions in the FCC unit cell. The size of the atom that can fit the tetrahedral void is $0.225r$. In the HCP crystal, the same types of octahedral and tetrahedral voids are present. In the BCC crystal, the tetrahedral voids at (½, ¼, 0) positions are larger ($0.29r$), as compared to the octahedral voids at (0, 0, ½) of size $0.15r$. Carbon atoms in BCC iron are located at the smaller (0, 0, ½) voids.

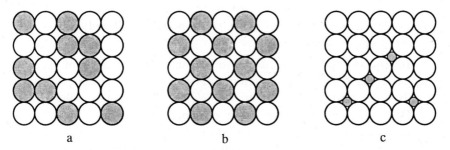

| a | b | c |

Figure 1.9   (a) Random substitutional solid solution, (b) ordered substitutional solid solution, and (c) interstitial solid solution.

Hume Rothery's rules   Hume Rothery studied a number of alloy systems and formulated the conditions that favour *extensive substitutional solid solubility*. These are known as Hume Rothery rules and are listed below.

1. The size difference between the parent atom and the solute atom must be less than 15%.

2. The electronegativity difference between the metals must be small.

3. The crystal structure of the metals and the valency of the atoms must be the same.

The more is the size difference, the more intense is the stress field around the solute atom. This is valid for both large and small atoms. A large atom induces a compressive stress field around it, whereas a small atom induces a tensile stress field. The stress field increases the potential energy of the crystal. So, *the solid solubility becomes more limited, as the size difference increases*.

The electronegativity difference between two elements can be computed from Pauling's electronegativity numbers. This difference is usually small between typical metallic elements.

Complete solid solubility, i.e. the mixing of the two atoms in all proportions can evidently occur only when the crystal structures are identical. In the unit cell of one of the metals, the atoms can be continuously substituted by the other, till the pure crystal of the substituting atom is obtained.

The valency must be the same for extensive solid solubility. When the valencies are different, it is generally found that an excess of electrons is readily tolerated rather than a deficiency of bonding electrons. For example, zinc with two valence electrons dissolves up to 38% in copper, whereas copper with one valence electron dissolves only about 3% in zinc.

Free energy of solid solutions When two metals A and B are mixed to form a solid solution, the Gibbs free energy G changes. The change in free energy (the free energy of the solid solution minus the free energies of the two pure metals) is called the free energy of mixing ΔG_{mix}. It can be written in terms of the enthalpy of mixing ΔH_{mix} and the entropy of mixing ΔS_{mix}:

$$\Delta G_{mix} = \Delta H_{mix} - T\Delta S_{mix} \tag{1.1}$$

1. For an *ideal solution*, $\Delta H_{mix} = 0$. Here, the A-A, B-B and A-B bonds are all *equally* favoured.

2. If $\Delta H_{mix} > 0$ (positive deviation from ideality), the formation of like bonds (A-A and B-B bonds) is preferred. For small positive values of ΔH_{mix}, there is a tendency for like atoms to *cluster* together in the solid solution. On an average, an A atom has more A neighbours than is the case for a perfectly random solid solution. At low temperatures or for large positive values of ΔH_{mix}, the clustering tendency increases. Eventually, *immiscibility* results. The solid solution splits into two separate phases, one rich in A and the other rich in B.

3. If $\Delta H_{mix} < 0$ (negative deviation from ideality), the formation of unlike bonds (A-B bonds) is preferred. Here, there is a tendency for *short range ordering*, i.e. A and B atoms show a preference to become nearest neighbours. At low temperatures, long range order may set in and an ordered solid solution may form. If ΔH_{mix} is only slightly negative, the ordering tendency may be so weak that long range ordering does not occur at any temperature. If ΔH_{mix} has a large negative value, the alloy may remain in the fully ordered state right up to the melting point, behaving like a chemical compound.

On mixing two metals at a constant temperature, a large number of distinguishable configurations w of equal potential energy result. The configurational entropy S_c is given by

$$S_c = k \ln w \tag{1.2}$$

where k is Boltzmann's constant. The entropy of mixing X_A mole fraction of A with X_B mole fraction of B ($X_A + X_B = 1$) in a random solid solution turns out to be

$$\Delta S_{mix} = - R (X_A \ln X_A + X_B \ln X_B) \tag{1.3}$$

X_A and X_B being fractions, the entropy of mixing is always positive. It tends to lower the free energy according to Eq. (1.1).

An ideal solid solution is random. For small deviations from ideality (either positive or negative), the solid solution can still be taken to be random for the purpose of computing the entropy of mixing. This is called a *regular solution* approximation. The free energy of mixing is then given by

$$\Delta G_{mix} = \Delta H_{mix} + RT(X_A \ln X_A + X_B \ln X_B) \tag{1.4}$$

The variation in the free energy of a solid solution as a function of composition is sketched schematically in Fig. 1.10. Figure 1.10a is for an ideal solution, where $\Delta H_{mix} = 0$. The free energy decreases with increasing concentration of either element reaching a minimum at the mid-composition, where the entropy of mixing is a maximum. Figure 1.10b is a case where $\Delta H_{mix} < 0$. The free energy curve has the same shape as in Fig. 1.10a, but more U-shaped. Figure 1.10c is for a solution where $\Delta H_{mix} > 0$. The free energy curve decreases initially at the two pure ends due to the dominance of the entropy term. With increasing concentration, however, the positive ΔH_{mix} term dominates and the free energy curve has two minima and a maximum. There is no complete solid solubility in this case. The maximum solid solubilities are obtained by drawing the *common tangent xy* to the free energy curve, Fig. 1.10c. The compositions corresponding to the points of tangency c_1 and c_2 give the limit of solubility at the two ends respectively. In between c_1 and c_2, the alloy is stable only as a mixture of two solid solutions of composition c_1 and c_2. With increasing temperature, however, the entropy term may dominate over the enthalpy term for all compositions, the free energy curve may become U-shaped and a single solid solution may become stable over the entire composition range.

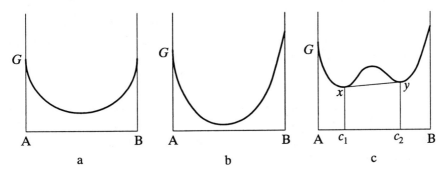

Figure 1.10 Free energy of solid solutions: (a) enthalpy of mixing ΔH_{mix} is zero (ideal solution), (b) ΔH_{mix} is negative, and (c) ΔH_{mix} is positive.

Intermediate phases Intermediate phases refer to alloy crystal structures which are different from either of the parent crystals. Some intermediate phases have a fixed composition and are called *intermetallic compounds*. Quite often, however, the intermediate phases have a significant composition range.

Only a few intermetallic compounds obey the *normal rules of valency*. Many of these are based on the cubic structures of sodium chloride (NaCl) or calcium fluoride (CaF_2). In the NaCl structure, the chlorine ions are at the FCC positions of the cubic unit cell and the sodium ions are at the octahedral voids. Examples of such intermediate phases are MgSe, PbSe and CdTe. In the CaF_2 structure, the calcium ions are at the FCC positions and the fluorine ions are at the tetrahedral void positions. Examples are Mg_2Si, Mg_2Sn, Cu_2S and Be_2C.

The *nickel arsenide* (NiAs) structure is often formed by the transition metals alloyed with the metalloids of the V and VI columns such as As, Bi, Sb, Se and

Te. The structure has the HCP stacking sequence with alternate layers of metal and metalloid atoms. These phases have a fairly wide range of solubility. Examples are CrSb, CuSn and MnSe.

Electron phases (also called electron compounds or Hume Rothery compounds) have a wide range of solubility. They occur at certain definite values of valence electrons to atom ratio in the alloy such as 3:2, 21:13 and 7:4. Typical examples are CuZn (3:2), Cu_5Zn_8 (21:13) and $CuZn_3$ (7:4).

Laves phases possess one of the three related structures with the general formula AB_2. Examples of the three prototype structures based on magnesium are: $MgCu_2$ (cubic), $MgZn_2$ (hexagonal) and $MgNi_2$ (hexagonal).

The *sigma phase* has a complex crystal structure and is very brittle. The unit cell is tetragonal with 30 atoms in the cell. This phase is a source of embrittlement in stainless steels.

Alloy carbides and nitrides form very hard and brittle compounds. They are often cubic with the formula MX, with the metal atoms (M) in FCC positions and the carbon or nitrogen (X) in interstitial positions (octahedral or tetrahedral). Examples are TiC, VC, NbC, TiN, VN and NbN. Examples of carbides with other structures are $Cr_{23}C_6$, Cr_7C_3, MoC and WC.

Like other solid solutions, intermediate phases may remain disordered at high temperatures and become ordered at low temperatures. The β (BCC) phase of the Cu-Zn alloy system is a typical example. The composition of β is around 50Cu50Zn. At temperatures above 465°C, the copper and zinc atoms are randomly distributed on the BCC sites. At lower temperatures, an ordered structure forms with the zinc atoms at the body corners and the copper atoms at the body centres (or vice versa). When this occurs, extra lines appear in the diffraction pattern, as the ordered structure corresponds to a simple cubic space lattice (with lattice points at the eight corners of the cube only) rather than the BCC space lattice. The ordered compound is known as a *superlattice*, as it gives rise to additional diffraction lines.

In general, intermetallic compounds and ordered solid solutions possess little ductility and are relatively brittle phases. They are useful for increasing the strength of a ductile matrix, but at the cost of reduced ductility.

1.4 IMPERFECTIONS IN CRYSTALS

Imperfections in crystals can be classified according to their geometry as point, line and surface imperfections. The characteristics of different imperfections are briefly considered below.

Point imperfections   There are point-like regions of distortion in the crystal. The common types are :

   (a) vacancy
   (b) interstitialcy

(c) interstitial impurity, and

(d) substitutional impurity

A *vacancy* is an atomic site from which the atom is missing, *a* in Fig. 1.11. An *interstitialcy* refers to an atom displaced from a regular site into an interstitial site, *b* in Fig. 1.11. An *interstitial impurity* is a small atom occupying an interstitial void space between parent atoms of the crystal, *c* in Fig. 1.11. A *substitutional impurity* is an impurity atom that has substituted for one of the parent atoms on a regular atomic site, *d* in the figure.

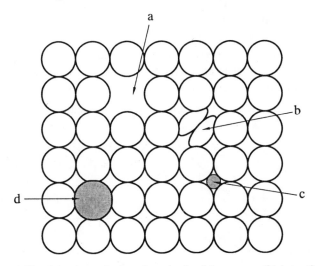

Figure 1.11 Point imperfections in crystals: (a) vacancy, (b) interstitialcy, (c) interstitial impurity, and (d) susbstitutional impurity.

Point imperfections increase significantly the configurational entropy of the crystal and thereby lower its free energy. So, a certain number *n* of point imperfections is in thermodynamic equilibrium in the crystal at a given temperature. For example, the fraction of vacancies n/N in a crystal at temperature T is given by

$$\frac{n}{N} = \exp\left(-\frac{\Delta H_f}{kT}\right) \tag{1.5}$$

where N is the total number of atomic sites and ΔH_f is the enthalpy of formation of a vacancy and is equal to the reversible work done at constant pressure in bringing an atom from inside the crystal to the surface.

Dislocations Line imperfections are known as dislocations. The geometry of dislocations can be understood with reference to the two limiting straight line types:

1. the edge dislocation, and
2. the screw dislocation

Figure 1.12a shows an *edge dislocation* extending from the front to the back face of the crystal. It is the distorted region all along the edge of an *incomplete plane* in the crystal. The atoms just above the edge are in compression, whereas those just below are in tension. A dislocation is characterized by a vector known as the *Burgers vector*. Figure 1.12a illustrates the procedure for determining the Burgers vector **b**. A Burgers circuit is drawn around the dislocation line. The vector needed to close the circuit, *QP*, is the Burgers vector of the dislocation. It is *perpendicular* to the edge dislocation line. A positive or a negative edge dislocation is defined, depending on whether the incomplete plane is from the top or from the bottom of the crystal. They are symbolically denoted by ⊥ and ⊤ respectively.

Figure 1.12b shows a *screw dislocation* extending from the right to the left side face of the crystal. It is characterized by a shear distortion. The Burgers vector is *parallel* to the screw dislocation line, as illustrated in the figure. Positive and negative screw dislocations are symbolically denoted by (⟳ and ⟲).

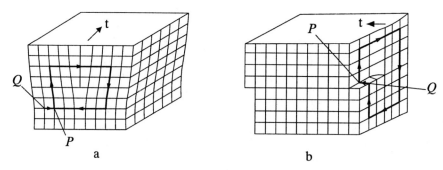

a   b

Figure 1.12 Edge and screw dislocations. The direction of the dislocation line lies along the direction vector **t**.

In general, the dislocations in real crystals are some combination of the edge and the screw types. These are called *mixed dislocations*. The Burgers vector of a mixed dislocation remains *invariant* along the length of the dislocation line. It can be resolved into two components, one parallel to the dislocation line (screw component) and the other perpendicular to the line (edge component). Two dislocations of opposite sign (either edge or screw) lying on the same plane attract and can mutually annihilate each other.

The elastic strain energy E per unit length of a dislocation line is

$$E = \frac{\mu b^2}{2} \tag{1.6}$$

where μ is the shear modulus of the crystal and b is the magnitude of the Burgers vector. As the elastic energy is proportional to the square of the Burgers vector, dislocations tend to have as small a Burgers vector as possible. The smallest distance between any two atomic sites lies along the close packed directions. Accordingly, the Burgers vector of full dislocations lies along close packed directions in typical crystals as listed below:

Crystal	BCC	FCC	HCP
Burgers vector	½ <111>	½ <110>	<11$\overline{2}$0>

Dislocations are present in crystals due to accidents during the growth of the crystal. The dislocation density in an annealed crystal ranges from 10^6 to 10^{10} m m^{-3}. If the growth of the crystal is done very slowly and carefully and if the volume of the grown crystal is small, many of the accidents can be averted. In a few cases, perfect crystals that are totally free of dislocations can be grown.

Dislocations play an important role in the plastic deformation of metals and alloys. Very thin perfect crystals that are totally free of dislocations known as *whiskers* possess very high strength. In ordinary crystals, however, the presence of even a few dislocations is sufficient to make the crystal weak. Dislocations move at relatively low stresses and cause plastic deformation. The methods of strengthening crystalline materials against this inherent weakness aim at increasing the resistance to dislocation motion.

The motion of a dislocation in response to an externally applied stress on a plane containing the Burgers vector and the dislocation line (called the slip plane) is known as *glide motion*. The atoms near the dislocation configuration are conserved during glide motion. Edge dislocations and mixed dislocations have uniquely defined slip planes. As the Burgers vector and the dislocation line are parallel in the case of a screw dislocation, there is *no uniquely defined slip plane* in this case. A screw dislocation can cross-glide or *cross-slip* from one slip plane to another, as illustrated in Fig. 1.13. The screw dislocation first

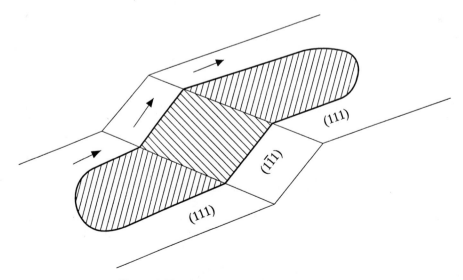

Figure 1.13 Cross-slip of a screw dislocation.
The hatched areas are the slipped regions.

glides on a (111) plane causing slip over the hatched region. It then cross-slips on to a nonparallel (1 $\bar{1}$ 1) plane. In the double cross-slip process illustrated, it again cross-slips back to a (111) plane, which is parallel to the initial plane.

Edge dislocations cannot cross-slip. When they move on a plane other than the slip plane, the motion involves *addition or subtraction of atoms to the edge*. This motion is nonconservative and is called *climb motion*. Addition or subtraction of atoms generally occurs at an atomic step called *jog* on the edge of the incomplete plane, Fig. 1.14. Edge dislocations climb up or climb down, depending on whether the incomplete plane shrinks or increases in extent. Addition of atoms is required for climbing down, whereas subtraction of atoms (or equivalently addition of vacancies) is required for climbing up. In Fig. 1.14, moving of the jog to the left is equivalent to climbing down; movement to the right is climbing up. Climb can clearly occur only when there is sufficient thermal energy for the diffusion of atoms to or away from the edge of the incomplete plane. It is, therefore, an important process in high temperature deformation known as *creep*, discussed under Sec. 5.4.

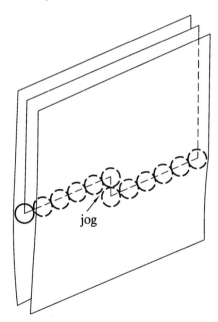

Figure 1.14   Jog is a step on the edge of the incomplete
plane of an edge dislocation.

Partial dislocations and stacking faults   Full dislocations described above have an integral lattice translation as the Burgers vector. For partial (or imperfect) dislocations, the Burgers vector is a fraction of an interatomic distance. As the elastic energy of dislocations is proportional to the square of their Burgers vector, the splitting of a full dislocation b_1 into two partial dislocations b_2 and b_3 is favoured energetically, when

$$b_1^2 > b_2^2 + b_3^2$$

A typical example of such a dislocation is the splitting of a full dislocation in an FCC crystal into two *Shockley partials*:

$$\tfrac{1}{2}[110] \rightarrow 1/6[2\,1\,\overline{1}] + 1/6[121]$$

The Burgers vectors of the Shockley partials lie on the slip plane (which is a close-packed plane in FCC crystals). They repel and tend to move away from each other. In the region of the slip plane between the two partials, the slip displacement is not a full interatomic distance. The region becomes a planar surface imperfection known as a *stacking fault*. The stacking sequence across the slip plane in the region between the two partials becomes ...*ABCACABC*..., i.e. a thin region of HCP stacking *CACA* occurs in the FCC crystal. Locally the stacking is improper or faulty, and so this region is called a stacking fault. Stacking faults possess surface energy. The surface tension due to this tends to minimize the area of the faulted region. Stacking fault energies for typical metals and alloys are given below.

Metal	Al	Cu	Ni	Cu25Zn	Fe18Cr8Ni
Stacking fault energy, J m^{-2}	0.2	0.04	0.03	0.007	0.002

The distance between the two Shockley partials is determined by a balance between the repulsive force acting on the partials and the attractive force due to the surface tension tending to shrink the area of the faulted region. The equilibrium distance of separation between the partials thus depends on the stacking fault energy. *The distance is less when stacking fault energy is high.* This fact has important consequences in the plastic deformation mechanisms. In order to cross-slip, a dissociated screw dislocation has to recombine over a critical distance and this is easier if the distance of separation between the partials is less. So, *cross-slip is easier in metals with a high stacking fault energy.*

High angle grain boundaries   When the orientation difference between two neighbouring crystals is more than 10–15°, the boundary between them is generally a curved surface known as a high angle *grain boundary*, Fig. 1.15. During solidification or recrystallization, crystals nucleate at different points of the parent phase independently of one another and grow until the neighbouring crystals impinge. The atoms that are caught in the boundary region take up uncoordinated positions, belonging to neither of the neighbouring crystals. In close packed crystals, the average number of nearest neighbours to an atom in the boundary region is 11, as compared to 12 inside the crystal. This missing bond accounts for the grain boundary energy, which is in the range of 0.5–1.0 J m^{-2} for most metals.

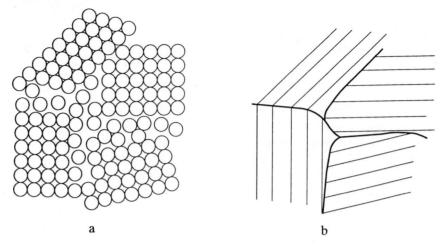

a   b

Figure 1.15 Grain boundaries in a polycrystalline metal. The atom
arrangements at the boundaries are distorted and unrelated.

The size of the grains in a polycrystalline metal greatly influences a number
of its mechanical and chemical properties. Grain sizes are specified using an
ASTM (American Society for Testing and Materials) designation. If n is the
ASTM *grain size number*, 2^{n-1} grains are present per square inch in the microstructure of the metal viewed under a magnification of 100 X (linear). Noting
that 1 sq.in. = 645 mm^2, for an ASTM grain size number of 7, 2^{n-1} = 64. There
are 64 × 10^4 grains per sq.in. or ~ 10^3 grains per mm^2. Along a length of one
mm, there are $\sqrt{10^3}$ grains. The average grain diameter is thus approximately
$1/\sqrt{10^3}$ = 0.03 mm.

Planar boundaries   One type of planar boundary, the stacking fault, has already
been discussed in relation to partial dislocations. The other types are described
below.

When the orientation difference between neighbouring crystals is less than
10°, the boundary is described as a low angle boundary. *Tilt boundaries* are
arrays of parallel edge dislocations of the same sign one below the other as
shown in Fig. 1.16. The tilt angle θ is given by

$$\tan \theta = \frac{b}{h} \tag{1.7}$$

where b is the Burgers vector of the edge dislocations and h is the vertical
distance of separation between two neighbouring edge dislocations on the
boundary. Tilt boundaries form during a process called *recovery*, when excess
dislocations of the same sign arrange themselves one below the other. *Twist
boundaries* refer to similar low angle boundaries formed by arrays of screw
dislocations.

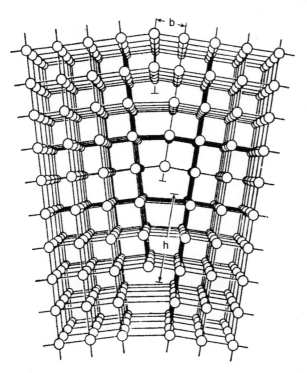

Figure 1.16   A tilt boundary consists of an array of edge dislocations of the same sign vertically one above the other.

When the arrangement of atoms on one side of a boundary is a mirror image of that on the other side, the boundary is known as a *twin boundary*, Fig. 1.17. Twin boundaries occur in pairs, where the orientation difference introduced by one twin of a pair is nullified by the other. Twin boundaries form during annealing (called annealing twins) or during deformation (deformation twins). The energy of twin boundaries is in the range of 0.01–0.05 J m^{-2}.

When the crystal structures of the two metals are similar and the lattice parameters are nearly equal, the boundary between the two crystals (called an interface) is *coherent*, with a *one-to-one correspondence of atoms* across the interface. The surface energy of this interface is small, in the range of 0.01–0.05 J m^{-2}. When there is no such similarity or matching of the two metals, the interface is *incoherent* and is similar in structure and energy to large angle grain boundaries.

Interaction between crystal imperfections   Different types of imperfections in crystals can interact with one another. The interaction is always such that the total distortional energy of the interacting imperfections is lowered.

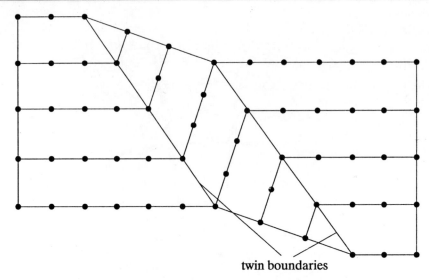

twin boundaries

Figure 1.17 The atomic arrangement on one side of a twin boundary
is a mirror reflection of that on the other side.

A large substitutional atom can interact with a vacancy in the same crystal to lower the distortional energy. The two defects stay together in close proximity. Point imperfections interact with the distortional geometry associated with dislocations. For example, a large substitutional atom can lower its distortional energy by staying in the tensile region just below the edge of the incomplete plane of an edge dislocation. An interstitial atom, that is too large for the void it occupies, can similarly lower its energy by staying in the core of an edge dislocation. Such an effect is particularly marked in low carbon and mild steels, where the oversized (interstitial) carbon atoms tend to segregate in voids around the tensile region of edge dislocations. Such solute atmospheres around dislocations are known as *Cottrell atmospheres*. Point imperfections also segregate at grain boundaries as the structure at the boundary is more open than that in the interior of the crystal. Such segregation results in several metallurgically important effects such as the solute drag effect on a migrating grain boundary and intergranular cracking.

Dislocations lie on slip planes within the crystal. As the crystal orientation across a grain boundary (or a twin boundary) changes abruptly, a dislocation on a slip plane in any one grain cannot cross the boundary and move on to the same slip plane of the next grain. Because of this, moving dislocations get piled up against grain boundaries. This results in an important influence of grain size on the yield strength of metals and alloys.

1.5 EXPERIMENTAL STUDY OF STRUCTURE

The structure seen with the naked eye or under low magnification by acid etching of steel bars, billets, castings and forgings is called *macrostructure*. It reveals pipes, segregation, flakes, cracks, inclusions, porosity and decarburized layers. A solution consisting of one part of HCl and one part of water is the most widely used etchant. For studying the structure at a finer level, a number of physical techniques are used.

The optical microscope   As metals are opaque, they can be viewed under an optical microscope only in reflected light. In the optical microscope, Fig. 1.18a, light from a lamp gets reflected by a semi-silvered glass kept at a 45° tilt, passes through the objective and then on to the specimen surface. It is reflected back by the metal surface and partly transmitted through the semi-silvered glass to the eyepiece. A *metallograph* is an instrument in which the structure as seen under the microscope called the *microstructure* is photographed.

To examine the metal specimen properly, the surface should be polished to a high degree of reflectivity. This is done by polishing the surface on successively finer grades of emery papers. Final polishing is done on cloth impregnated with a very fine powder of alumina or diamond. After polishing, the specimen is etched with a dilute acid to selectively attack the features of the structure. Figure 1.18b shows the profile of a polished surface of a polycrystalline sample after etching. The grain boundaries are selectively attacked by the etchant, as they

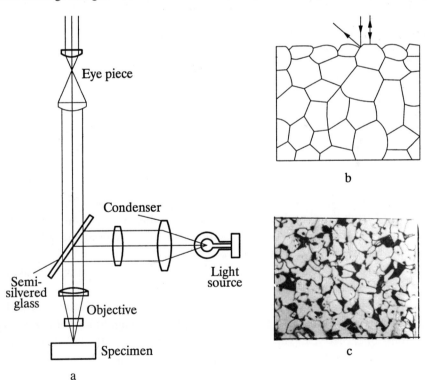

Figure 1.18   (a) The optical microscope. (b) Etching produces grooves along grain boundaries and the light that falls on the grooves is not reflected back into the objective. (c) The network of dark lines are grain boundaries as seen under the optical microscope.

possess a higher energy than the interior of the crystal. No light is reflected from the grooves that form along grain boundaries and they appear as a network of dark lines under the microscope, Fig. 1.18c. Sometimes, the grains are also attacked at different rates depending on their orientation with respect to the plane of observation. They may reflect different amounts of light and the grain structure can be identified.

A number of accessories and attachments are available to the optical microscope. It continues to be an important tool for the study of the structure, despite the advances in recent years in high resolution microscopes.

The electron microscope The source of illumination in an optical microscope is the ordinary visible light with a wavelength of about 5000 Å. In an electron microscope, the source of illumination is a beam of electrons with a wavelength of about 0.05 Å. As the resolving power of a microscope is inversely proportional to the wavelength of the illumination used, the electron microscope has a much better resolving power and can show up details as small as 10 Å. In addition to this, the electron microscope provides facilities for *selected area diffraction*, i.e. a diffraction pattern can be obtained from a very small particle in the structure along with its micrograph.

The illuminating system is the *electron gun*, Fig. 1.19a, consisting of a heated filament held at a high accelerating potential of 100–200 kV.

Magnetic lenses are used in the electron microscope. The condenser lenses (usually two in number) focus the electron beam on to the specimen. The objective lens produces a first magnified image, which is further magnified by an intermediate lens. The final magnification is by the projector lens, which produces the image on a fluorescent screen. For recording the image, a photographic plate or film is put in place of the screen.

A dark field image can be formed from one or more of the diffracted beams (instead of from the main beam), by moving the objective aperture to transmit the diffracted beam and block the main beam. This enables the diffracting precipitate particles to be seen more easily than in the normal bright field image. For metallurgical work, a tilting stage is indispensable. Tilting should be about two orthogonal axes with at least 25° of tilt about each axis.

Metals may be examined in two ways: by making a replica of a suitably etched surface or by making a piece of metal thin enough to be transparent to electrons. In earlier years, the replica was made from a plastic called *formwar*. The film about 1000 Å thick is stripped and examined under the electron microscope. In carbon extraction replica, a film of about 100–200 Å is evaporated on the etched surface, stripped off and examined. The resolution of the carbon replica is much better than the plastic replica. In addition, the particles in the microstructure that stand out in relief are transferred to the replica and may not be dissolved during the subsequent step of dissolving out the metal matrix. By obtaining a diffraction pattern, the particles can be identified. Extremely fine particles of NbC (about 20 Å in size) in microalloyed steels have been identified this way.

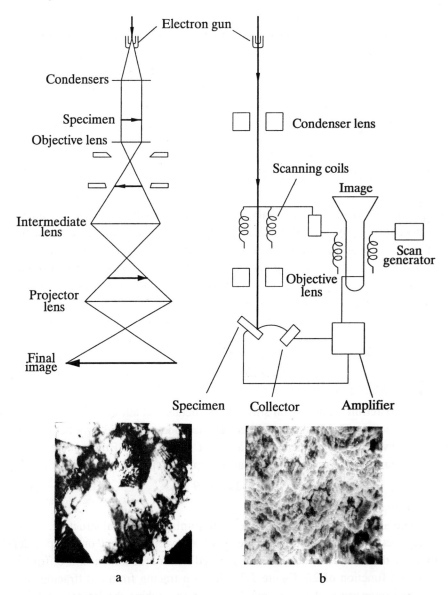

Figure 1.19 Line diagram of (a) the transmission electron microscope, and (b) the scanning electron microscope. Typical electron micrographs are also shown.

Thin foils of the metal (less than 2500 Å thick) can be directly examined in a *transmission electron microscope* (TEM). The thin foil is obtained by electropolishing. In the window technique, pointed electrodes are used. The metal directly in front of the pointed electrode is dissolved more rapidly and perforates. The metal adjacent to the perforation is thin enough to transmit the electrons. Diffraction patterns can be obtained over any selected area of the matrix or of particles embedded in it.

The scanning electron microscope   In the *scanning electron microscope*, Fig. 1.19b, a beam of electrons is moved over the specimen surface in a sequence of closely spaced lines. The electrons interact with the surface atoms and the output depends on the composition and topography. The output signal is picked up and used to modulate the brightness of a cathode ray beam, which is moving synchronously with the scanning search beam. The depth of focus of the scanning electron microscope is so high that a fracture surface can be directly examined without any polishing. In metallurgical studies, fractographic examination and, to a lesser extent, examination of polished and etched surfaces are carried out with the scanning electron microscope.

The electron probe microanalyzer   The composition of alloys can be determined by conventional chemical analysis and other modern instrumental methods such as spectroscopy or x-ray fluorescence. These give only the average composition. The electron probe microanalyzer (EPMA) is a tool for determining the composition on a micron scale relevant to metallurgical problems such as identification of very small inclusions and precipitates and composition gradients on a micron scale. In this instrument, a beam of electrons about ½ μm diameter strikes the specimen surface, interacting with the atoms of the specimen to produce x-rays. By measuring the wavelength and intensity of the x-rays produced, it is possible to determine which elements are present and their respective concentrations.

X-ray diffraction   The crystal structure of metals and alloys is determined by x-ray diffraction. The Bragg law describes the effect produced by a beam of x-rays of wavelength λ incident at an angle of θ (called the Bragg angle) on to a set of parallel atomic planes with an interplanar spacing of d:

$$n\lambda = 2d \sin \theta \qquad (1.8)$$

where n is an integer.

There are a number of methods for determining the crystal structure. In the powder method, a monochromatic beam of x-rays is incident on the powder sample of the unknown metal. The diffracted beam is recorded in a diffractometer as a function of 2θ. Figure 1.20 shows a tracing from a diffractometer, where the intensity peaks correspond to positions, where the Bragg condition given in Eq. (1.8) is satisfied. Computer software packages are now available for analyzing the diffraction data and ascertaining the crystal structure.

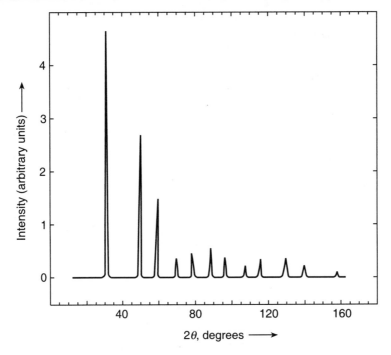

Figure 1.20 Tracing from an x-ray diffractometer.

SUGGESTED READINGS

Barrett, C.S. and T.B. Massalski, *The Structure of Metals*, 3rd revised edition, Pergamon Press, Oxford (1980).

Smallman, R.E., *Modern Physical Metallurgy*, Butterworths, London (1985).

Weinberg, F. (Ed.), *Tools and Techniques in Physical Metallurgy*, Vols. 1 and 2, Marcel Dekker (1970).

QUESTIONS

1. The resistivity of copper is 10^{-9} ohm m, whereas that of germanium is 10^{-1} ohm m and of diamond is 10^{11} ohm m. What is the reason for such large variations in resistivity of different materials?

2. The density of BCC chromium is 7190 kg m^{-3}. Find its lattice parameter. *Answer:* 2.88 Å.

3. Show that the packing efficiency of an FCC crystal is 0.74.

4. What is the difference between the hexagonal space lattice and the HCP crystal ? *Hint:* Compare Fig. 1.3a and 1.3b.

5. Explain why an ... *ABBA* ... stacking is not stable.

6. Show that the ideal *c/a* ratio of an HCP crystal is 1.633.

7. Draw a cubic unit cell and sketch the following planes and directions within the unit cell: (132), (322), [312] and [102].

8. Draw a $(1\bar{1}0)$ plane in the unit cell of a BCC crystal and show the close packed directions that lie on it.

9. If two metals show only limited solid solubility in each other, is it positive or negative deviation from ideality ? Explain.

10. Explain why complete solid solubility is not possible in an interstitial solid solution.

11. Explain the differences between a chemical compound, an ordered solid solution and a random solid solution.

12. The enthalpy of formation of vacancies in aluminium is 68 kJ mol^{-1}. Calculate the fraction of vacancies in equilibrium at room temperature and just below the melting point.
    Answer: at 300 K, 1.44×10^{-12} and at 930 K, 1.52×10^{-4}.

13. A cold worked copper sample has a dislocation density of 10^{15} m m^{-3} Estimate the strain energy stored in the metal.
    Answer: 1.48 MJ m^{-3}.

14. Calculate the spacing between edge dislocations in a tilt boundary in iron, when the angle of misorientation between the subgrains is 2°.
    Answer: 71Å.

15. Calculate the average grain diameter for ASTM grain size number 14. By how much would this change, if the ASTM number is 12?
    Answer: 2.8 μm; increase by 100%.

2

PHASE DIAGRAMS

The relationships between phases in a system as a function of temperature, pressure and composition are depicted in the form of maps. Generally, these are equilibrium relationships in that they correspond to the state of the minimum free energy of the system. Such maps are called *equilibrium diagrams* (also phase diagrams or constitutional diagrams). Sometimes, metastable phases may also be shown on a phase diagram, especially if they are present in alloys of engineering interest. In such cases, the phase diagram depicts the metastable equilibrium.

2.1 THE PHASE RULE

The Gibbs phase rule can be stated as follows :

$$F = C - P + 2 \tag{2.1}$$

where F is the degrees of freedom,
C is the number of components, and
P is the number of phases in the system.

Phases   Different states of aggregation of matter such as solid, liquid and gas form separate phases. The gaseous phase is always a single phase, as atoms (or molecules) in the gaseous phase are mixed at the atomic level. A liquid solution is by the same token a single phase. For example, in salt solution, i.e. salt dissolved in water, the sodium ions, the chlorine ions and the water molecules are mixed at the atom level. A liquid mixture of .water and oil forms separate phases. A solid solution of an alloy with the component atoms mixed at the unit cell level constitutes a single phase.

Components   Components refer to the *independent chemical species* that constitute an alloy. For plain carbon steel, iron and carbon are the chemical species; so, the components are Fe and C (graphite). However, carbon almost always occurs in the combined form as cementite (Fe_3C) in steels, even though cementite is metastable and has a higher free energy as compared to graphite. So, it is common to show the phase relationships in the Fe-C system on a metastable phase diagram with Fe and Fe_3C as the components. The choice of all the three (Fe, C and Fe_3C) as components does not constitute a set of independent chemical species.

Degrees of freedom   The degrees of freedom refer to the number of *independent variables* associated with the system. The total number of variables is the external variables (temperature and pressure) plus the composition variables. The number of composition variables required to express the concentration of C components in a phase is $(C - 1)^*$. For a system with P phases,

$$\text{total variables} = P\,(C - 1) + 2 \tag{2.2}$$

The degree of freedom F is equal to or less than the total number of variables :

$$F = C - P + 2 \leq P\,(C - 1) + 2 \tag{2.3}$$

When there is only one phase in a system, F is equal to the total number of variables. For $P > 1$, F is less than the total number. The minimum value for the degree of freedom is zero and this sets an upper limit on the number of phases that can coexist in a system under equilibrium.

2.2   BINARY PHASE DIAGRAMS

The most commonly used phase diagrams are those that depict the equilibrium between two components. These are known as *binary phase diagrams*. Many engineering alloys contain more than two components. Nevertheless, the binary diagram between the two major components is still useful in interpreting the phase relationships. For example, the Fe-Fe_3C phase diagram is used in the study of carbon steels, which usually contain small quantities of S, P, Si and Mn, in addition to Fe and C. In other cases, more complex phase relationships have to be studied. For equilibrium in a system containing three components, ternary phase diagrams are used. Further, it is possible to depict the more complicated phase relationships between a number of components on a pseudo-binary diagram.

For graphical representation of the binary phase relationships, we need a map with three axes corresponding to temperature, pressure and composition. As three-dimensional diagrams are difficult to draw on paper, for binary phase diagrams it is customary to ignore the pressure variable and the vapour phase.

*Note that every phase in equilibrium in a system will have all the components in it, however small may be the concentration of a component.

As one of the variables has been arbitrarily omitted, the phase rule for condensed phases (i.e., liquids and solids) only is written as

$$F = C - P + 1 \tag{2.4}$$

The binary phase diagram is drawn with temperature on the y-axis and composition on the x-axis. For a binary system of A and B, the x-axis reads % B from left to right (or % A from right to left). The composition is either weight % or atom %. It is usually in weight %, unless stated otherwise. The weight % of A in an alloy of A and B can be converted into atom % A as follows:

$$\text{Atom\% A} = \frac{\dfrac{\text{wt.\% A}}{\text{atomic wt. of A}}}{\dfrac{\text{wt.\% A}}{\text{atomic wt. of A}} + \dfrac{\text{wt.\% B}}{\text{atomic wt. of B}}} \times 100$$

Isomorphous systems The simplest binary phase diagram is for a system exhibiting complete liquid solubility as well as solid solubility. This is called an *isomorphous system*, to indicate that the crystal structures of the two components and the solid solution are the same. As an example, the copper-nickel phase diagram is shown in Fig. 2.1. Pure copper (FCC) melts at 1083°C. Pure nickel (FCC) melts at 1455°C. The liquid solution extends over all compositions.

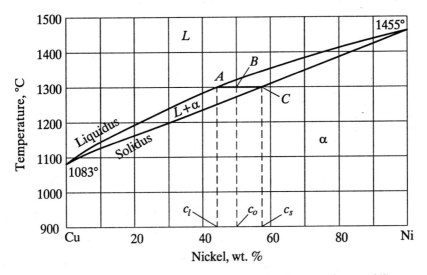

Figure 2.1 The copper-nickel phase diagram, showing complete solubility both in the liquid and in the solid states.

Similarly, the solid solution (α), which is also FCC, covers the entire composition range.* The liquid and the solid regions are separated by a two-phase region, where both the phases coexist. The boundary between the two-phase region and the liquid is called the *liquidus*. The boundary between the two-phase region and the solid is called the *solidus*.

---

*The α solid solution splits into two different solid phases at temperatures below 322°C.

In certain systems, the liquidus and the solidus may coincide at some composition. The alloy of this composition melts and solidifies at a constant temperature like a pure metal without passing through the two-phase region. Such a composition is said to be *congruently melting*.

The tie-line rule The compositions of the phases in the two-phase region are *not* equal. Nickel (or copper) *redistributes or partitions itself in different concentrations in the two phases*. The compositions of the co-existing phases are determined from the *tie-line rule*. A horizontal line (called the tie-line) is drawn at the temperature of interest T, say, 1300°C in Fig. 2.1. The intersection of this line with the liquidus gives the composition of the liquid c_l and the intersection with the solidus gives the composition of the solid c_s. Referring to Fig. 2.1, at 1300°C,

composition of the liquid c_l = 46% Ni (54% Cu)

composition of the solid c_s = 58% Ni (42% Cu)

This is applicable for any overall composition of the alloy that lies along the tie-line within the two-phase region. In the above example, as the overall composition of the alloy is varied between 46 and 58% Ni, the liquid and the solid compositions remain constant. A little reflection shows that this will be possible only if the relative amounts of the coexisting phases also change, as the overall composition is varied.

The lever rule The relative amounts of the coexisting phases at a specified temperature are given by the *lever rule*. The tie-line is taken to be a lever arm CA, with the fulcrum at the overall composition c_o (point B), Fig. 2.1. The solid and the liquid compositions lie at the two ends C and A of the lever arm. The fraction of the liquid f_l for the overall composition c_o is given by the ratio of the lever arm length on the other side of the fulcrum (CB) to the total length of the lever arm (CA):

$$f_l = \frac{CB}{CA} = \frac{c_s - c_o}{c_s - c_l}$$

Similarly, the fraction of the solid f_s is given by

$$f_s = \frac{BA}{CA} = \frac{c_o - c_l}{c_s - c_l}$$

Referring to Fig. 2.1, for the overall composition c_o = 50% Ni at 1300°C,

$$f_l = \frac{58 - 50}{58 - 46} = 0.67$$

$$f_s = \frac{50 - 46}{58 - 46} = 0.33$$

It must be clearly understood that the tie-line rule gives the concentration of the components in each phase, whereas the lever rule gives the fractions of the phases. Stating the two rules together, for the above example, at 1300°C,

fraction of liquid of composition 46% Ni = 0.67
fraction of solid of composition 58% Ni = 0.33

$$\text{Total} = \underline{1.00}$$

$$0.67 \times 46 + 0.33 \times 58 = 50\% \text{ Ni}$$

which is the overall composition of the alloy.

Phase rule applied to the isomorphous system   In the liquid or in the solid region of the Cu-Ni phase diagram, only one phase exists. Noting that $C = 2$ and $P = 1$ here, from Eq. (2.4), the degrees of freedom $F = 2 - 1 + 1 = 2$. Both the temperature and composition can be varied within limits in the single phase region. In the two-phase region, we have three variables,

> temperature,
> composition of the liquid phase, and
> composition of the solid phase.

From Eq. (2.4), $F = 2 - 2 + 1 = 1$. So, only one of these three variables can be changed *independently*. For example, if we choose the temperature arbitrarily and thereby exercise one degree of freedom, the other two variables, namely, the compositions of the two phases are automatically fixed, as per the tie-line rule.

The eutectic phase diagram   All systems do not exhibit complete solid solubility. The Hume-Rothery's conditions for extensive solid solubility are not ideally obeyed for many pairs of elements. This usually results in limited solid solubility with two terminal solid solutions, each based on the crystal structure of a pure component. Two types of phase diagrams result :

(i) the eutectic diagram, and
(ii) the peritectic diagram

When the melting points of the components are comparable, the eutectic phase diagram is usually obtained. The Ag-Cu eutectic phase diagram is shown in Fig. 2.2. A maximum of 8.8% of copper dissolves in silver at 780°C, forming the terminal solid solution α (FCC). A maximum of 7.9% of silver dissolves in copper at 780°C, forming the other terminal solid solution β (also FCC). The solubility in both cases decreases with decreasing temperature along the solvus line. The *solvus* is the solid-state phase boundary between the terminal solid solution and the two-phase region, see Fig. 2.2.

The alloy with 28.1% Cu has the minimum melting point among all the alloys of this system. This composition is known as the *eutectic composition* c_e and the corresponding temperature (780°C) is the *eutectic temperature* T_e. The liquid of eutectic composition solidifies isothermally as a mixture of α and β crystals on cooling through T_e. The characteristics of this eutectic reaction are summarized as follows:

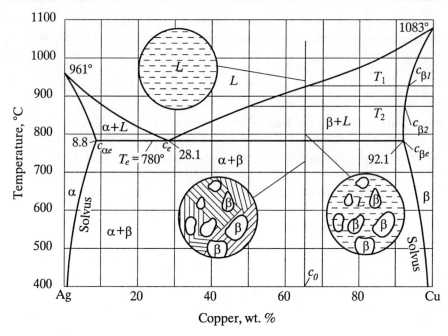

Figure 2.2 The silver-copper phase diagram is a simple eutectic system.

		cool $\longrightarrow$		
reaction	:	$L \longleftrightarrow$	α +	β
structure	:	–	FCC	FCC
composition	:	c_e	$c_{\alpha e}$	$c_{\beta e}$
wt% Cu	:	28.1	8.8	92.1

Plate-like crystals (or rod-like crystals) of α and β arranged in an alternating, parallel fashion are the characteristic structure of the eutectic mixture as shown in Fig. 2.3a. Sometimes, an *abnormal* or *divorced* eutectic structure is observed. Here, the eutectic is present in so small a volume fraction that the plate-like structure does not form. Instead the minor phase of the eutectic forms and grows as islands that appear unconnected on a polished surface. The other phase forms the continuous matrix. Abnormal eutectic structures are observed, when one of the phases forms strong covalent bonds, e.g. the Al-Si and Fe-graphite systems. Chinese script is a structure between the lamellar (normal) eutectic and the abnormal eutectic. Here, the lamellar morphology has degenerated into a pattern that looks like a Chinese script, Fig. 2.3b.

An alloy to the left of the eutectic is known as a *hypoeutectic* alloy. An alloy to the right is called a *hypereutectic* alloy. In both these cases, on cooling below the liquidus boundary, the *proeutectic* phase (α or β) separates out first. On further cooling, the fraction of the proeutectic phase increases, till the eutectic temperature is reached. Just above the eutectic temperature T_e, the tie-line indicates that the composition of the proeutectic phase is $c_{\alpha e}$ (or $c_{\beta e}$) and the liquid is of the eutectic composition c_e. On cooling through T_e, the eutectic reaction occurs in that part of the system which is in the liquid form. The proeutectic phase appears as equiaxed crystals in the eutectic matrix and is clearly distinguishable from the plate-like crystals of the eutectic mixture. This structure for a hypereutectic alloy is schematically shown in Fig. 2.2.

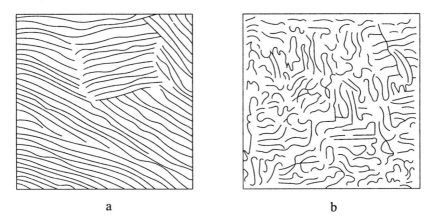

a   b

Figure 2.3 (a) Microstructure of a normal eutectic. (b) Microstructure of a eutectic mixture that lies between normal and abnormal, known as the Chinese script.

At the eutectic temperature, all the three phases, α, β and liquid are present. Here, the total variables are 4 in number: temperature (1) and compositions of the three phases (2-4). From Eq. (2.4), $F = 2 - 3 + 1 = 0$. With the zero degree of freedom, none of the four variables can be independently changed. The eutectic temperature is a fixed value for a given system and the compositions of the three phases at the eutectic temperature are also fixed. To denote the zero degree of freedom, the eutectic reaction is called the *invariant reaction* and the eutectic temperature is known as the *invariant temperature*. Note that, for all compositions which undergo the eutectic reaction (the eutectic, the hypoeutectic and the hypereutectic alloys), three-phase equilibrium prevails at the eutectic temperature and the degree of freedom is zero.

The lever rule cannot be applied at an invariant temperature, where three phases coexist. However, it can be applied just above or just below the eutectic temperature to determine the fraction of

(i) a proeutectic phase,

(ii) the eutectic mixture, and

(iii) a phase that forms part of the eutectic mixture.

The peritectic phase diagram When the melting points of two components showing limited solid solubility are quite different, a peritectic diagram usually results. Figure 2.4 illustrates the simple peritectic system between nickel (Ni) and rhenium (Re), the respective melting points being 1455°C and 3186°C.

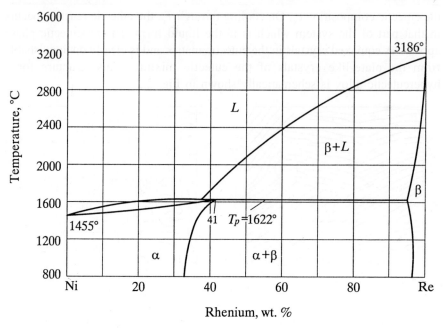

Figure 2.4   The nickel-rhenium phase diagram is a simple peritectic system.

The peritectic reaction occurs at the peritectic temperature T_p (1622°C).

reaction	:	L	+	β	$\xleftarrow[\quad]{\text{cool} \rightarrow}$	α
structure	:	–		HCP		FCC
composition	:	c_{lp}		$c_{\beta p}$		$c_{\alpha p}$
wt.% Re	:	36		94		41

Here, one liquid and one solid react to form a single solid phase on cooling through the peritectic temperature. Three phases are in equilibrium at the peritectic temperature and zero degree of freedom prevails. Accordingly, the peritectic reaction is invariant. Note that the peritectic temperature T_p lies *between* the melting points of the two components, whereas in the eutectic reaction, T_e is lower than either of the melting points.

Other invariant reactions   We have considered above the simple phase diagrams of the eutectic or the peritectic type. Binary diagrams may have other invariant reactions, a number of which are described below.

In the *eutectoid reaction*, a solid phase decomposes isothermally on cooling through a fixed temperature into two other solid phases:

$$\gamma \xleftarrow[\quad]{\text{cool} \rightarrow} \alpha + \beta$$

The initial liquid phase of the eutectic reaction is replaced by the solid phase in this reaction. Corresponding to the peritectic reaction, we have the *peritectoid reaction* that occurs entirely in the solid state:

$$\gamma + \alpha \xrightleftharpoons[]{\text{cool} \rightarrow} \beta$$

In the *monotectic reaction*, a liquid phase on cooling decomposes to another liquid and a solid phase:

$$L_I \xrightleftharpoons[]{\text{cool} \rightarrow} L_{II} + \alpha$$

In the *syntectic reaction*, two liquids combine to yield a single solid phase on cooling:

$$L_I + L_{II} \xrightleftharpoons[]{\text{cool} \rightarrow} \alpha$$

Three-phase equilibrium and zero degree of freedom prevail at the invariant temperature of all the above reactions. The following table is a summary of the invariant reactions.

Name	Invariant reaction direction of cooling $\rightarrow$	Phase boundaries near the invariant composition
Eutectic	$L \rightleftharpoons \alpha + \beta$	L / $\alpha + \beta$
Eutectoid	$\gamma \rightleftharpoons \alpha + \beta$	γ / $\alpha + \beta$
Monotectic	$L_I \rightleftharpoons L_{II} + \alpha$	L_I / $L_{II} + \alpha$
Peritectic	$L + \alpha \rightleftharpoons \beta$	$L + \alpha$ / β
Peritectoid	$\gamma + \alpha \rightleftharpoons \beta$	$\gamma + \alpha$ / β
Syntectic	$L_I + L_{II} \rightleftharpoons \alpha$	$L_I + L_{II}$ / α

2.3 FREE ENERGY COMPOSITION CURVES FOR BINARY SYSTEMS

The free energy of each of the phases present on a phase diagram can be plotted as a function of composition at a series of temperatures. The phases that coexist in equilibrium are those that correspond to the lowest free energy of the system.

For a binary system exhibiting complete solid solubility, the free energy-composition curves for the liquid and the solid phases are shown at three temperatures in Fig. 2.5. In Fig. 2.5a (the phase diagram), the temperature T_1 lies above the liquidus across the entire composition range. Figure 2.5b shows the free energy curves for this temperature. The liquid phase has a lower free energy than the solid at all compositions; so, it is the stable phase. The next lower temperature T_2 cuts across the two phase region in Fig. 2.5a. The corresponding free energy curves intersect each other, Fig. 2.5c. There is a certain range of composition over which the free energy of a mixture of the liquid and the solid phases is lower than either of the phases. This composition range is obtained by drawing a *common tangent xy* to the two curves, see Fig. 2.5c. The compositions at points x and y are c_l and c_s respectively. Over the range of composition to the left of c_l, the free energy of the liquid is lower; so, it is the stable phase. For compositions that lie between x and y, two-phase equilibrium prevails. The mixture of the two phases in the proportion given by the lever rule has the lowest free energy. For compositions to the right of c_s, the solid phase is the stable phase. At temperature T_3, Fig. 2.5d, the solid phase has lower free energy and is stable over the entire composition range.

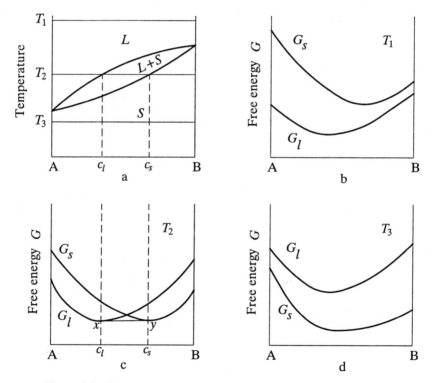

Figure 2.5 Free energy-composition relationships for an isomorphous system at three temperatures.

For a eutectic system, three free energy-composition curves are drawn, one for each of the phases: α, β and liquid. The sketches in Fig. 2.6a-d illustrate the relationships. At T_1, Fig. 2.6a, the liquid phase is stable over the entire composition range, as it has a lower free energy. At T_2, the liquid free energy curve intersects both the α and β free energy curves, Fig. 2.6b. Two common tangents are drawn to delineate the two two-phase regions, on either side of the eutectic composition. At the eutectic temperature T_e, all three phases have the same free energy. A single straight line is tangential to all the three free energy curves, Fig. 2.6c. At T_3, the liquid phase has a higher free energy than either of the solid phases at all compositions and there is no liquid present at this temperature. The α and β free energy curves intersect each other, the common tangent delineating the ($\alpha + \beta$) region of the phase diagram, Fig. 2.6d.

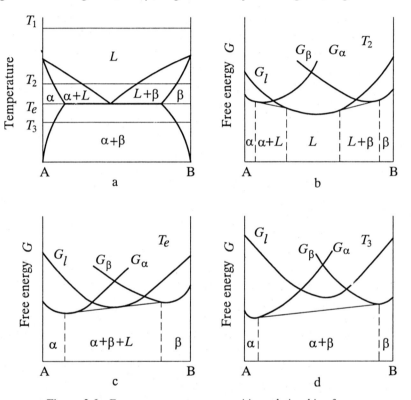

Figure 2.6 Free energy versus composition relationships for a simple eutectic system at different temperatures.

The common tangent principle described above serves to explain why the solubility is more in a phase which is in equilibrium with a metastable phase than with a stable phase. In Fig. 2.7, the free energy-composition curves for the terminal solid solution α, the stable intermediate phase θ, and the metastable intermediate phase θ' are shown. If the α solid solution is in equilibrium with θ, the maximum solubility is c_α as given by the common tangent. If it is in equilibrium with the metastable θ', the maximum solubility is c'_α. It is easily seen that $c'_\alpha > c_\alpha$.

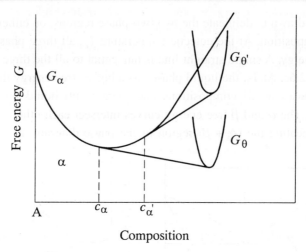

Composition

Figure 2.7 The solubility in the matrix (α) is more, when the matrix is in equilibrium with a metastable precipitate (θ'), as compared to a stable precipitate (θ).

2.4 MICROSTRUCTURAL CHANGES DURING COOLING

Slow equilibrium cooling It is instructive to consider first the changes that occur microstructurally during extremely slow cooling, approximating the equilibrium conditions. Consider the hypereutectic alloy of composition c_o in the Ag-Cu system, Fig. 2.2. As this alloy is cooled below the liquidus temperature, solidification starts. The first solid to crystalize has a composition $c_{\beta 1}$ as given by the first tie-line. As the temperature falls further, more and more of the liquid crystallizes. At the same time, the compositions of the solid and the liquid phases continuously change with the tie-line, which occupies successive horizontal positions with decreasing temperature. At T_2, the solid composition is $c_{\beta 2}$. Just above the eutectic temperature, the composition of the solid is $c_{\beta e}$ and that of the liquid is c_e. On cooling through T_e, the eutectic reaction occurs in the liquid region, yielding the eutectic mixture of α and β. On further cooling below T_e, the solubilities of copper in silver and silver in copper decrease along the solvus lines and more α and β form by precipitation from the supersaturated phases. Figure 2.2 also shows the successive changes in the microstructure during cooling.

Nonequilibrium cooling In practice, the cooling rates are rarely slow enough to obtain equilibrium conditions. The continuous adjustments in compositions of the phases required for equilibrium may not take place.

Consider an alloy of composition c_o cooled from above the liquidus, Fig. 2.8a. The first solid to crystallize has a composition $c_{\alpha 1}$. As further solidification occurs, the composition of the solid phase should shift along the solidus to $c_{\alpha 2}$, $c_{\alpha 3}$, etc. Diffusion of atoms inside the solid phase is required to bring about these compositional changes. Diffusion in the solid phase is many orders of magnitude slower than in the liquid phase. So, only the solid that crystallizes at any instant is in local equilibrium with the liquid with which it is in contact. The solid that formed earlier at a higher temperature does not change its composition according to the new tie-line, as diffusion is slow through the solid. Thus a gradient of composition develops from $c_{\alpha1}$ at the centre of the crystal which solidifies first to $c_{\alpha5}$ at the periphery of the crystal which solidifies last, Fig. 2.8b. The average composition of the crystal is shown by the dotted line in Fig. 2.8a. This lags behind the equilibrium composition, so that some liquid is left over, even after crossing the equilibrium solidus at T_s. Solidification is complete at a lower temperature, T_s', where the average composition of the solid becomes equal to the overall composition of the alloy. This phenomenon is called *coring* and is seen under the microscope through an etching effect produced by the compositional gradient, as schematically shown in Fig. 2.8b. Figure 2.8c shows the coring effect, when the growing crystals have the shape of a *dendrite*. *The extent of coring increases, with increasing separation between the liquidus and the solidus, i.e. in alloys with a wide freezing range.*

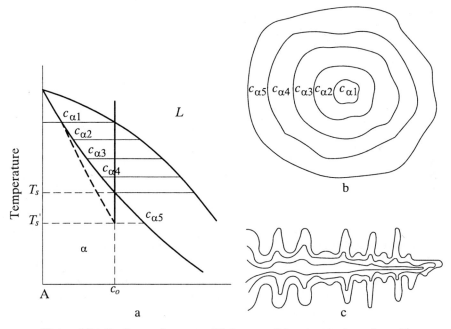

Figure 2.8 Cooling under nonequilibrium conditions results in coring with compositional gradients from the centre to the periphery of the growing crystals.

Under nonequilibrium conditions of cooling of an alloy of a eutectic system, the proeutectic crystals are cored. Due to this, more liquid is left over on reaching the eutectic temperature. The fraction of the eutectic mixture formed is correspondingly larger in the final microstructure. The coring effect may also produce some eutectic mixture in an alloy of overall composition that lies outside the eutectic horizontal.

Deviation from equilibrium is a serious problem in alloy systems in which a peritectic reaction occurs. Recall that this reaction is between a liquid and a solid. The product of the reaction is a solid, which forms at the boundary between the two parent phases. As soon as some solid product (α) forms, the parent phases (*L* and β) get separated and are no longer in contact. This phenomenon is known as *surrounding or enveloping*, Fig. 2.9. Further reaction

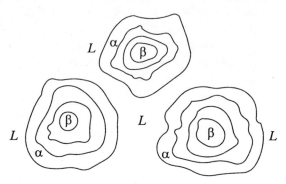

Figure 2.9   In the peritectic reaction $L + \beta \rightarrow \alpha$, surrounding or enveloping occurs, when the product α phase surrounds the unreacted β phase.

can occur only through solid state diffusion through the intervening product layer. Solid state diffusion being very slow, peritectic alloys solidify with large deviations from the equilibrium composition and structure.

A homogenizing treatment is required to remove the compositional variations that accompany coring or surrounding. The alloy is heated to a high temperature and held there for a prolonged period, during which diffusion levels out the compositional gradients and yields a homogeneous solid solution. Extreme care is required during heating not to cross the solidus. Note that, for a cored structure, the effective solidus is lower than the equilibrium solidus. If this solidus is crossed, melting occurs near the grain boundaries. Liquation is often accompanied by grain boundary oxidation and the phenomenon is called *burning*. A burnt alloy is permanently damaged, as the oxidized grain boundaries cannot be restored to the initial unoxidized condition by means of a heat treatment or by mechanical working. *Overheating* refers to heating close to the solidus, but without causing liquation. Overheating impairs the properties of steels through loss of ductility and toughness. It is associated with the segregation of impurities and subsequent precipitation along grain boundaries. The effects of overheating are not permanent and can be removed by a subsequent heat treatment.

2.5   THE IRON CARBON EQUILIBRIUM DIAGRAM

In Fe-C alloys, carbon may be present either in the form of free carbon (graphite) or as iron carbide (Fe_3C). The most frequently occurring form in steels is Fe_3C, known as *cementite*. As already pointed out, *cementite is metastable with respect to graphite.* The phase diagram in Fig. 2.10 shows Fe and Fe$_3$C as the two components. In cast irons, carbon is present either as graphite or cementite. To denote this possibility, Fig. 2.10 has dotted phase boundaries corresponding to the graphite equilibrium.

Phases in the Fe-C system   *α-ferrite* is an interstitial solid solution of carbon in BCC iron. It is stable over the temperature range from − 273°C to 912°C. Carbon is present in a few of the (0, 0, ½) and other equivalent interstitial sites in the BCC unit cell. The size of the largest atom that can fit in this site is 0.19Å, which is much smaller than the size of the carbon atom (0.71Å). So, the solubility is extremely limited. The maximum solubility is 0.02 wt% (0.10 at %) at 727°C.

Austenite (γ) is an interstitial solid solution of carbon in FCC iron. It is stable from 912 to 1394°C. Carbon is present in some of the (0, 0, ½) and other equivalent positions which includes the body centre (½, ½, ½). The size of the largest atom that can fit this void is 0.52 Å. Correspondingly, the solubility is larger here as compared to ferrite. The maximum solubility is at 1146°C and is 2.1 wt% (9.1 at %)

δ-ferrite (BCC) is stable from 1394 to 1539°C, the melting point of iron. The maximum solubility of carbon here is 0.09 wt%.

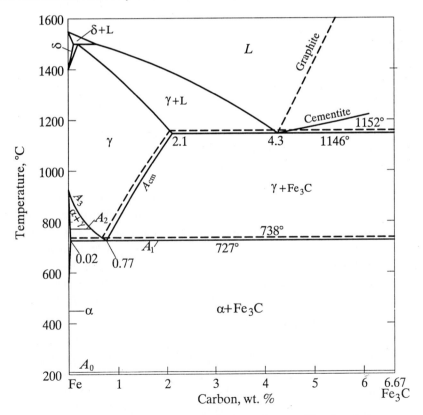

Figure 2.10   The Fe-Fe$_3$C metastable phase diagram. The dotted phase boundaries correspond to the stable graphite equilibrium.

Cementite is an intermetallic compound with the formula Fe_3C. The atomic percent of carbon in cementite is 25 and the weight percent is 6.67. Cementite has a complex orthorhombic crystal structure, with twelve iron atoms and four carbon atoms in the unit cell.

Graphite has a hexagonal crystal structure, in which sheets of primarily-bonded carbon atoms are held together by secondary bonds.

Invariant reactions Three invariant reactions occur in the Fe-Fe_3C system. A *peritectic reaction* occurs at 1495°C:

reaction	:	δ	+	L	$\longleftrightarrow$	γ
structure	:	BCC		−		FCC
composition, wt.% C	:	0.09		0.53		0.17

On cooling through the peritectic temperature, δ-ferrite reacts with the liquid to yield austenite (γ).

A *eutectic reaction* occurs at 1146°C:

reaction	:	L	$\longleftrightarrow$	γ	+	Fe_3C
				austenite		cementite
structure	:	−		FCC		orthorhombic
composition, wt.% C	:	4.3		2.1		6.67

On cooling through the eutectic temperature, the lowest melting liquid of the system decomposes to two solid phases, austenite and cementite. This eutectic mixture is known as *ledeburite*.

A eutectoid reaction occurs at 727°C:

Reaction	:	γ	$\longleftrightarrow$	α	+	Fe_3C
		austenite		ferrite		cementite
structure	:	FCC		BCC		orthorhombic
composition, wt.% C	:	0.77		0.02		6.67

On cooling through the eutectoid temperature, austenite decomposes into a lamellar mixture of ferrite and cementite crystals, called *pearlite*.

Critical temperatures Critical temperatures are those at which phase changes occur during heating or cooling an alloy. Certain symbols are used to denote the critical temperatures in steels.

The eutectoid reaction during heating and cooling sets in at the critical temperatures A_{c1} and A_{r1} respectively. The letters stand for the French words:

    A for arrêt (means arrest)
    c for chauffage (means heating), and
    r for refroidissement (means cooling).

If extremely slow rates of heating or cooling are employed, the corresponding critical temperatures are nearly equal, i.e. $A_{c1} = A_{r1} = A_1 = 727$°C (eutectoid temperature). At ordinary rates of heating or cooling, there is a thermal hysteresis, and $A_{c1} > A_{r1}$.

The next higher critical temperature A_2 is the Curie temperature of iron (768°C), where ferrite undergoes the magnetic transition from the ferromagnetic to the paramagnetic state on heating. There is no hysteresis in this electronic transition.

The temperature corresponding to the $(\gamma + \alpha)/\gamma$ phase boundary for hypoutectoid steels is termed A_{c3} or A_{r3}. Unlike A_1, the A_3 temperature is a function of carbon content. It decreases from 912°C at 0% C to 727°C. in hypereutectoid steels, the $\gamma/(\gamma + Fe_3C)$ phase boundary is called A_{cm}. The A_{cm} line is considerably steeper than the A_3 line.

The Curie temperature of cementite (210°C) is called A_0.

Microstructure of Slowly Cooled Steels

Eutectoid steel   The microstructure of eutectoid steel (0.77% C) is all pearlite. Pearlite is a lamellar arrangement of alternate, parallel plates of ferrite and cementite, Fig. 2.11. The relative amounts of ferrite and cementite in pearlite can be determined from lever rule:

$$f_\alpha = \frac{6.67 - 0.77}{6.67 - 0.02} = 0.89$$

$$f_{Fe_3C} = 1 - 0.89 = 0.11$$

The weight fractions of the phases are in the ratio 8:1. The densities of ferrite and cementite are comparable (7870 and 7700 kg m^{-3} respectively). The volume fractions of ferrite and cementite in pearlite are also approximately in the ratio of 8:1. Correspondingly, the cementite plates are much thinner than the

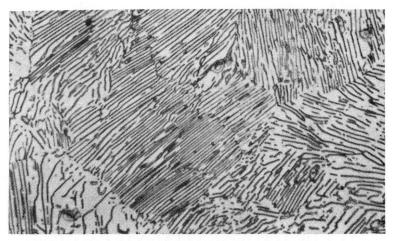

Figure 2.11   The microstructure of pearlite, showing the lamellar arrangement of ferrite and cementite plates.

ferrite plates. When *nital* (a dilute solution of nitric acid in alcohol) is used as the etchant, the boundaries between ferrite and cementite are selectively attacked.

As the two boundaries of a cementite plate are close together, they may not be resolved as separate lines. Cementite often appears as a single dark line. At higher magnifications or in a coarse distribution in pearlite, the cementite boundaries show up as separate lines.

Hypoeutectoid steels   The composition of hypoeutectoid steels is less than 0.77% C. In addition to pearlite, *the proeutectoid ferrite* (pro α) is present, Fig. 2.12. The fraction of the pro α can be estimated from lever rule. For example, in mild steel of 0.2% C,

$$f_{\text{pro}\,\alpha} = \frac{0.77 - 0.2}{0.77 - 0.02} = 0.76$$

$$f_{\text{pearlite}} = 1 - 0.76 = 0.24$$

The proeutectoid ferrite forms at the austenite grain boundaries between A_3 and A_1 temperatures.

Hypereutectoid steels   Here, the proeutectoid phase is cementite. It separates between A_{cm} and A_1 temperatures as a thin network along the austenite grain boundaries. In a 1.2% C steel, applying lever rule, we have

$$f_{\text{pro Fe}_3\text{C}} = \frac{1.2 - 0.77}{6.67 - 0.77} = 0.07$$

$$f_{\text{pearlite}} = 1 - 0.07 = 0.93$$

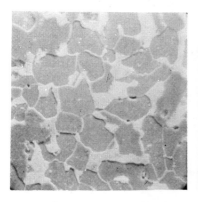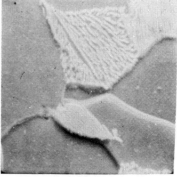

Figure 2.12   Scanning Electron Micrograph of mild steel, showing proeutectoid ferrite and pearlite.

2.6   EFFECT OF ALLOYING ELEMENTS ON THE Fe-C DIAGRAM

The effect of alloying elements on the Fe-C phase relationships is best understood by first considering the two types of phase diagrams obtained, when iron is alloyed with a substitutional element.

Ferrite stabilizers Some alloying elements tend to stabilize the ferrite phase in preference to austenite. Many of these elements have the same crystal structure as ferrite, i.e. BCC. They reduce the extent of the austenitic area on the equilibrium diagram, by forming a *gamma loop*, as illustrated for the Fe-Cr system in Fig. 2.13. Austenite (γ) is enclosed within the loop. At chromium contents greater than 12.7%, the δ-ferrite and the α-ferrite regions merge and become continuous. Such compositions exist only in the BCC form from the lowest temperature up to the melting point. *As austenite cannot be produced in such compositions, they are not heat treatable.* The critical compositions at which the austenite phase disappears are given below for some typical ferrite-stabilizing elements.

Element	Cr	Si	Mo	W	V
Crystal structure	BCC	DC	BCC	BCC	BCC
Critical composition, wt%	12.7	3	3	6	2

DC = Diamond cubic.

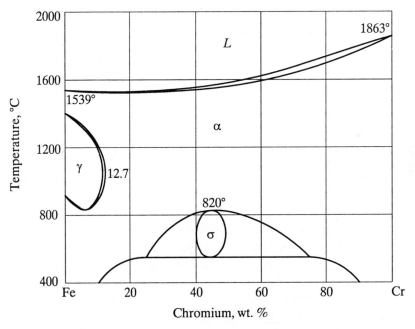

Figure 2.13 The iron-chromium phase diagram illustrates the formation of a gamma loop.

Austenite stabilizers Manganese and nickel are the common austenite-stabilizing elements. They enlarge the area of the austenite phase on the phase diagram, as shown for the Fe-Ni system in Fig. 2.14. When sufficient amount of nickel (or manganese) is present, austenite may be present at room temperature, as the low temperature reactions seen in Fig. 2.14 may be too slow to occur.

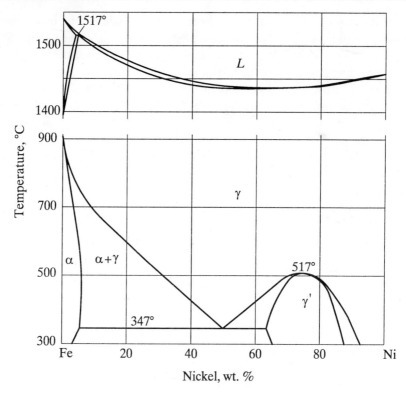

Figure 2.14 The iron-nickel phase diagram, showing the
stabilization of the austenite phase by nickel.

The interstitial elements carbon and nitrogen are also austenite stabilizers.
Referring to the Fe-C diagram in Fig. 2.10, carbon is seen to extend the temperature range over which austenite (γ) is stable, as compared to the range for
pure iron.

Effect on eutectoid temperature and composition   Figure 2.15a shows the
effect of different alloying elements on the eutectoid temperature. When the
alloying element is a ferrite stabilizer, the eutectoid temperature is raised above
727°C, as the concentration of the elements is increased. Ti and Mo are among
the most effective elements in raising the eutectoid temperature. With an austenite stabilizer, the eutectoid temperature is depressed below 727°C, see the
effect of Ni and Mn in Fig. 2.15a.

Figure 2.15b shows the effect of alloying elements on the eutectoid composition. *Both* ferrite and austenite stabilizers decrease the eutectoid composition from 0.77% C to lower values.

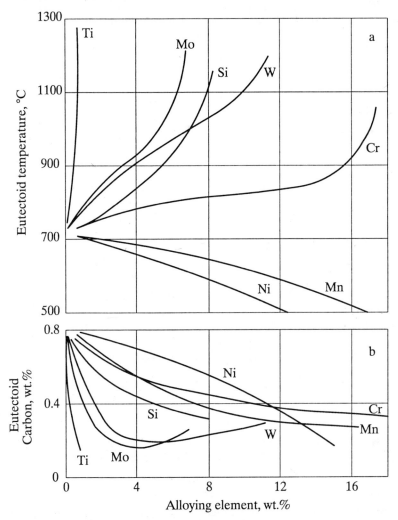

Figure 2.15 The effect of common alloying elements on
(a) the eutectoid temperature, and (b) the eutectoid composition.

The Fe-C-X phase relationships The effect of alloying elements on the
important phase boundaries of the Fe-C system is illustrated below using
pseudobinary plots. Figure 2.16 shows the A_3 and A_{cm} lines for different
manganese contents. As the manganese content increases, the austenite phase
field is enlarged, the eutectoid temperature moves down, and the eutectoid
composition shifts to lower carbon contents. Figure 2.17 shows the effect of
a ferrite stabilizer (chromium) on the Fe-C diagram. As the concentration of
chromium increases, the four phase boundaries enclosing the austenite field

move closer, thus restricting the extent of the austenite phase. To the left of the field are austenite and ferrite and to the right austenite and carbide. The eutectoid temperature moves up. The eutectoid composition shifts to lower carbon contents. With Cr > 19%, the austenite phase field disappears altogether. The critical composition at which this happens are given below for a few typical cases.

Ferrite stabilizer	Cr	Si	Mo	W	V
Critical composition, wt.%	19.5	8.1	6.4	10.8	4

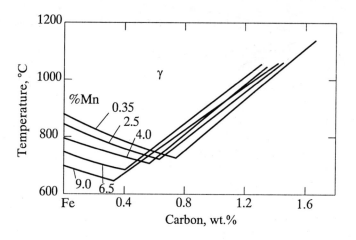

Figure 2.16   The shifting of the A_3 and A_{cm} phase boundaries in the presence of manganese.

Carbon being an austenite stabilizer, a higher concentration of a ferrite stabilizing element (19.5% Cr for Fe-C-Cr as compared to 12.7% Cr for Fe-Cr) is required in the presence of carbon to eliminate the austenite field.

For low alloy steels containing C between 0.08 and 1.4 wt%, A_{c1} and A_{c3} critical temperatures are given by the following empirical equations:

$$A_{c1} \ (°C) = 723 - 10.7Mn - 16.7Ni + 29.1Si \\ + 16.9Cr + 290As + 6.38W$$

$$A_{c3} \ (°C) = 910 - 203\sqrt{C} - 30Mn - 20Cu - 15.2Ni \\ - 11Cr - 700P + 44.7Si + 31.5Mo \\ + 104V + 460Al + 13.1W + 120As$$

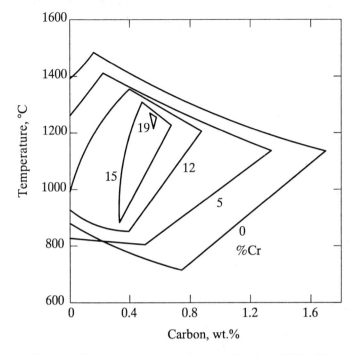

Figure 2.17   The shrinking of the austenite phase field with increasing concentration of chromium in steels.

2.7   THE COPPER-ZINC PHASE DIAGRAM

A number of important binary phase diagrams of nonferrous alloys are known. As an example, the Cu-Zn phase diagram is discussed below. The relevant parts of many other diagrams such as Al-Zn, Cu-Sn, Cu-Al and Cu-Be are introduced at appropriate places, when discussing engineering alloys in Chap. 7.

The melting points of copper (1083°C) and of zinc (419°C) are quite different. The Cu-Zn phase diagram shown in Fig. 2.18 has a number of peritectic reactions and intermediate phases. The α terminal solid solution is based on the crystal structure of copper (FCC), with zinc substitutionally dissolved. It is a commonly occurring phase in commercially important Cu-Zn alloys. It has excellent mechanical properties, with both strength and ductility increasing with increasing zinc content.

The intermediate phase β has the BCC crystal structure. It undergoes an order-disorder transformation on heating above 465°C. In the disordered β phase, the copper and zinc atoms are randomly distributed on the BCC sites. In the ordered β' phase, copper occupies the body corners and zinc the body centres of BCC (or vice versa). The β' phase has little ductility, but on disordering, the β phase becomes quite ductile. The γ, δ and ε phases of the Cu-Zn system have complex crystal structures and are too brittle to be of any commercial use.

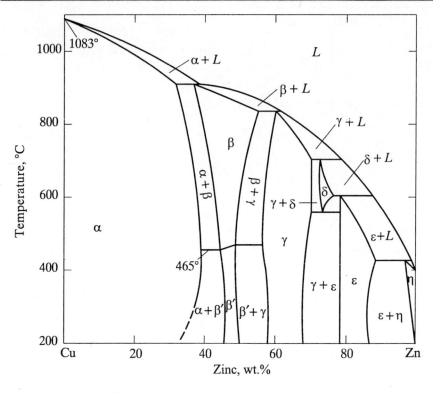

Figure 2.18 The copper-zinc phase diagram has a number of peritectic reactions and intermediate phases.

Within the α and β composition ranges, only one peritectic reaction occurs.

reaction	:	L	+	α	$\longleftrightarrow$	β
structure	:	–		FCC		BCC
composition, wt% Zn	:	37.5		32.5		36.8

The slopes of the $\alpha/(\alpha + \beta)$ and $(\alpha + \beta)/\beta$ boundaries are unusual. Between 900 and 400°C, the solubility of zinc in copper increases with decreasing temperature (as opposed to the normal decrease). A 37.5% Zn alloy is all β at 900°C. On slow cooling, the alloy gradually transforms into a mixture of $(\alpha + \beta)$. Below 550°C, it is fully converted to α. On further cooling below 300°C, under equilibrium conditions, the alloy should become $(\alpha + \beta')$ mixture, even though this may not happen at such low temperatures.

Commercial alloys of copper and zinc are discussed in Chap. 7.

2.8 TERNARY PHASE DIAGRAMS

Ternary phase diagrams depict the equilibrium between three components. As in binary diagrams, it is common to omit the pressure variable. The remaining variables are two compositions and temperature, requiring three axes for graphical representation. As perspective three-dimensional diagrams are not easy to draw or understand on paper, complex ternary relationships are usually presented as isothermal sections, i.e. each diagram corresponds to the phase equilibrium at a specified temperature. A number of such isothermal sections describe fully the ternary system.

The composition variables at a constant temperature are best represented in the form of an equilateral triangle (called the Gibbs triangle), the corners of which correspond to the three pure components, Fig. 2.19a. Each side of the triangle shows the variation in the concentration of the two components at the two ends of that side, just as the x-axis of a binary phase diagram. All compositions that lie on a side consist of two components only. Compositions that lie within the triangle contain all the three components. For reading the compositions of an alloy at point o within the triangle, lines xy, $x'y'$ and $x''y''$ parallel to the three sides BC, CA and AB of the triangle are drawn through the point o as in Fig. 2.19a. The length Bx or Cy is equal to the percentage of component A which is at the apex with respect to the lines BC and xy. Thus,

$$\% \; A = Bx = Cy$$

$$\% \; B = Cx' = Ay'$$

$$\% \; C = Ax'' = By''$$

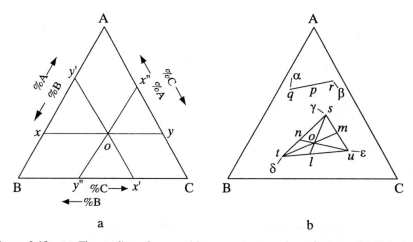

Figure 2.19 (a) The reading of composition on a ternary phase diagram. (b) Use of the tie-line and the tie-triangle to calculate the relative amounts of coexisting phases.

The level rule to determine the relative proportions of two coexisting phases is applied in the same way as in the binary diagram. For example, if the overall composition p in Fig. 2.19b exists as a mixture of two phases α and β of compositions q and r, then the relative amounts of α and β are given by:

$$f_\alpha = pr/qr$$
$$f_\beta = qp/qr$$

If three phases coexist, their relative proportion is determined from a tie-triangle. For example, if the overall composition o in Fig. 2.19b exists as a mixture of γ, δ and ε, the respective compositions being s, t and u, the relative proportions of the three phases are given by (see Fig. 2.19b):

$$f_\gamma = ol/sl$$
$$f_\delta = om/tm$$
$$f_\varepsilon = on/un$$

An example of an isothermal section of the Fe-Cr-Ni system at 650°C is shown in Fig. 2.20. Two tie-triangles are seen in this section. Three phases are present in each of the tie-triangles.

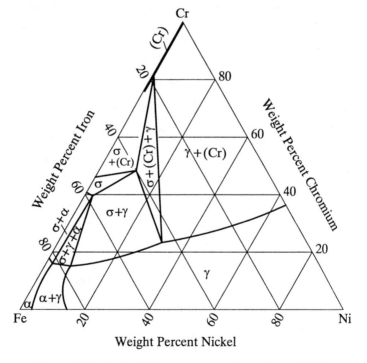

Figure 2.20 Fe-Cr-Ni ternary isothermal section at 650°C.

Another common way of presenting the ternary phase relationships is to draw vertical sections (called *isopleths*), keeping the concentration of one component constant. The *x*-axis then gives the variation of one of the other two components. Temperature is plotted on the *y*-axis. Figure 2.21 shows a vertical section of the Fe-Cr-Ni system at a constant Fe content of 74 wt%.

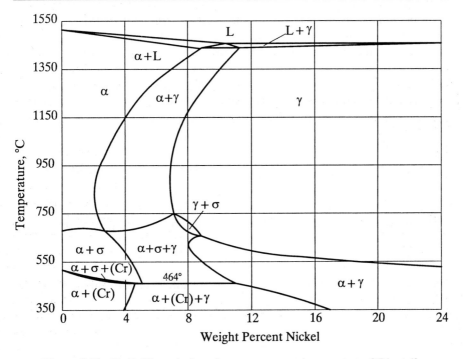

Figure 2.21 Fe-Cr-Ni vertical section at a constant iron content of 74 wt.%.

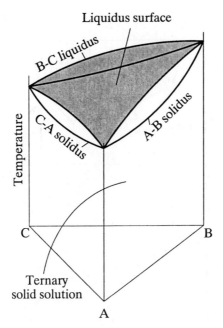

Figure 2.22 The three-dimensional view of the ternary phase diagram for the case of complete liquid and solid solubility.

Perspective views of ternary phase diagrams can be drawn on a triangular prism. They are useful in visualizing the phase relationships in simple cases. The vertical axis of the prism is the temperature axis and any section parallel to the base is an isothermal section. Figure 2.22 shows a perspective view of the ternary system, in which all the three pairs of binaries exhibit complete solid solubility. Within the triangle, the (liquid + solid) two-phase field is a three-dimensional space enclosed by the liquidus surface at the top and the solidus surface at the bottom. Above the liquidus surface, a ternary liquid solution exists. Below the solidus surface, it is a ternary solid solution.

Figure 2.23 shows a ternary phase diagram formed by three components, which pair up as simple eutectic systems. There are four phases in the system, corresponding to the liquid and the three terminal solid solutions α, β and γ. Three-phase eutectic reactions occur over a range of temperatures, along liquidus lines e_1e, e_2e and e_3e. For example, the three-phase eutectic reaction:

$$L \longleftrightarrow \alpha + \beta$$

occurs along line e_1e. Note that this eutectic reaction is not invariant. For $C = 3$ and $P = 3$, the phase rule Eq. (2.4) gives $F = 1$.

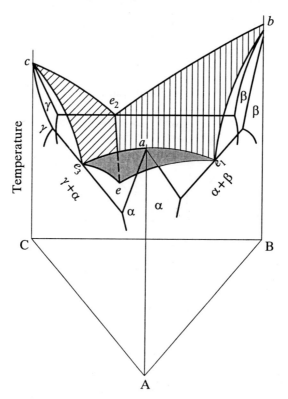

Figure 2.23 The three-dimensional view of the ternary phase diagram between three components, which pair up as simple binary eutectic systems.

e is an invariant point in the ternary system, where all the four phases coexist, with zero degree of freedom. When the liquid has this composition, a four-phase eutectic reaction occurs isothermally:

$$L \longleftrightarrow \alpha + \beta + \gamma$$

2.9 QUATERNARY PHASE DIAGRAMS

With increasing complexity of industrial alloys, multi-component systems, in which the number of components may be more than three, are gaining importance. A quaternary system comprises four components A, B, C and D. After omitting the pressure variable, there are still four variables to be shown on a graphical representation. If the temperature is kept constant, a three-dimensional regular tetrahedron (Fig. 2.24) can show the phase relations. The four components are located at the four corners A, B, C and D, the six sides of the tetrahedron represent the six binaries AB, AC, AD, BC, BD and CD, and the four faces of the tetrahedron are isothermal sections of the four ternaries ABC, ABD, ACD and BCD. Any composition inside the quaternary space has all the four components in it. The equilibrium between four phases in the quaternary space is represented by a tie-tetrahedron (similar to the tie-triangle in ternary systems). A tie-tetrahedron can be of any irregular shape. The equilibrium between α, β, τ, and σ phases is schematically sketched in Fig. 2.24.

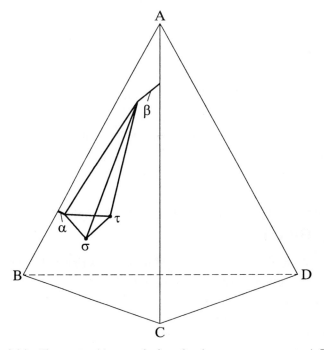

Figure 2.24 The composition tetrahedron for the quaternary system A-B-C-D. A tie-tetrahedron depicting four-phase equilibrium lies within.

For two-dimensional representation, the concentration of one of the components and temperature is to be kept constant. Figure 2.25 shows an isothermal section of the Fe-Cr-V-C system at 700°C and at a constant C content of 0.2 wt%. $M_{23}C_6$, M_7C_3 and MC are alloy carbides, with M standing for (Fe, Cr, V). ABC is the triangular section of a tie-tetrahedron, showing a four-phase equilibrium.

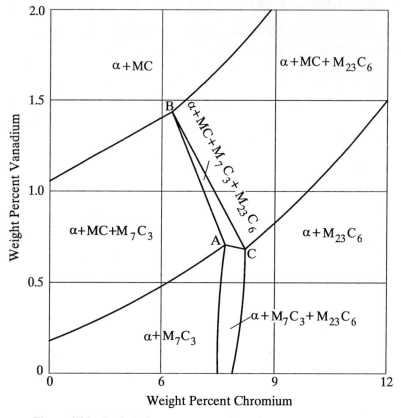

Figure 2.25   Fe-Cr-V-C quaternary isothermal section at 700°C and at a constant carbon content of 0.2 wt%.

2.10   EXPERIMENTAL DETERMINATION OF PHASE DIAGRAMS

A variety of physical techniques are used for the experimental determination of phase diagrams. Among these, the more important are:

(i) thermal analysis,
(ii) microscopic examination, and
(iii) x-ray diffraction.

Other auxiliary techniques are dilatometry, electrical resistivity and magnetic measurements.

Determination of the liquidus and the solidus   *Thermal analysis* is by far
the most important method employed for determining the liquid-solid transformations. The method is based on the fact that evolution or absorption of heat
occurs during a phase change. When the temperature of an alloy sample is
plotted as a function of time during heating or cooling, abrupt changes in slope
of the plot occur at points corresponding to the start or finish of a phase change.

Figure 2.26 illustrates some typical cases. Figure 2.26a is the cooling curve
for a pure metal. As the liquid is cooled to the freezing point, solidification
starts with the evolution of latent heat. The heat evolved compensates for the
heat lost to the surroundings, so that the temperature of the sample remains
constant. The cooling curve becomes horizontal and remains so, till the solidification is complete. Thereafter, the temperature drops again with time, with an
abrupt change in slope at the point of completion of the solidification. Often,
a liquid may *supercool* below the freezing point. But once solidification starts,
heat evolution raises the sample temperature back to the freezing point as
shown in Fig. 2.26b.

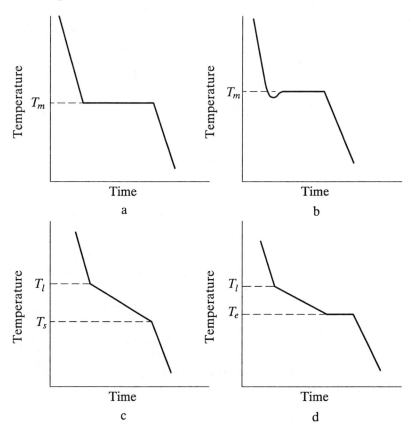

Figure 2.26   Thermal analysis. Cooling curves (a) for a pure metal without
supercooling, (b) for a pure metal with supercooling,
(c) for a solid solution alloy, and (d) for a hypoeutectic alloy.

When heating a pure solid metal, similar breaks in the heating curve occur. In the horizontal part of the curve, the heat input is used up for the latent heat absorbed during melting. No superheating is known to occur. The temperature corresponding to the horizontal part of the cooling and heating curves must coincide. This gives the true freezing/melting point of the metal.

Figure 2.26c is the cooling curve for the solidification of a *solid solution*. The first arrest indicating an abrupt decrease in the cooling rate occurs as the liquidus temperature T_l is crossed. There is no horizontal portion in the cooling curve here, as solidification occurs over *a range of temperature* between the liquidus and the solidus. The second arrest is observed at the solidus temperature T_s, when the cooling rate starts to increase again.

Figure 2.26d is the cooling curve for a proeutectic binary alloy. The first arrest occurs at the liquidus temperature and the cooling rate decreases. At the eutectic temperature T_e, the cooling curve becomes horizontal, as the invariant eutectic reaction occurs isothermally. The cooling rate increases again, when the eutectic solidification is complete. If the alloy has exactly the eutectic composition, only the horizontal part in the cooling curve is seen, corresponding to the eutectic solidification. In principle, a peritectic alloy should show a similar behaviour. However, the phenomenon of surrounding prevents the peritectic reaction from going to completion isothermally. The horizontal part in the cooling curve may not be clearly defined.

The following *precautions* are taken in determining cooling curves:

1. Local fluctuations of temperature in the furnace should be avoided.
2. The rate of cooling must be as slow as feasible for near equilibrium conditions to be achieved.
3. The molten alloy should be stirred for uniform temperature and to reduce supercooling.
4. The analysis for composition must be accurate.
5. No contamination must occur from the crucible, thermocouple sheath, etc.

The *solidus* is determined only approximately from the break in the cooling curve, as coring tends to lower the solidus temperature. A more accurate determination can be carried out by holding the solidified alloy for a long time for homogenization just below the approximate solidus temperature determined from the cooling curve. The alloy is heated again to find the break in the heating curve. This break is at a higher temperature than that determined during cooling, as coring effects are removed by homogenization. The thermal analysis is supplemented with microscopic examination. The alloy is heated close to the solidus and quenched to ascertain microscopically the appearance of the first chilled liquid.

Using the breaks in the cooling and heating curves for a series of compositions covering the entire binary range, the liquidus and the solidus boundaries can be fully determined, as illustrated in Fig. 2.27 for an isomorphous system.

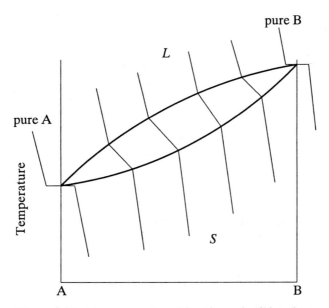

Figure 2.27 The construction of liquidus and solidus phase boundaries from cooling curves. Each cooling curve (shown in perspective view) corresponds to a single composition.

Determination of the solvus The common methods for determining the solvus are microscopic examination and x-ray diffraction. A series of small ingots of alloys of different compositions are prepared and homogenized. They are then annealed at various temperatures for a prolonged time (a few days) and quenched. In some cases, the high temperature phases may be retained on quenching. In such cases, subsequent metallographic and x-ray studies at room temperature disclose the appearance of the second phase at some known composition. In other cases, the high temperature phase may decompose on quenching. If this happens, room temperature x-ray studies are not suitable. A high temperature x-ray camera may be used. Even after the decomposition during quenching, the metallographic method may be useful, if the transformed phase is in an easily recognizable form. A phase boundary is first bracketed between two compositions, as illustrated in Fig. 2.28. The exact location of the boundary is determined by studying a few more alloys of closely varying composition in the boundary region.

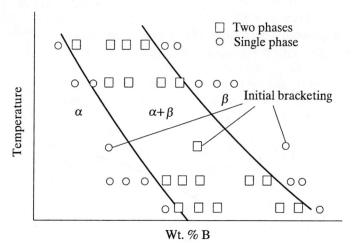

Figure 2.28   The determination of solvus boundaries by the metallographic and x-ray methods.

Auxiliary techniques   *Dilatometry* is based on the volume change associated with most phase changes. It is common to record the length changes of a specimen as a function of temperature during heating or cooling. Figure 2.29

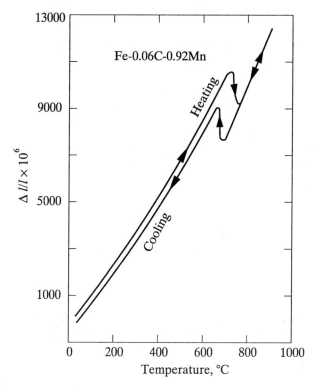

Figure 2.29   The fractional change in length of a low carbon steel on heating and cooling. The abrupt changes in slope correspond to phase changes.

shows the length changes in a low carbon steel during heating and cooling. The interpretation of the curve is similar to that for thermal analysis. Note the appreciable thermal hysteresis that occurs during this solid state phase change.

The *electrical resistivity* of a solid solution changes nonlinearly with the concentration of the solute. However, the resistivity of a mixture of two phases changes linearly with the volume fraction of the phases. The resistivity of the alloys of a simple eutectic system is shown in Fig. 2.30a. The abrupt change in slope of this plot indicates the location of a phase boundary (solvus). The electrical resistivity of an ordered solid solution is low as compared to that of the random solid solution. Figure 2.30b shows the electrical resistivity as a function of composition for the Au-Cu system. The resistivity falls to a minimum at compositions corresponding to the ordered compounds, AuCu and $AuCu_3$. An order-disorder transition can thus be identified.

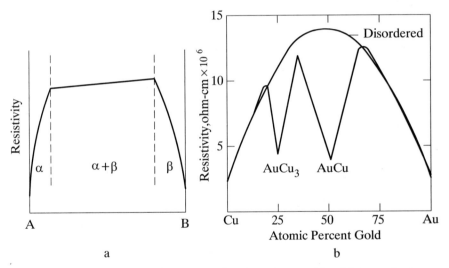

Figure 2.30   Resistivity changes as a function of composition (a) in a eutectic system, and (b) in a solid solution, where ordering occurs.

The *saturation magnetic intensity* of a ferromagnetic phase is very large as compared to a paramagnetic phase. This fact can be used to detect the appearance or disappearance of a phase, if one of the phases involved is ferromagnetic. This method is suitable only when it is used in conjunction with one or more of the other methods described above.

SUGGESTED READINGS

Metallography and Microstructures, *Metals Handbook*, Vol. 9, ASM International, Materials Park, Ohio (2000).

Prince, A., *Alloy Phase Equilibria*, Elsevier, Amsterdam (1966).

QUESTIONS

1. In a three component system, what is the maximum number of phases that can coexist in equilibrium?

    Answer: 5 (taking pressure variable into account).

2. Find the atomic % of carbon in mild steel containing 0.2 wt.% C.

    Answer: 0.92

3. A binary eutectic freezes at a fixed temperature, whereas in a ternary system with three-phase equilibrium, freezing is over a range of temperature. Explain why this is so.

4. Explain why coring occurs to a greater extent in Cu-Sn alloys than in Cu-Zn alloys.

5. Explain why a eutectic composition does not show coring, whereas a solid solution does.

6. Compare and contrast the phenomena of overheating and burning.

7. Give the invariant reactions (and their names) in the Cu-Zn phase diagram.

8. Explain the relative positions of the A_{cm} line and the corresponding graphite line on the Fe-C diagram, on the basis of free energy composition relationships.

9. Calculate the fractions of proeutectoid ferrite, eutectoid ferrite and total ferrite in a 0.2% C steel.

    Answer: 0.76, 0.21, 0.97.

10. What is the fraction of pearlite in a slowly cooled 0.6% C steel? If the steel contains in addition 1% Mn and 0.5% Si, what is the fraction of pearlite?

    Answer: 0.77, ~ 0.9.

11. Sketch the microstructural changes that occur in a brass of 37.5% Zn, when cooled slowly from 900°C to room temperature.

12. Draw a set of cooling curves obtained from thermal analysis of a simple binary eutectic system.

13. Draw heating curves for a proeutectic and a eutectic composition.

Chapter 3

PHASE CHANGES

The properties of engineering alloys are optimized by a careful control of the microstructure. Phase changes (also called phase transformations) that occur in an alloy determine its microstructural features. For understanding the underlying principles in the control of microstructure through thermal or thermomechanical treatments, a knowledge of the mechanism and kinetics of phase changes is essential.

3.1 TYPES OF PHASE CHANGES

A phase change may involve a change in the state of aggregation (e.g. liquid $\rightarrow$ solid), in the crystal structure (e.g. BCC $\rightarrow$ FCC) or in composition (e.g. 0.77%C in austenite $\rightarrow$ 0.02%C in ferrite + 6.67%C in cementite). Compositional changes require long-range diffusion, where the atoms move through several thousands of interatomic distances to bring about the change. Phase transformations without a change in composition can occur by short-range diffusion, where the atoms move only over one or two interatomic distances from the parent phase to the product phase across an interface. Such transformations can also occur by a shear process, where a coordinated movement of atoms (each by a fraction of an interatomic distance only) can change the parent crystal structure to the product structure.

There are two basic mechanisms of phase transformations. In the nucleation-and-growth mechanism, a tiny particle identical in structure and composition to the product phase nucleates and then grows in size. In spinodal decomposition, compositional fluctuations occur in the parent phase. These fluctuations grow in intensity with time, until two discrete phases corresponding to the equilibrium compositions form. Many metallurgical transformations occur by nucleation and growth. We will consider only this mechanism.

3.2 DIFFUSION IN SOLIDS

Diffusion is the mass flow process in which atoms change their positions relative to their neighbours in a phase under the influence of thermal energy and a concentration gradient.

Fick's laws   Fick's first law describes steady state diffusion and is written as

$$J = -D \frac{dc}{dx} \tag{3.1}$$

where J is the diffusional flux in the x-direction (number of atoms transported per unit area per unit time), dc/dx is the concentration gradient, and D is the diffusion coefficient.

Under steady-state conditions, the flux remains independent of time t and position x.

Fick's second law is applicable to nonsteady state diffusion. Here, the flux is changing as a function of position and time. When the diffusion coefficient is not a function of concentration, the second law is of the form:

$$\frac{\partial c}{\partial t} = D \frac{\partial^2 c}{\partial x^2} \tag{3.2}$$

Solutions to the second law for different initial and boundary conditions are available, but will not be covered here. A quick but approximate estimate of the depth of penetration x during nonsteady state diffusion is given by

$$x = \sqrt{Dt} \tag{3.3}$$

Atomic model of diffusion   In interstitial diffusion, Fig. 3.1a, the diffusing atom jumps from one interstitial site to a neighbouring interstitial site in executing a unit step. The neighbouring site is usually vacant in dilute solutions. The activation energy for interstitial diffusion is simply the energy barrier along the path from one interstitial site to the next. Substitutional diffusion occurs with the aid of vacancies, Fig. 3.1b. A substitutional atom jumps from a regular site into a neighbouring vacant site in executing the unit step. Here, in addition to considering the probability of an atom crossing the activation barrier along the path, the probability of the neighbouring site being vacant has also to be taken into account. Because of this, substitutional diffusion is generally 4–6 orders of magnitude slower than interstitial diffusion.

The unit step in diffusion is executed with the help of thermal energy. So, the diffusion coefficient D is strongly dependent on temperature and is of the form

$$D = D_0 \exp\left(-\frac{Q}{RT}\right) \tag{3.4}$$

where D_0 is the pre-exponential constant and Q is the activation energy for diffusion.

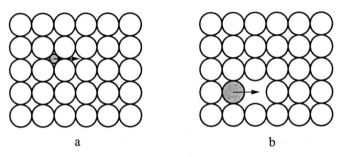

a   b

Figure 3.1 Atomic model of (a) interstitial diffusion, and (b) substitutional diffusion by the vacancy mechanism.

In several phase changes, diffusion occurs along special paths such as grain boundaries or across interfaces separating two phases. The activation barrier for diffusion along such special paths is lower and D is correspondingly larger than that for lattice diffusion described above. However, the cross-sectional area across which mass transfer can occur is limited for grain boundaries as compared to the lattice. Due to this, grain boundary diffusion tends to dominate only at low temperatures. At higher temperatures, lattice diffusion becomes more important.

3.3 NUCLEATION AND GROWTH KINETICS

When the free energy of the parent phase becomes higher than that of the product phase through a change in temperature or pressure, a driving force for a phase change arises. Figure 3.2 shows the free energy of a pure metal per unit volume as a function of temperature for the liquid phase g_l and for the solid phase g_s. If T_m is the melting point of the metal, the free energy change Δg for the liquid $\rightarrow$ solid transformation is:

above T_m, $g_s - g_l = \Delta g > 0,$

at T_m, $g_s - g_l = 0,$ and

below T_m, $g_s - g_l < 0.$

Thus, the free energy change becomes negative only below the melting point. Only then, the liquid can spontaneously transform to the solid.

When $\Delta g < 0$, thermal fluctuations result in the formation of very tiny particles (containing only a few atoms) of the product phase within the parent volume. Such a tiny particle has an interface that separates it from the parent matrix. It grows by transfer of atoms across this interface. The transformation can be divided into two steps that occur sequentially:

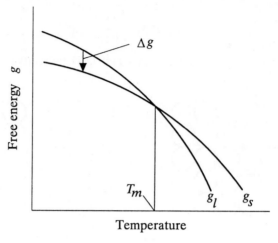

Figure 3.2 A driving force for the liquid-to-solid transformation arises below the melting point T_m.

1. the formation of tiny particles that are stable to further thermal fluctuations and will not dissolve; and

2. the increase in the size of these particles.

Step 1 is called *nucleation* and step 2 is *growth*.

The interface that separates the two phases has a surface energy. This energy has to be supplied during nucleation. It acts as an inhibiting factor for the phase change to occur. A very small particle has a large surface area-to-volume ratio and can, therefore, be unstable.

Homogeneous nucleation   In homogeneous nucleation, the probability of nucleation remains constant throughout the volume of the parent phase. If Δf is the free energy change during nucleation of a spherical particle of radius r, we can write

$$\Delta f = (4/3)\pi r^3\, \Delta g + 4\pi r^2 \sigma \qquad (3.5)$$

where σ is the specific surface energy of the interface. When a driving force exists for the phase change, Δg is negative, but σ is always positive. When the particle is initially very small, Δf increases with r. As r increases further, Δf reaches a maximum and then decreases, Fig. 3.3. The value of Δf corresponding to the maximum is called the critical nucleation barrier (or the activation free energy of nucleation) Δf^* and is found by setting $d\Delta f/dr = 0$:

$$\Delta f^* = \frac{16\pi\sigma^3}{3(\Delta g)^2} \qquad (3.6)$$

The corresponding radius of the nucleating particle r^* is given by

$$r^* = -\frac{2\sigma}{\Delta g} \qquad (3.7)$$

Δg is zero at the equilibrium temperature; so $\Delta f^* = \infty$. When $\Delta g < 0$, the nucleation barrier becomes finite. With increasing driving force and super cooling, both the barrier energy and the critical radius decrease, see Fig. 3.3.

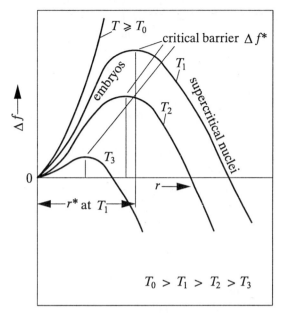

Figure 3.3 The free energy of nucleation Δf as a function of radius r of a spherical nucleating particle.

The barrier to nucleation is overcome with the aid of thermal fluctuations. At the equilibrium temperature T_0, Δf^* is infinite and the nucleation rate I is zero. At 0 K, there are no thermal fluctuations and the nucleation rate is again zero. It passes through a maximum at some intermediate temperature, as shown in Fig. 3.4.

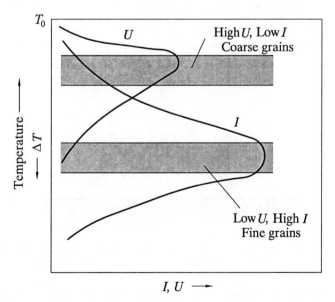

Figure 3.4 The nucleation rate I and the growth rate U as a function of temperature below T_0, which is the equilibrium temperature.

When both the parent and the product phases are solids, volume or shape changes introduce elastic strains during nucleation. The strain energy is added as a positive energy term to the nucleation Eq. (3.5). This has an additional inhibiting effect on the transformation. To minimize the total energy, the particle usually assumes a nonspherical shape such as a disc or a plate.

The increase in the size of the particle beyond the critical size is called *growth*. Like nucleation, growth is dependent on thermal fluctuations. The growth rate U is zero at the equilibrium temperature T_0, as well as at 0 K. It passes through a maximum at some intermediate temperature, which turns out to be higher than that for the nucleation maximum, as shown in Fig. 3.4.

Heterogeneous nucleation   Here, there are certain preferred sites in the parent phase, where the probability of nucleation is much greater than that at other sites. The preferred sites are the walls of the container (in the case of a liquid), inclusions, grain boundaries, stacking faults and dislocations (in the case of solids).

In Fig. 3.5, the nucleation of the new phase β on the surface of an inclusion δ embedded in the parent α phase is schematically shown. The β particle is in the form of a spherical cap. The contact angle θ is determined by equilibrium between surface tension forces (γ) acting at the periphery of the β particle. The energy of the inclusion surface is utilized during nucleation. The barrier for heterogeneous nucleation Δf^*_{het} turns out to be

$$\Delta f^*_{het} = \frac{1}{4} \Delta f^*_{homo} \, (2 - 3 \cos \theta + \cos^3 \theta) \qquad (3.8)$$

The key to the reduction of the nucleation barrier is a small value of θ. When the crystal structures of δ and β are similar and the lattice parameters are nearly equal, a low energy interface forms between them. The contact angle θ is then small and the nucleation barrier is very effectively lowered.

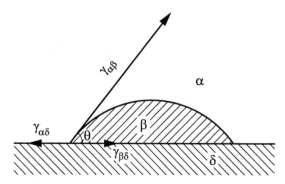

Figure 3.5   The nucleation of a β phase particle on the surface of a nucleating agent δ. The surface tension forces $\gamma_{\alpha\beta}$, etc. act along the indicated directions.

Overall transformation rate   The overall transformation rate dX/dt, where X is the fraction of the product formed, is a function of both the nucleation rate and the growth rate. It has the same temperature dependence as nucleation and growth, i.e. it is zero at T_0, increases with decreasing temperature (or increasing supercooling), reaches a maximum and then decreases to zero at 0 K. The data on transformation rate are usually plotted in the form of a T-T-T (temperature-time-transformation) diagram. The time for a fixed fraction of transformation is plotted as a function of temperature. This has a C-shape, where the nose of the C-curve corresponds to the minimum time (or the maximum in the transformation rate).

The grain size of the product phase depends on the relative rates of nucleation and growth. Each nucleating particle becomes a grain in the final product. So, a high nucleation rate means a large number of grains. Also, when this is combined with a low growth rate, more time is available for further nucleation to take place in the parent phase that lies between slowly growing particles. So, *the combination of a high nucleation rate and a low growth rate yields a fine grain size*, see Fig. 3.4. On the other hand, a low nucleation rate combined with a high growth rate yields a coarse grain size.

In Fig. 3.4, the temperature of maximum rate of nucleation is lower than the temperature of maximum growth rate. An increase in cooling rate lowers the effective transformation temperature and results in the combination of a high nucleation rate and a relatively slow growth rate and, therefore, yields a fine grain size. A progressive increase in cooling rate may show the following phenomena.

Cooling rate °C/sec	Structure	Typical industrial process
10^2	Fine grain size	Chill casting
10^3–10^4	Very fine grain size	Rapid solidification processing
10^5–10^6 10^7	Metastable crystal structures Metallic glass (if the parent phase is liquid)	Splat quenching

3.4 SOLIDIFICATION

Solidification refers to the phase change from the liquid state to the solid crystalline state. Its study is important in physical metallurgy, as it is directly related to the industrial production of castings and ingots and the growth of single crystals from the melt.

Grain structure of an ingot   In addition to aspects of nucleation and growth, the rate of heat flow from the cast liquid to the surroundings through the solidified layer and the mould wall is equally important in industrial processes. Figure 3.6 shows the typical grain structure of a cross-section of a large ingot. The outer zone called the chill zone consists of small, equiaxed crystals that form under the large supercooling that occurs as soon as the liquid metal comes into contact with the cold mould walls. Some of the crystals of the chill zone grow preferentially in a direction perpendicular to the mould wall (opposite to the direction of heat flow) into long columnar crystals. The liquid at the centre undergoes solidification under a relatively small undercooling, forming large *equiaxed crystals.*

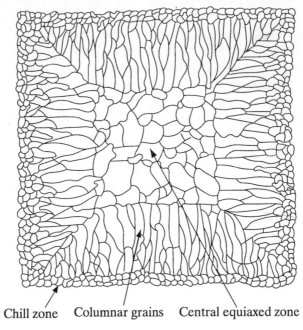

Chill zone   Columnar grains   Central equiaxed zone

Figure 3.6   The grain structure of a large ingot, showing the chill zone, the columnar grains and the central equiaxed zone.

Nucleation and grain size   The nucleation principles described in the previous section can be applied to solidification. No strain energy is usually involved in solidification, as the volume change is accommodated by the flow of the liquid around. An increase in cooling rate means more supercooling and the solidification occurs nearer the temperature of the maximum nucleation rate, resulting in a fine grain size. For example, *chill casting (casting in a metal mould) yields a finer grain size as compared to a sand casting.*

In industrial practice, nucleating agents are added to promote heterogeneous nucleation. Titanium and boron are added to aluminium alloy melts, ferrosilicon to cast iron (to promote the nucleation of graphite) and zirconium to magnesium alloys. The lattice parameter of zirconium (HCP: $a = 3.23$ Å) is close to that of magnesium (HCP: $a = 3.21$ Å), suggesting a small contact angle during heterogeneous nucleation, when close-packed planes of the two crystals can have a one-to-one correspondence of atoms at the interface. This effectively lowers the nucleation barrier, increases the nucleation rate and produces a fine grain size in the casting. In addition to lowering the contact angle by good lattice matching, a successful nucleating agent should be stable in the molten metal and possess a *large surface area and roughness.*

Another way to stimulate nucleation in undercooled melts is to introduce vibrations in the liquid. Vibrations can be applied by mechanical, sonic or ultrasonic means. A pulse of sufficient intensity causes cavitations (formation of voids in the liquid). When the voids collapse, large pressure differences are created and this promotes nucleation.

In recent years, in addition to nucleation, grain multiplication is also considered important in controlling the final grain size. In grain multiplication, some arms of the dendrite crystals break off by melting and move over to other parts of the melt. If there is undercooling at the new location, these broken arms grow into new separate crystals. Vibrations can aid in the break away of the dendrite arms.

The solidified grain structure may be further modified by solid state phase changes during cooling of the casting or ingot. This has an important grain refining effect in steels. Solidification starts as δ-ferrite. This changes to austenite on further cooling, which in turn transforms into α-ferrite and pearlite. Where no such solid state changes are available to exploit, grain refinement of a casting, which cannot be cold worked subsequently, is possible only by the methods outlined earlier.

Constitutional supercooling Referring to the schematic phase diagram in Fig. 3.7a, at temperature T, liquid of composition c_l is in equilibrium with solid of composition c_s as given by the tie-line. During solidification, if the interface that separates the solid and the liquid phases is at temperature T, the liquid near it is of composition c_l, which is greater than the average composition c_0 of the melt. The liquid composition decreases with increasing distance from the interface, as shown in Fig. 3.7b. With the aid of the phase diagram, the equilibrium liquidus temperature can be plotted as a function of distance, Figs. 3.7c and d. In Fig. 3.7c, the actual temperature gradient in the liquid ahead of the interface is such that the liquid at every point is at a temperature above the liquidus temperature for that point. Therefore, there is no supercooling ahead of the interface, which is stable and flat, Fig. 3.7e. Any protrusions that may form on the flat interface "feels superheated" and melts back.

In Fig. 3.7d, the actual temperature profile in the liquid is such that the temperature at every point between x and y is lower than the equilibrium liquidus temperature corresponding to that point. Any protrusion formed in this region "feels supercooled" and does not melt back. As the supercooling here is due to a compositional effect, this phenomenon is known as *constitutional supercooling*. This effect occurs, when the temperature gradient in the liquid ahead of the interface is small or when the interface velocity is large. Under unstable conditions of growth, an interface with protrusions develops, see Fig. 3.7f.

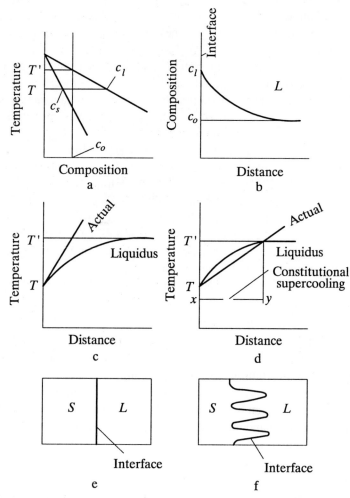

Figure 3.7 Constitutional supercooling: (a) the phase diagram, (b) the composition profile in the liquid ahead of the interface, (c) and (d) the temperature profiles ahead of the interface, and (e) and (f) the profiles of the interface.

Formation of dendrites Under conditions of constitutional supercooling, a cell structure with protrusions forms. If the velocity of the interface (the growth rate of the cells) increases further, the cells tend to grow along certain preferred directions such as <100> for cubic metals. Then a dendrite structure develops, where the growing crystal is in the form of a Christmas tree, Fig. 3.8. Recall that the <100> directions are three mutually perpendicular directions. One of them coincides with the growth direction of the central (primary) arm of the dendrite. The other two perpendicular <100> directions correspond to the secondary and tertiary arms of the dendrite. A number of primary dendrites might have branched off from the same nucleus and thus be part of the same grain, see Fig. 3.8. The spacing between dendrite arms decreases with increasing cooling rate.

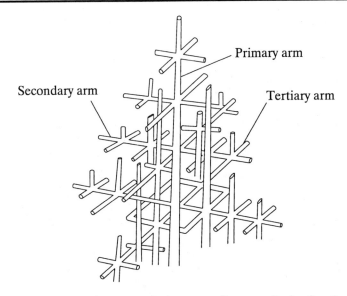

Figure 3.8 A dendrite grows in three mutually perpendicular directions, giving rise to primary, secondary and tertiary arms.

Directional solidification As described above, the dendrites grow along certain preferred crystallographic directions. When the dendrites of neighbouring grains grow in the same direction, we obtain the columnar structure. The direction of columnar growth is always the preferred dendritic direction, i.e. one of the <100> directions for cubic metals. The grains are randomly oriented in the chill zone of an ingot. When columnar growth begins, the most favourably oriented grains crowd out the less favoured ones and grow preferentially. An additional factor that may favour selective growth is that such grains provide the most favourable path for heat flow.

The improved properties of unidirectionally solidified alloys have been exploited in a number of applications. The alignment of the boundaries of the columnar grains in relation to the direction of stress leads to better creep resistance in turbine blades. The columnar structure of directionally solidified *Alnico* permanent magnets nearly doubles the magnetic energy product. Aligned composites with finely-distributed phases can be obtained by directional solidification of eutectics.

Microsegregation During solidification of an alloy, the solute atom partitions itself in different proportions in the liquid and the solid. Under nonequilibrium conditions of cooling, coring manifests itself and the solute gets segregated in the volume of the liquid that solidifies last. During dendritic growth, the liquid to solidify last is in the spaces between the dendritic arms. This segregation of the solute in the solid that forms last is known as *microsegregation*. Compositional variations due to this segregation are seen in a composition-distance profile across dendritic arms obtained from an electron probe microanalyzer. The "wavelength" of the compositional variation gives the dendritic arm spacing.

Homogenization is the process of heating the casting for a prolonged time at a high temperature. This allows diffusion to occur in the solid state and tends to wipe out or reduce microsegregation. The distance over which diffusion is to occur and the time of annealing during homogenization are determined by the dendritic arm spacing. Interstitial elements such as carbon in steel become fully homogeneous, whereas substitutional elements, which diffuse much more slowly, may be only partly homogenized. Homogenization does not remove macrosegregation described below, where the diffusion distances are much larger.

Macrosegregation   Figure 3.9 illustrates some common types of macro-segregation in a large ingot. *The chill zone which solidifies first is usually purer.* The central part of the ingot has a concentration of solutes higher than the average. Macroetched sections show *channel segregates* arranged in a V pattern along the centre line. Vertical channels of segregates also occur in the upper part of the ingot. *A cone type of segregation* is present at the base of the ingot. In large steel ingots, it is not uncommon to find variations in carbon and other alloying elements up to ± 30% of the mean value.

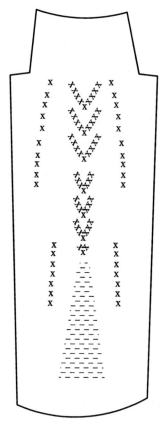

Figure 3.9   The macrostructure of a large ingot shows different types of segregation.

Macrosegregation is caused by the *physical movement of the liquid and the solid* in the semi-solidified "mushy" region. The liquid flows as a result of thermal contraction, solidification shrinkage and density differences. In addition, solid crystals can either settle down or float depending on the density. A segregation known as kishing of graphite in hypereutectic cast irons is due to the floating of the lighter graphite flakes. The cone segregation at the bottom of the ingot in Fig. 3.9 is due to the settling down of the heavier crystallites.

When an ingot of wide freezing range (e.g. Cu-Sn alloys) is poured against a chill mould, a solute-rich region (instead of the usual pure, solute-poor region) may be obtained in the vicinity of the chill. This phenomenon is called *inverse segregation*. The shrinkage during solidification causes the solute-rich liquid to flow through the interdendritic channels in a direction opposite to the interface motion. Inverse segregation does not occur in alloys that expand on solidification. Another form of inverse segregation known as *exudation* refers to the sucking out of the liquid by a pressure difference created by the separation of the metal from the mould due to shrinkage or by the pressure build up inside the metal due to gas evolution. The exuded solute-rich liquid solidifies on the surface of the metal in the form of small drops known as "sweat". *Tin sweat* occurs as a coating of tin-rich white layer on the yellow surface of a bronze casting.

Porosity and inclusions   As the fraction of the solid in the "mushy" region increases, the liquid is not able to flow freely and compensate for shrinkage. This results in *microporosity*. The strains generated by shrinkage can fracture the weak solid. This phenomenon is known as *hot tearing*.

When a deoxidizer is added to a melt, the deoxidation product is often a solid. When aluminium or silicon is used to deoxidize molten steel, Al_2O_3 or SiO_2 particles form in the melt. These are called *primary inclusions*, as they form before solidification starts. Secondary inclusions form during or after solidification, e.g. MnS in steels. Secondary inclusions are usually present in interdendritic regions. Primary inclusions are present within the dendrites, but sometimes found in interdendritic regions, if they have been pushed by the thickening dendrites.

A troublesome class of impurities in cast metals is the *dissolved gases*. In aluminium, there is an abrupt decrease in the solubility of hydrogen, when solidification occurs. The gas precipitates in the form of H_2 bubbles. The decrease in solubility of oxygen in steel results in the reaction between oxygen and carbon in the steel to produce bubbles of CO. These are examples of gas porosity.

Killed and rimmed steels   In a *fully-killed* steel, the residual oxygen in the melt is removed by reaction with aluminium. No gas evolution occurs during solidification. The normal shrinkage gives rise to pipes in the ingot, Fig. 3.10a. In a semi-killed steel, the oxygen is partly removed by the deoxidants. The evolution of CO is just enough to compensate for shrinkage and avoid the formation of pipe, Fig. 3.10b. The CO bubbles are closed during the subsequent working.

In a *rimming ingot*, Fig. 3.10c, no deoxidants are added. Gas evolution occurs with effervescence during solidification. Large bubbles of CO are swept out of the ingot. The left-over CO is in the form of bubbles or wormholes between columnar grains. The turbulence during gas evolution in a rimmed ingot physically transports the metal to different parts, causing macrosegregation to a greater extent. *Capping* is a variation of rimming. After the ingot has rimmed for some time, a cast iron cap is placed on top of the mould to freeze the top and stop the rimming action.

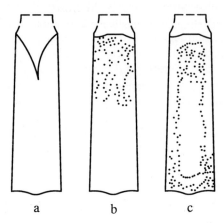

a   b   c

Figure 3.10   (a) Killed ingot, showing the shrinkage cavity at the top,
(b) semikilled ingot, with CO bubbles near the top half, and
(c) rimmed ingot with CO bubbles throughout the volume.

The upper part containing the exposed pipe in killed steels has to be rejected and this decreases the yield to about 80%. The yield from a rimmed ingot is higher.

Continuous casting   Continuous casting is now an established method of producing semi-finished steel products like billets, blooms and slabs. In this method, the liquid steel is first poured from a ladle into a refractory-lined tundish, which directs the flow into a vertical water-cooled copper mould. The strand of steel which comes out of the mould is semi-solid, with a liquid core encased in a thick solidified shell. After solidification is complete, a welding torch cuts the strand into the desired lengths. The structure of the continuously-cast steel is similar to that of an ingot: a chill zone on the surface, followed by columnar grains and a central equiaxed zone.

Continuous casting offers several advantages. It yields a semi-finished shape (billet, bloom or slab), in contrast to the unfinished shape obtained in ingot casting. It provides better productivity and yield, reduced energy and manpower, improved product quality and consistency of quality, as compared to ingot casting. Only a killed steel can be continuously cast. The yield here is about 10% more, as there is no rejection in the form of the exposed pipe of an ingot. A rimmed steel cannot be continuously cast, as the rimming action can puncture holes in the solidified shell, with liquid pouring out.

Rapid solidification processing   The cooling rate in rapid solidification processing (RSP) is in excess of 10^3 °C per second. In the *melt spinning* method, a jet of liquid metal is ejected by an applied pressure through an orifice on to a rotating wheel, Fig. 3.11. Typically, ribbons of 5 mm wide and 20–100 μm thick are produced. The thickness is proportional to the orifice diameter and inversely proportional to the speed of the rotating wheel. The structural features of the product include an extremely fine grain size, metastable extension of solid solubility limits, formation of metastable or glassy products and retention of disordered high-temperature structures. Microsegregation is reduced and the manufacture of near-net shape products is made possible. Some examples of RSP products are soft magnetic ribbons and metallic glasses of Fe-B based alloys.

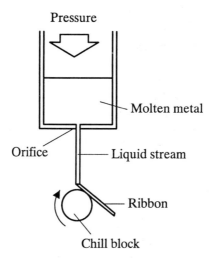

Figure 3.11 The melt spinning method of rapid solidification processing.

Gas jets can also be directed on to the liquid metal stream to atomize the liquid into fine droplets, which solidify by impinging on a substrate forming a dense coating.

3.5 PEARLITIC TRANSFORMATIONS

On cooling a steel below the eutectoid temperature, austenite transforms to pearlite, consisting of a mixture of alternate parallel plates of ferrite and cementite:

Reaction	:	γ	⟷	α	+	Fe_3C
		austenite		ferrite		cementite
Structure	:	FCC		BCC		orthorhombic
Composition, wt%C	:	0.77		0.02		6.67

In the T-T-T diagram for a eutectoid steel, Fig. 3.12, the upper half of the C-curve pertains to pearlitic transformation. In alloy steels, the T-T-T diagram may have two separate C-curves, the upper one for the pearlitic transformation and the lower one for the bainitic transformation.

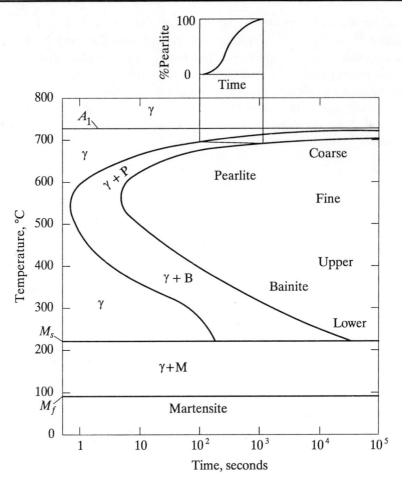

Figure 3.12   The T-T-T diagram for a eutectoid steel.

Nucleation and growth of pearlite   Pearlite nucleates at the austenite grain boundaries. The finer is the austenite grain size, the more is the grain boundary area per unit volume and also more is the number of potential nucleation sites. The nucleation rate of pearlite increases with decreasing austenitic grain size. This explains the increase in the transformation rate with decreasing grain size (see Fig. 3.14). The C-curve shifts to the left, i.e. to shorter times in fine grained austenite.

Nucleation of pearlite occurs in two stages. First, a cementite plate nucleates at the grain boundary and grows inwards into one of the austenite grains. As the cementite plate thickens, the carbon content of the austenite on either side of the cementite plate decreases. When it falls to a critical value, two ferrite plates, one on either side of the cementite plate, nucleate. They grow by rejecting carbon in excess of ~ 0.02% into the adjacent austenite, thereby enriching it. As the carbon content of the austenite increases to a critical value, two cementite plates nucleate on either side and grow. Thus the *side-wise nucleation* and growth of pairs of lamellae continues in a pearlitic colony.

The *edgewise growth* of pearlite is illustrated in Fig. 3.13. In the austenite ahead of the growing plates, the carbon content opposite to a ferrite plate is higher than at a point opposite to the next cementite plate. Carbon diffuses down this concentration gradient, as indicated by arrows in Fig. 3.13.

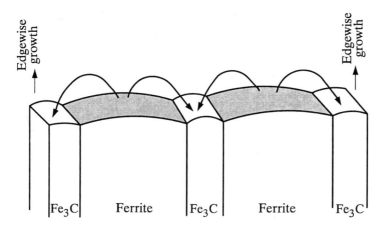

Figure 3.13 The edgewise growth of a pearlite colony takes place by carbon diffusion in the austenite ahead, along directions indicated by arrows.

Several colonies form together in an approximately spherical volume called a pearlitic *nodule*. The radius of a nodule increases linearly with time. The volume of the nodule increases initially as the cube of time, until impingement of neighbouring nodules occurs. The transformation fraction plotted as a function of time has a sigmoidal shape as shown in Fig. 3.14.

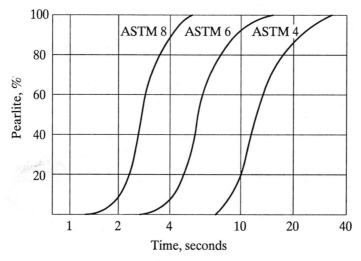

Figure 3.14 The plot of % pearlite against time has a sigmoidal shape.

The interlamellar spacing   If the steel is cooled slowly, the effective transformation temperature is just below the eutectoid temperature. This corresponds to a combination of a high growth rate and a relatively low nucleation rate, see Fig. 3.4. The crystals of ferrite and cementite are relatively coarse. If the steel is cooled more rapidly, the effective transformation temperature is lower and corresponds to a high nucleation rate and a relatively low growth rate. Note that carbon diffusion is required for growth and that the diffusion rate of carbon decreases with decreasing temperature. The crystals formed are, therefore, finer. The size of the crystals in pearlite is measured by a parameter called the interlamellar spacing.

The *interlamellar spacing* of a pearlite colony is defined as the distance from the centre of a ferrite (or cementite) plate to the centre of the next ferrite (or cementite) plate. The true spacing is seen under the microscope, when lamellae of a colony are perpendicular to the plane of observation. When they are inclined at an angle other than 90°, the measured spacing is larger than the true spacing. Experimentally, it is observed that the true interlamellar spacing is constant for a constant transformation temperature. It decreases with decreasing reaction temperature. In Fig. 3.15, the logarithm of interlamellar spacing in Å is plotted against the degree of supercooling ΔT below the eutectoid temperature. Transformation very near the eutectoid temperature yields coarse pearlite, with the interlamellar spacing of about 1–2 µm. Coarse pearlite is soft, with a hardness of about 5 R_c. The pearlite formed near the nose of the C-curve (550°C) is very fine, the spacing being less than 0.1 µm. Hardness of very fine pearlite can be as high as 40 R_c.

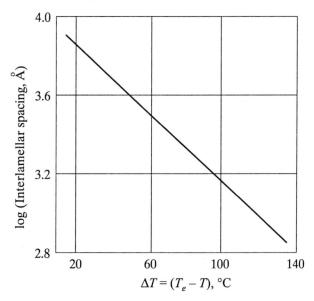

Figure 3.15   The variation of the interlamellar spacing with the degree of supercooling ΔT below the eutectoid temperature T_e.

Cooling of austenite in a furnace yields coarse pearlite, whereas air cooling gives fine pearlite of hardness of 20–25 R_c. The extremely fine pearlite (unresolved under the optical microscope)) formed near the nose of the C-curve is sometimes called *troostite* and the air-cooled fine pearlite as *sorbite*. However, in modern usage, only the terms coarse, fine and very fine pearlite are used, as all these are lamellar structures with different interlamellar spacings.

Effect of alloying elements   Common alloying elements such as Ni, Cr, Mn, Si and Mo (with the exception of Co) shift the nose of the C-curve to the right. They markedly slow down the growth rate of pearlite. For example, the addition of 0.5% Mo decreases the growth rate of pearlite by a factor of 100.

Austenite stabilizing elements such as Ni and Mn lower the eutectoid temperature. In the presence of these elements, for the same cooling rate, the effective transformation temperature is lowered and a finer pearlite results.

3.6   BAINITIC TRANSFORMATIONS

When austenite is cooled rapidly past the nose of the C-curve in Fig. 3.12 and kept isothermally in a constant temperature bath, it transforms to an extremely fine *nonlamellar* mixture of ferrite and carbide known as *bainite*. Several definitions and descriptions of bainite are in use. The subject is complicated by experimental difficulties and the lack of general agreement. We will follow the classical definition, which divides bainite into upper bainite and lower bainite. Upper bainite forms between about 550 and 350°C. Lower bainite forms below 350°C. In both upper and lower bainite, the ferrite units grow by rejecting the excess carbon into the surrounding regions, where the carbides eventually nucleate. In order to proceed, *the bainitic transformation requires the diffusion of carbon.*

Upper bainite has the morphology of a feathery-shaped ferrite. The feathery appearance arises from clusters of fine parallel *ferrite laths*, Fig. 3.16. Cementite platelets precipitate at the austenite grain boundaries, at ferrite/austenite interfaces or between ferrite laths in a direction approximately *parallel* to the length of the laths. The cementite plates are resolved only by an electron microscope. The hardness of upper bainite in a 0.8%C steel is in the range of 40–50 R_c.

In *lower bainite*, the ferrite is a *plate-like unit*, inside which *transition carbides* such as ε carbide ($Fe_{2.4}C$) have precipitated at an angle of 55° to the axis of the ferrite plate. The carbide units are even finer than those in upper bainite. The hardness of lower bainite is in the range of 50–55 R_c. Generally, the mechanical properties of lower bainite are better than those of upper bainite.

Sometimes, two temperatures B_s and B_f are used to denote the start and finish of the bainitic transformation. No bainite forms above B_s. The amount of bainite formed increases with decreasing temperature below B_s. At B_f, the austenite transforms to 100% bainite, if held long enough isothermally.

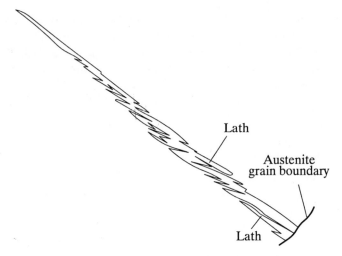

Figure 3.16 The feathery morphology of upper bainite.

Ferrite nucleation is believed to be the first step in bainite formation, in contrast to cementite nucleation in pearlite. The ferrite plate may form by a shear mechanism, as in martensitic transformations discussed in the next section. On the other hand, like in pearlite reactions, diffusion of carbon is also essential for bainite to form. As the diffusion rate of carbon is slow, the distance over which diffusion occurs is very small. This explains the submicroscopic size of the crystals in bainite.

3.7 MARTENSITIC TRANSFORMATIONS

Below the bainitic transformation range, the diffusion rate of carbon becomes so negligible that the austenite transforms without a change in composition to a new product called *martensite*. For eutectoid steel,

$$
\begin{array}{ccc}
 & \text{quench} & \\
\text{austenite} & \xrightarrow{\hspace{2cm}} & \text{martensite} \\
\text{FCC} & & \text{BCT} \\
0.8\%\text{C} & & 0.8\%\text{C}
\end{array}
$$

The shear mechanism The FCC crystal of austenite is converted to the BCT structure of martensite in a diffusionless manner by means of a shear. The basic mechanism is illustrated in Fig. 3.17. A body centred tetragonal (BCT) unit cell is outlined within two adjacent FCC unit cells. The interstitial carbon occupies the octahedral voids of FCC, located at the body centre and at the twelve edge centres of the FCC unit cell. During the shear transformation, the vertical c axis of the BCT unit cell (which is the same as the cube edge a) contracts by about 20% and the horizontal, a_1 and a_2 axes (which are half of the face diagonal of the cube) expand by about 12% each, so that the c/a ratio decreases to the value characteristic of the martensitic crystal. The iron atoms move in a coordinated fashion, by a fraction of an interatomic distance. As the carbon atoms are all located at the middle of the c-axis (or equivalent positions), the shear displacement of the iron atoms is obstructed along the c-axis by the carbon in between. There are no carbon atoms along the a_1 and a_2 axes. The obstruction along the c-axis results in a tetragonal product, with the c/a ratio slightly greater than unity. The c/a ratio is a function of the carbon content and increases from ~ 1.00 at 0.2%C to 1.04 at 0.8%C. In pure iron, where there are no carbon atoms, rapid quenching converts the FCC crystal to BCC by a shear mechanism. Here, the c-axis contracts by a sufficient amount to make all three axes exactly equal, as in the BCC unit cell.

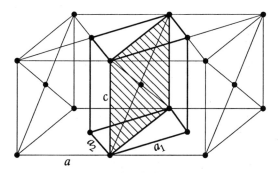

Figure 3.17 The correspondence between the BCT unit cell (martensite) and the FCC unit cell (austenite) in the shear transformation.

Progress of the martensitic reaction Martensite starts to form at a well-defined temperature (below the bainitic range) called M_s (martensite start). The transformation progresses essentially by the nucleation of new plates on cooling. The amount of martensite that forms is a function of the temperature to which the steel is cooled below M_s and not of the time of holding at that temperature. The fraction of martensite formed increases slightly at first just below M_s and then more rapidly with falling temperature. The transformation tails off again and is virtually complete at M_f (martensite finish) temperature.

Both M_s and M_f decrease with increasing carbon (Fig. 3.18) and other alloying elements in the steel (with the exception of cobalt). The following empirical equation gives M_s as a function of composition (wt%).

$$M_s \; (°C) = 561 - 474C - 33Mn - 17Ni - 17Cr - 21Mo \qquad (3.9)$$

M_f decreases in a similar manner. With increasing carbon and alloying elements, M_f shifts below room temperature. Such steels have some untransformed austenite, when quenched to room temperature. This is called *retained austenite*. Further cooling to subzero temperatures is necessary to convert the retained austenite to martensite. As a fully martensitic condition is desirable after hardening, subzero treatment is a standard practice in the heat treatment of alloy steels such as tool steels.

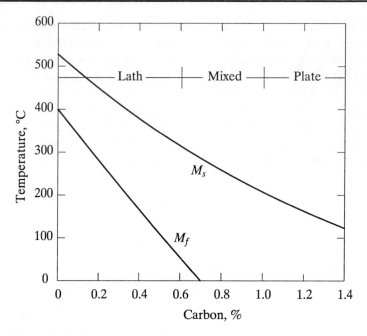

Figure 3.18 The effect of carbon on the M_s and M_f temperatures and on the morphology of martensite in plain carbon steels.

Other characteristics Two morphologies of martensite are commonly observed:

1. lath martensite, and

2. plate martensite.

At low concentrations of carbon and alloying elements and at high temperatures, lath martensite forms (see Fig. 3.19). The lath unit has the shape of a strip. A number of laths form in a parallel fashion, more or less completely filling austenite, Fig. 3.19a. At higher concentrations of carbon and alloying elements and at lower transformation temperatures, plate martensite forms. The plates are arranged in a non-parallel fashion, partitioning the austenite grains into several smaller pockets, Fig. 3.19b.

The hardness of martensite is a function of its carbon content, as shown in Fig. 3.20. The hardness values at 0.1 wt% C intervals are also listed below.

Carbon, wt.%	0.1	0.2	0.3	0.4	0.5	0.6	0.8
Hardness, R_c	38	44	50	57	60	63	65

To realize the full hardness, the steel should have at least 0.6% C. *Alloying elements have no significant effect on the hardness of martensite.* Martensite with hardness below 55 R_c has some amount of ductility. Those with hardness more than 60 R_c are generally brittle.

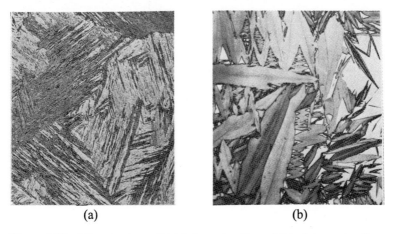

(a)   (b)

Figure 3.19 Microstructure of (a) lath martensite and (b) plate martensite.

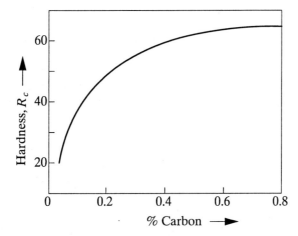

Figure 3.20 The hardness of martensite is a function
of the carbon content of a steel.

Tempering of martensite Reheating of martensite to higher temperatures is
called *tempering*. Tempering is done to eliminate quenching stresses and to
restore some ductility in the quenched steel, at the expense of some hardness.
With the increase in temperature, carbon diffusion becomes appreciable and the
metastable martensite decomposes to more stable products. Five stages of tempering are known. In the *preliminary stage*, recent studies indicate that ageing
effects occur around room temperature and are associated with the clustering of
carbon atoms in martensite prior to precipitation.

Stage I of tempering extends from room temperature to 200°C. During this
stage, the martensite decomposes to two phases: a low-carbon martensite with
0.2%C and ε (HCP, $Fe_{2.4}C$), a transition carbide, which is metastable with
respect to cementite. With increase in the carbon content of the steel, more ε
carbide forms. It precipitates in a very fine form and is resolved only under the

electron microscope. The hardening effect due to this precipitation is usually offset by the softening effect associated with the loss of carbon in martensite. At high carbon levels, e.g. in a 1.4%C steel, the hardness may initially increase on tempering due to the dominance of the precipitation of ε carbide. Other transition precipitates such as η and χ carbides have also been reported.

Stage II tempering occurs in the range of 100–300°C. The structural change here is the *decomposition of retained austenite to bainite* as a function of time at the tempering temperature. The hardness increase due to this reaction may not be evident due to the simultaneous occurrence of other softening effects.

Stage III tempering consists of the decomposition of martensite to ferrite and cementite (Fe_3C). This reaction occurs in the range of 250–400°C. The cementite particles that form are submicrocopic in size. If the steel had already been tempered at a lower temperature, the reaction consists of the decomposition of the low carbon martensite into ferrite and cementite, dissolution of ε carbide and its reprecipitation as cementite.

Stage IV of tempering is the coarsening of cementite particles, which results in further softening of the steel. The coarsened particles become visible under the optical microscope, when tempering is done above 500°C.

The hardness change as a function of tempering temperature is depicted in Fig. 3.21. The carbon steels show a continuous decrease in hardness with increasing temperature. The time at a given tempering temperature is a less important parameter. When hardness changes are to be specified as a function of both temperature and time of tempering for carbon steels, the Hollomon-Jaffee parameter $T(c + \log t)$ is used as the x-axis in Fig. 3.21. Here, T is absolute temperature, t is time in seconds and c is a constant.

Effect of alloying elements on tempering The influence of alloying elements on the tempering behaviour of steels is of two types. Noncarbide forming elements may slow down the decrease in hardness during tempering and also strengthen the ferrite by solid solution. Silicon is particularly effective in this respect, see Fig. 3.21a. For example, at 550°C, the carbon steel has a tempered hardness of 28 R_c, whereas the silicon steel has a hardness of 45 R_c (both of the same carbon content).

The carbide forming alloying elements give rise to an important effect known as *secondary hardening* (sometimes termed Stage V of tempering). The effect of molybdenum is shown in Fig. 3.21b. At about 550°C, a peak in hardness appears. Precipitation of very fine alloy carbide particles is responsible for the peak. The hardness of the molybdenum steel tempered at 550°C is about 55 R_c, as compared to 26 R_c of the carbon steel (both of the same carbon content).

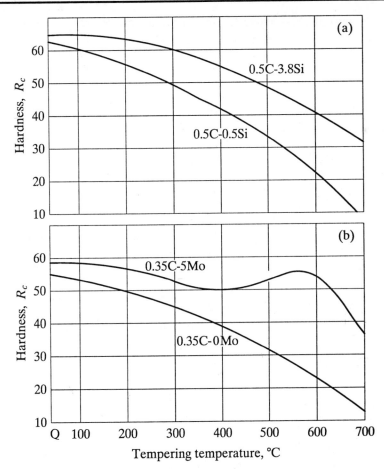

Figure 3.21 The variation of hardness with tempering temperature for different steels.

Thermoelastic martensite In alloys, where the tempering reaction does not intervene, the martensite phase may revert back to austenite on heating. This is illustrated in Fig. 3.22 for Fe-30% Ni, Au-47.5% Cd and Fe_3Pt alloys. Corresponding to M_s, there is A_s (the austenite start temperature) during the reversal. The temperature interval between the forward and reverse transformations (called *thermal hysteresis*) in Fe-Ni is more than 400°C, whereas it is only 16°C for the Au-Cd alloy (Fig. 3.22a). In Fe_3Pt (Fig. 3.22b), the hysteresis is large when the transformation occurs in the disordered alloy and is small when the alloy is ordered.

The alloys exhibiting a small hysteresis show thermoelastic behaviour. Here, the martensite plates nucleate and grow continuously on cooling. If cooling is stopped, growth ceases. If cooling is resumed, further growth of the martensitic plates occur. On heating, the reverse transformation takes place. The plates shrink and disappear exactly in the reverse order of their appearance. An externally applied stress above M_s (in place of a temperature change) can cause the same cyclic phenomenon, i.e. the plates appear and grow on increasing the applied stress; they shrink on decreasing the stress and disappear when the stress falls to zero. Some of the factors which favour the thermoelastic behaviour are a small hysteresis, a small shear strain associated with the martensitic transformation and accommodation of transformation strains *elastically*, without the occurrence of the irreversible plastic deformation.

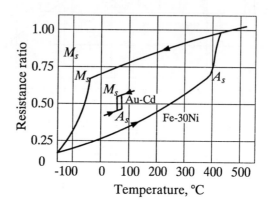

a

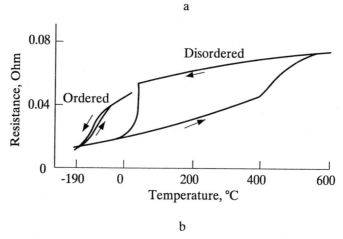

b

Figure 3.22   The reverse transformation of martensite to austenite starts at A_s.

Shape memory alloys   The fact that the martensitic transformation in thermoelastic alloys can be brought about by thermal and/or mechanical means has led to the development of shape memory alloys. A well-known shape memory alloy NiTi (called *Nitinol*) has nearly equiatomic proportions of Ni and Ti. The stress-strain curve of nitinol at 10°C is compared with the normal elastic behaviour of stainless steel in Fig. 3.23. The stainless steel exhibits a usual linear elastic region as per Hooke's law. The elastic strain is less than half of a percent. The deformation beyond the elastic region (not shown in Fig. 3.23) is permanent plastic deformation in stainless steel. In contrast, nitinol exhibits a nonlinear

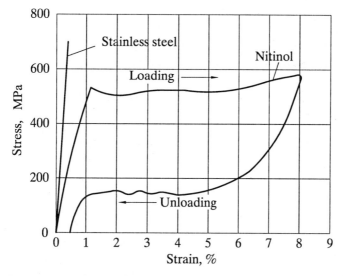

Figure 3.23 The stress-strain curve in the elastic region of a shape memory alloy (Nitinol) is compared with that of stainless steel.

elastic behaviour with elastic strains up to 8%. On removal of the stress, the strain is more or less completely recovered. The forward martensitic transformation takes place during loading and the reverse transformation occurs on unloading, with a hysteresis. A simple example of a combination of thermal and mechanical application is as follows. A straight rod of nitinol can be bent by hand into an L-shape just above M_s. On release of the hand load, the rod comes back to the initial straight form. If, in the bent condition, the rod is cooled below M_s, the rod remains L-shaped even after the removal of the load. If the bent rod is now heated above A_s, it springs back to the straight form "remembering" its original shape.

Manipulation of the martensitic transformation within specified limits of temperature and stress levels has resulted in the development of numerous devices such as dental arch wires in orthodontics, heat activated fasteners or couplings (eliminating welding) in inaccessible locations like nuclear equipment, deep sea and space systems, medical instruments such as catheters and guidewires used in surgery.

Smart materials are materials systems that combine the use of sensors, signal processing and actuation functions into the material structural system. The smart materials have the ability to change physically in response to temperature, load, pressure or other environmental factors. In recent years, numerous international symposia have been held on shape memory alloys, with more than 10,000 patents of shape memory devices on record.

3.8 PRECIPITATION AND AGE HARDENING

In many alloy systems, the solubility in a terminal solid solution decreases with decreasing temperature. An alloy that is undersaturated or just saturated with solute at a high temperature is in the form of a single phase. On cooling, the alloy may become supersaturated with respect to the solute. Then a driving force arises for rejection of the excess solute in the form of a precipitate. Several industrially important alloys such as Al-Cu and Cu-Be alloys undergo precipitation. Precipitation of carbides occurs during tempering of a quenched steel (as discussed in the last section) or during ageing of rapidly cooled low carbon steel. When the precipitates are in a very fine form, an increase in hardness and strength of the alloy usually results. Careful control of the precipitation process is an important step in the heat treatment of such alloys.

Precipitation in Al-4.5% Cu alloy The precipitation process can be described with reference to the Al-4.5% Cu alloy known as *duralumin*. Duralumin contains small quantities of other alloying elements, but, for our present purposes, we can assume it to be a binary alloy of Al and Cu. The relevant portion of the Al-Cu phase diagram is shown in Fig. 3.24. The solubility of copper in aluminium decreases from 4.5% at 500°C, to less than 0.2% at room temperature, see the θ solvus in Fig. 3.24.

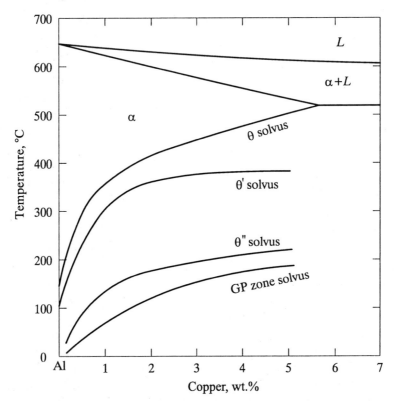

Figure 3.24 The aluminium-rich end of the Al-Cu phase diagram. The positions of the solvus corresponding to the metastable transition precipitates are also shown.

If the Al-4.5%Cu alloy is cooled slowly from 500°C, it becomes supersaturated and tends to form particles of θ precipitates (CuAl$_2$):

$$\alpha_{\text{supersat}} \longrightarrow \alpha_{\text{sat}} \quad + \quad \theta$$

α_{supersat}	α_{sat}	θ
FCC	FCC	tetragonal
4.5%Cu	0.2%Cu	52%Cu

During slow cooling, the precipitates that form are coarse and do not cause any improvement in mechanical properties. If the alloy is quenched to room temperature, no time is available for diffusion to occur to bring about the compositional changes. If the alloy is left at room temperature for a prolonged period or reheated to slightly higher temperatures, precipitation occurs. Due to the limited diffusion rates at these temperatures, the solute atoms move through only a few tens of interatomic distances, giving rise to extremely fine precipitates. This process is called *ageing*.

Steps in the ageing process   The nucleation barrier for the formation of the equilibrium precipitate θ at room temperature is too high. So, precipitation occurs in steps involving several *transition phases*. These are metastable with respect to θ, but still their formation is favoured because of the favourable nucleation conditions.

First, the *Guinier-Preston (GP) zones* form. These zones are ordered, copper-rich clusters of atoms, which are only one or two atoms thick. They are coherent with the matrix and may cause considerable elastic strains. GP zone formation occurs by copper diffusion, aided by quenched-in vacancies over relatively short distances. *The GP zone solvus is below and to the right of the θ solvus* (see Fig. 3.24). So, GP zones do not form above 200°C, as the supersaturation with respect to the GP zone solvus disappears. If the alloy is heated above 200°C after the formation of GP zones, the zones redissolve and the process is called *reversion*.

Overlapping with the GP zone formation, the transition precipitates θ' and θ'' form. These are much larger than GP zones and are partially coherent with the matrix. They have a definite composition and crystal structure, which are slightly different from those of the equilibrium precipitate θ. The transition precipitates may nucleate at GP zones or on dislocations.

Complete loss of coherency at the interface occurs when the final equilibrium precipitate θ forms. It forms only at higher temperatures in a coarsely dispersed form.

Age hardening   Controlled precipitation hardens the alloy. As hardness increases as a function of time of ageing, this process is known as age hardening. The heat treatment consists of several steps:

1. *Solutionizing* is the process of heating above the solvus to produce a single-phase solid solution. It is essential that the alloy is not heated

above the solidus temperature. If coring persists in the cast alloy, even heating close to the equilibrium solidus may cause burning, i.e. melting and oxidation at the solute-rich grain boundaries, with an adverse effect on ductility. Special problems are encountered in Al-Cu-Mg alloy where effective solutionizing requires heating to within a few degrees of the solidus.

2. *Quenching* or rapid cooling to retain the single phase solid solution at room temperature. Cold water quenching is very effective in achieving a maximum supersaturation. It is frequently necessary for thicker cross-sections to obtain the required cooling rate at the centre of the section. Slower cooling rates are achieved by quenching in hot or boiling water or even by aircooling in some cases.

3. Controlled decomposition of the solution by ageing at one or two ageing temperatures. *Natural ageing* refers to holding the alloy at room temperature, whereas *artificial ageing* is holding at slightly elevated temperatures (100–200°C). Figure 3.25 shows the increase in hardness

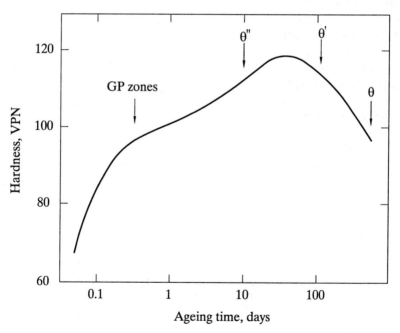

Figure 3.25 The variation in hardness as a function of ageing time at 130°C for an Al-4%Cu alloy. The appearance of the various transition precipitates is indicated.

of an Al-4%Cu alloy at 130°C. The hardness increases with the formation of GP zones and the intermediate transition precipitates. Maximum hardening results in an alloy when there is a critical dispersion of GP zones or a transition precipitate (θ' or θ'') or both.

After the peak hardness, further ageing tends to decrease the hardness. This phenomenon is called *overageing*. The precipitate particles coarsen during overageing. During coarsening,

1. the average particle size increases,
2. the number of particles decreases, and
3. the interparticle distance increases.

The dislocations moving in the matrix face less resistance in an over-aged alloy, which becomes softer.

The service temperature of an age-hardened alloy has to be appreciably less than the ageing temperature. This will ensure that there is no overageing during service. For example, some supersonic aircrafts operate in service with the skin temperature attaining 100–110°C. The ageing temperature for the aluminium alloy used for the body of this aircraft is 190°C.

Quench ageing The solubility of carbon in ferrite decreases from 0.02% at 727°C to less than 0.001% at room temperature. On quenching a low carbon steel from above 500°C, a supersaturated ferrite is obtained. Quench ageing refers to the precipitation as a function of ageing time of iron carbide (or iron nitride) from the supersaturated ferrite. The phenomenon is the same as in age hardenable aluminium alloys.

Between 20–200°C, the transition phase ε carbide precipitates in a submicroscopic form. Above 200°C, cementite precipitates. Figure 3.26 shows the increase in hardness as a function of ageing time at different temperatures. Overageing occurs beyond the hardness peak, as the carbide particles coarsen and the inter-particle distance increases. If an appreciable amount of nitrogen is present in the steel, similar precipitation of iron nitrides can cause hardening.

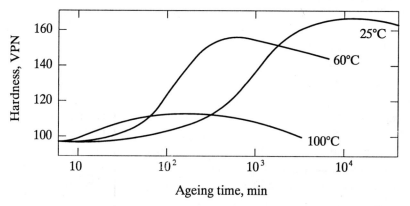

Figure 3.26 Ageing of a quenched low-carbon steel at different temperatures.

Quench ageing has significance in industrial processes such as galvanizing. When the low carbon steel sheet emerges from the molten zinc bath at 500°C, it is cooled with a blast of cold air. Supersaturation occurs at room temperature and precipitation ensues. An annealing treatment after galvanizing to coarsen the precipitate particles may be necessary to have the maximum ductility in the sheet.

3.9 RECOVERY, RECRYSTALLIZATION AND GRAIN GROWTH

These processes refer to the microstructural changes that take place on heating a cold worked metal. In none of these phenomena, a change in composition or crystal structure is involved, unlike a typical phase change. However, the boundary migration processes are quite similar to the growth process.

On cold working, the density of point imperfections and dislocations increases. These structural imperfections have strain energy associated with them. On annealing, the metal tends to lose the excess energy acquired during cold working and revert back to the initial state. This loss of the excess strain energy provides the driving force for these relaxation processes. On heating, recovery, recrystallization and grain growth occur in that order at successively higher temperatures.

Recovery   Recovery is the annihilation and rearrangement of point imperfections and dislocations *without the migration of high angle grain boundaries.* As the annealing temperature is increased, the excess point imperfections anneal out in different ways. A vacancy and an interstitialcy pair can mutually annihilate each other. The point imperfections also find a sink at high angle grain boundaries and at edge dislocations. Excess vacancies can disappear at edge dislocations making them to climb up. On further increase of the annealing temperature, dislocation recovery processes start. A positive and a negative edge (or screw) dislocation on the same slip plane can mutually annihilate each other. Excess dislocations of the same sign left over after this, lower their energy by arranging themselves in low angle boundaries. This process is known as *polygonization.*

Recrystallization   Recrystallization is the nucleation and growth of new, strain-free crystals from the cold worked metal. The driving force for recrystallization is the stored energy in the cold worked metal. Nucleation in the usual sense may not occur in recrystallization. An existing grain boundary with local differences in dislocation density on either side may simply migrate into the region of higher dislocation density. The recrystallization temperature can be defined as that temperature at which 50% of the metal recrystallizes in 1 hour.

Some well-known laws of recrystallization are the following:

1. The higher is the amount of cold work, the lower is the recrystallization temperature.

2. The finer is the initial grain size, the lower is the recrystallization temperature. This is so, as the prior grain boundaries act as sites from where the recrystallized grains start to grow.

3. Increasing amount of cold work and decreasing initial grain size produce finer recrystallized grains as shown in Fig. 3.27.

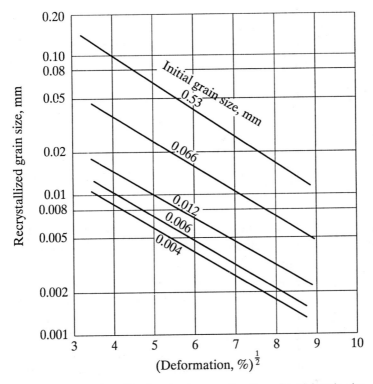

Figure 3.27 Recrystallized grain size as a function of initial grain size and amount of prior deformation in a 70/30 brass.

4. The higher is the temperature of cold working, the less is the strain energy stored in the metal. The recrystallization temperature is correspondingly higher.

5. The recrystallization rate increases exponentially with temperature.

Solute drag and pinning effects   The recrystallization temperature is strongly dependent on dissolved impurities (solutes) in the metal. Commercial purity aluminium recrystallizes at 275°C, whereas high purity aluminium recrystallizes at 75°C. The impurity atoms in commercial aluminium segregate at the grain boundaries and retard the migrating boundaries during recrystallization. This is known as the *solute drag effect*.

Recrystallization is also slowed down in the presence of fine second phase particles such as alloy carbides in steels. When the particle lies on the migrating boundary during recrystallization, the grain boundary area is reduced by an amount equal to the cross-sectional area of the particle. When the boundary moves further, it has to pull away from the particle and thereby create new boundary area equal to the cross-section of the particle. This increases the energy and manifests itself as a *pinning action* of the particle on the boundary. Consequently, the rate of recrystallization decreases.

Grain growth   Grain growth is the increase in the average grain size following recrystallization. The grain size distribution does not change during normal grain growth. During abnormal grain growth called *secondary recrystallization*, the grain size distribution may radically change, i.e. some very large grains may be present along with fine grains.

When the average grain size increases, the grain boundary area per unit volume of the metal decreases, with a corresponding decrease in grain boundary energy per unit volume. This provides the driving force for grain growth, which is about an order of magnitude smaller than that for recrystallization.

The solute drag effect and the pinning action of second-phase particles retard the movement of a migrating boundary during grain growth as well. Thus, aluminium killed steels tend to remain fine grained during austenitization in the presence of aluminium oxide and nitride particles.

The effect on mechanical properties of cold work, recovery, recrystallization and grain growth processes are summarized in Fig. 3.28.

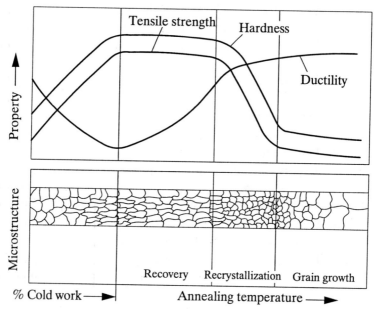

Figure 3.28   Microstructural and property changes during cold working and subsequent annealing, when recovery, recrystallization and grain growth occur at successively higher temperatures.

SUGGESTED READINGS

Shewmon, P.G., *Transformations in Metals*, McGraw-Hill Book Co., New York (1969).

Sinha, A.K., *Physical Metallurgy Handbook*, McGraw-Hill, New York (2003).

QUESTIONS

1. In order to increase the diffusion penetration distance by a factor of two, by how much should the diffusion time be changed and why?
2. Why is a nickel steel heated in air prone to decarburization and not to denickelization?
3. Derive the results given in Eqs. (3.6) and (3.7).
4. Explain how the grain size is determined by the nucleation and growth rates.
5. List the methods available to you for refining the grain size of a casting.
6. Distinguish between:
   (i) microsegregation and macrosegregation, and
   (ii) normal segregation and inverse segregation.
7. Compare the characteristics of pearlite, bainite and martensite transformations in a tabular form.
8. Arrange the following microconstituents in order of decreasing free energy: pearlite, martensite, tempered martensite, ferrite and graphite, spheroidized cementite and ferrite.
9. What is the purpose of tempering a quenched steel? How can the tempered properties be optimized? Discuss with examples.
10. Duralumin alloy rivets used in aircraft construction are kept at $-40°C$ after the solution treatment. Whenever required, they are taken out and riveted on the spot. Explain the reason for keeping them at $-40°C$ and how the riveting operation at room temperature strengthens the rivet.

    (*Hint:* Strain-induced precipitation is faster than normal precipitation).
11. Very fine alloy carbide particles effectively pin down the austenite grain boundaries during recrystallization. Explain how this results in grain refinement.

4

HEAT TREATMENT OF STEELS

The age hardening treatments based on the precipitation reaction were discussed in the last chapter. In this chapter, the heat treatments given to steels, which form an important area of application of physical metallurgy, are discussed. Some heat treatment processes such as annealing and stress relieving discussed here are based on the same general principles applicable to both ferrous and nonferrous alloys. Specific details of heat treatment applicable to individual ferrous and nonferrous alloys are discussed in Chap. 7.

4.1 THE T-T-T DIAGRAMS

The Fe-C phase diagram (Fig. 2.10) depicts phases that form at extremely slow rates of cooling. In industrial practice, the cooling rates may not be very slow. More importantly, *a cooling rate may be deliberately chosen to obtain a desired transformation product in the steel.* For understanding the effect of cooling rates, we need to follow the transformation as a function of both temperature and time. The T-T-T (temperature-time-transformation) diagrams, also known as I-T (isothermal-transformation) diagrams, depict the relationships between phases, temperature and time. The T-T-T diagram for a 0.8%C eutectoid steel was given in Fig. 3.12. Recall the relevant descriptions of it from Chap. 3.

Determination of the T-T-T diagram The T-T-T diagram is experimentally determined as follows. A steel specimen is first heated to the austenitic range and then quenched into a molten salt or metal bath, maintained at a constant temperature, e.g. 625°C in the pearlite region, Fig. 4.1. The specimen is allowed to transform partially to pearlite by holding for a certain length of time in the bath, after which it is quenched to room temperature. The untransformed austenite is converted to martensite on quenching. As pearlite and martensite can be readily distinguished under the microscope, the fraction of pearlite formed corresponding to that holding time in the bath is estimated. By reacting a series of about ten specimens in a similar fashion, it is possible to bracket the times for 1% and 99% pearlite formation. Similar tests are conducted at other temperatures in the pearlitic and bainitic regions to determine the full C-curves for the start and finish of these two transformations.

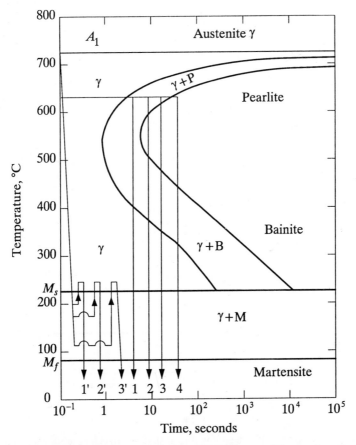

Figure 4.1 Experimental determination of the T-T-T diagram. The numbers 1, 2, 3 and 4 indicate increasing times of holding in the pearlitic region. 1', 2' and 3' indicate quenching to successively lower temperatures within the martensitic region.

Following this, the austenitized specimens are quenched to different temperatures in the martensitic range. They are then heated to temper the martensite formed and cooled back to room temperature, see Fig. 4.1. In the last step, the remaining austenite is converted to martensite. Tempered martensite is dark and can be distinguished under the microscope from untempered martensite, which etches lightly. So, the fraction of martensite corresponding to the first quenching temperature can be determined. In this manner, the amount of martensite formed at different temperatures as well as the M_s and M_f temperatures are obtained.

T-T-T diagrams for hypo- and hypereutectoid steels In a hypoeutectoid steel, *proeutectoid ferrite* forms between A_3 and A_1. An additional curve that starts from A_3 depicts the beginning of the proeutectoid ferrite formation on the T-T-T diagram in Fig. 4.2a, which should be compared with Fig. 4.1. The equilibrium amount of ferrite forms only at temperatures near A_3. At lower temperatures, the amount of ferrite is less. Near the nose of the C-curve, the proeutectoid ferrite curve merges with the pearlite curve. Under such conditions, the transformation is mostly to pearlite but the carbon content of pearlite is less than 0.77%.

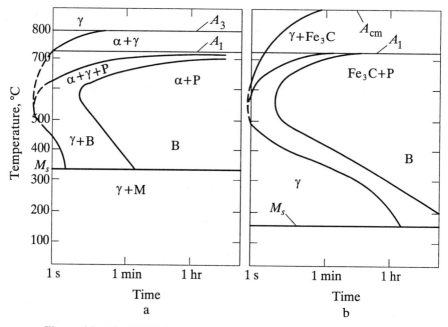

Figure 4.2 The T-T-T diagrams for (a) 0.35%C hypoeutectoid steel, and (b) 1.1%C hypereutectoid steel.

In hypoeutectoid steels, the nose of the C-curve (shown dotted) is much closer to the temperature axis than in the eutectoid steel. Compare the nose position in Figs. 4.2a and 4.1. The nose time is 1 sec for the eutectoid steel and about 0.2 sec for the 0.35%C steel. The hardenability of a hypoeutectoid steel is correspondingly less and very drastic quenching is required to produce all martensite. The reason for the shift of the C-curve to the left is that the proeutectoid ferrite provides sites for pearlite nucleation and enhances its rate of formation.

A hypereutectoid steel has a similar T-T-T diagram, Fig. 4.2b. The upper limiting temperature here is the A_{cm} temperature and the proeutectoid phase is cementite. The shift of the nose to the left occurs here as well.

Effect of alloying elements *All common alloying elements (except cobalt) shift the nose of the C-curve to the right*, thus making it easier to quench the steel past the nose without any transformation on the way. They are said to *increase the hardenability* of the steel. Also, in a number of cases, in the presence of an alloying element, separation of the pearlitic and the bainitic noses occurs. Figure 4.3 is the T-T-T diagram for a Ni-Cr-Mo low alloy steel with 0.4%C, 1.8%Ni, 0.8%Cr and 0.3%Mo. The pearlite nose is at 650°C and the nose time is ~100 s. The bainite nose is at 450°C and at ~10 s. The shorter time at the bainitic nose determines the hardenability of the steel. This time is still an order of magnitude larger than the nose time for a eutectoid steel.

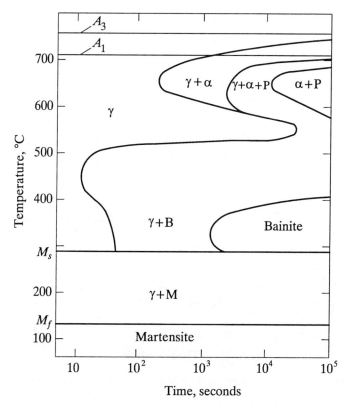

Figure 4.3 The T-T-T diagram for a low-alloy Ni-Cr-Mo steel, depicting two separate C-curves for the pearlitic and the bainitic transformations.

4.2 THE C-C-T DIAGRAMS

The T-T-T diagrams discussed above depict the isothermal transformation of austenite. In industrial practice, a steel is rarely quenched to a constant temperature and isothermally transformed. Rather the steel is continuously cooled from the austenitizing temperature to room temperature at different cooling rates. Continuous-cooling-transformation (C-C-T) diagrams depict the transformation, temperature and time relationships during continuous cooling.

Determination of the C-C-T Diagram   Figure 4.4 shows the C-C-T relation-ships for a eutectoid steel. It is determined as follows. Specimens are cooled from the austenitic range at a constant cooling rate. The pearlite start (point *a*) and the pearlite finish (point *b*) are determined, by the metallographic method

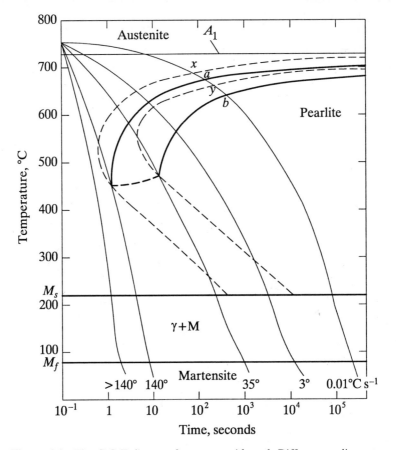

Figure 4.4   The C-C-T diagram for a eutectoid steel. Different cooling rates are indicated. The corresponding T-T-T diagram is shown dotted.

outlined for the determination of the T-T-T diagram. Points *a* and *b* are at a lower temperature and a longer time than the corresponding points *x* and *y* on the T-T-T diagram (shown dotted). This is so, because the specimen has spent much of the cooling time at higher temperatures, where the times for the pearlite start are longer. Experiments with different cooling rates yield the locus of points *a* and *b*. The C-C-T diagram is thus constructed.

The C-C-T diagram for a eutectoid steel A very slow cooling rate of $0.01°C$ s^{-1} crosses both the pearlite start and finish curves of the C-C-T diagram at fairly high temperatures, Fig. 4.4. The resulting microstructure is coarse pearlite. A cooling rate of $3°C$ s^{-1} gives fine pearlite. A higher cooling rate of $35°C$ s^{-1} crosses the pearlite finish near the nose, yielding very fine pearlite. A cooling rate of $140°C$ s^{-1} just misses the pearlite start curve, does not enter the bainitic region and transforms to all martensite. This critical cooling rate must be exceeded to obtain full hardening of the steel. For cooling rates between $35°$ and $140°C$ s^{-1}, the steel crosses the pearlite start curve, but not the pearlite finish curve. Such cooling rates convert a part of the austenite to pearlite. Even though the untransformed austenite passes through the bainitic range of the T-T-T diagram, it turns out that the bainite start curve for continuous cooling shifts so far to the right that very little austenite transforms to bainite. It passes untransformed into the martensitic range. Thus in a eutectoid steel, continuous cooling does not yield bainite. The transformation products as a function of cooling rate are summarized below.

Cooling rate, °C s^{-1}	Transformation product
< 35	all pearlite
35–140	pearlite and martensite
>140	all martensite

The C-C-T diagram for the Ni-Cr-Mo Steel The C-C-T diagram for the Ni-Cr-Mo steel given in Fig. 4.5 should be compared with the corresponding T-T-T diagram in Fig. 4.3. For cooling rates less than $0.006°C$ s^{-1}, the structure is proeutectoid ferrite and pearlite. Between 0.006 and $0.02°C$ s^{-1}, partial transformation to pearlite occurs. The untransformed austenite transforms to bainite and martensite at lower temperatures. Between 0.02 and $0.3°C$ s^{-1}, no pearlite forms. The final structure is ferrite, bainite and martensite. Between 0.3 and $8°C$ s^{-1}, the products are bainite and martensite. Note that bainite forms on continuous cooling in this steel, whereas it does not in the eutectoid steel. The critical cooling rate to produce all martensite is $8°C$ s^{-1}, which is 1/20th of that for the eutectoid steel.

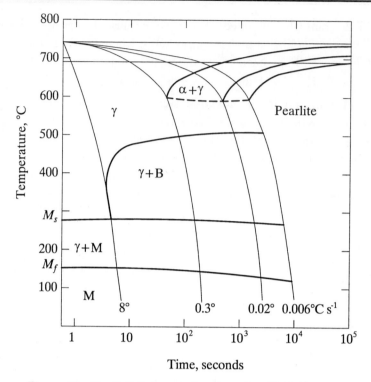

Figure 4.5 The C-C-T diagram for a low-alloy Ni-Cr-Mo steel. Different cooling rates are shown.

4.3 FUNCTION OF ALLOYING ELEMENTS

An alloy steel contains, in addition to Fe and C, one or more substitutional alloying elements such as Mn, Ni, Cr, Mo, W and V. When the total alloy content is small (5–10%), the steel is known as a *low alloy steel*. When the alloy content is more than 10%, it is a *high alloy steel*.

The alloying elements may be present in the steel in the following forms:

1. Substitutional solutes in ferrite or austenite.

2. Nonmetallic inclusions such as sulphides, oxides, and silicates, e.g. MnS, Al_2O_3 and $MnSiO_3$.

3. Dissolved in cementite as part of the orthorhombic structure, e.g. $(Fe,Mn)_3C$.

4. Fine alloy carbides and nitrides, e.g. NbC, VN, WC and $Cr_{23}C_6$.

5. Insoluble metals, e.g. Cu and Pb.

As substitutional solutes in ferrite or austenite, the alloying elements *strengthen* the steel. However, they are rarely used for improving the strength this way, as it is too expensive a method.

Chromium and nickel in solution in ferrite or austenite improve the corrosion resistance of iron remarkably. Stainless steels, which contain chromium with or without nickel, are discussed in Chaps. 6 and 7.

An important function of alloying elements in steels is to *increase the hardenability*, by shifting the nose of the C-curve to the right on the T-T-T diagram. *To be effective, the alloying element must be in solution in austenite.*

Second phase particles have both desirable and undesirable effects in steels. They are the initiators of voids during deformation, which coalesce ultimately to cause fracture. Silicates and sulphides get elongated during hot rolling, which result in poor toughness, when tested transverse to the direction of rolling. MnS removes *hot shortness* (brittleness at elevated temperatures). Sulphides, phosphides and insoluble metals improve the *machinability* of steels.

Fine spherical particles of alloy carbides pin down the migrating boundaries during recrystallization and grain growth. Thus they help in maintaining a fine grain size. In the presence of alloy carbides, the abrasion and wear resistance of steels is improved. Some alloy carbides such as MoC and VC enhance the high temperature (creep) strength, by providing a fine stable dispersion of particles in the matrix.

The order of increasing stability of carbides in a steel is as follows:

Ni   Si   Al   Fe   Mn   Cr   W   Mo   V   Ti   Nb

noncarbide formers   increasing carbide stability ⟶

When nitrogen is present, many of the carbide formers listed above form carbonitrides or nitrides, which are also very stable and abrasion resistant.

4.4   FORMATION OF AUSTENITE

In many heat treatment processes, the first step consists of heating the steel into the austenitic range, the process known as *austenitization*. Austenite starts to form when the steel is heated above A_{c1}. The kinetics of its formation depends to some extent on the initial microstructure. With tempered martensite as the initial structure, austenitization occurs more rapidly than with coarse pearlite.

The rate of austenitization can be shown on a T-T-T diagram, Fig. 4.6. The carbon content is 0.8% and the initial microstructure is fine pearlite. The rate of austenite formation increases rapidly with temperature. For example, full austenitization occurs in less than 5 s at 800°C. However, some residual carbides are left over, as cementite dissolves more slowly than ferrite. The third curve on the right in Fig. 4.6 indicates the completion of *cementite dissolution*. Even after this, the austenite is not homogeneous, as it has less carbon in regions which were initially ferrite and more carbon in regions of initial cementite. The fourth and the last curve on the right shows the *homogenization* of austenite. It is seen that the time for complete homogenization is much longer than for the formation of 99% of austenite (second curve in Fig. 4.6)

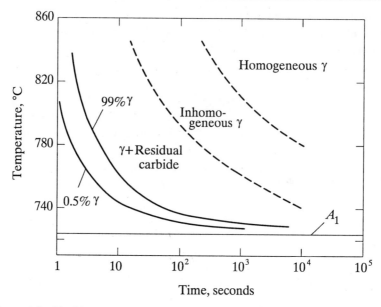

Figure 4.6 The kinetics of austenite formation on heating above A_1. Even though 99% austenite forms rapidly, the time for complete homogenization is very long.

In alloy steels, alloy carbides dissolve much more slowly than cementite. The difference is marked, when the carbide is very stable. For example, vanadium carbide starts to go into solution at around 1100°C, whereas niobium carbide does so only at around 1150°C. These temperatures are much higher than those required for cementite solution. Even after the alloy carbides have dissolved, homogenization of austenite is a very slow process, as substitutional diffusion of alloying elements is involved.

Austenite undergoes grain growth, when held at high temperatures and for long austenitizing times. A coarse austenite grain size is not desirable, as it results in *poor impact properties* of the heat treated steel. Figure 4.7 illustrates the grain growth characteristics of two low carbon steels. In the aluminium-killed steel, a fine dispersion of Al_2O_3 and AlN particles is present. Here, grain growth is much slower at the normal austenitizing temperatures as compared to the unkilled steel. This difference arises from the pinning action of Al_2O_3 and AlN particles on the migrating boundaries during grain growth of austenite. At temperatures above 1100°C, the pinning action is not effective, as the particles dissolve. The grain size of the austenite increases abruptly. Note that the difference between killed and unkilled steels is significant only around 950°C, the temperature at which carburization is carried out. At the hardening temperatures (800–900°C) and at the forging temperature (above 1000°C), the grain size is approximately the same in both the steels.

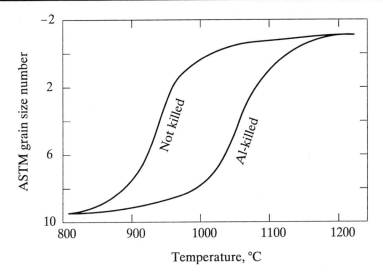

Figure 4.7 The grain growth characteristics of aluminium-killed and unkilled steels.

Effect of undissolved carbides The undissolved alloy carbides produce the following effects:

1. They help to keep the austenite grain size fine. The fine grain size results in better mechanical properties in the heat treated steel. With fine grain size, however, the C-curve shifts to the left, decreasing the ability of the steel to harden.

2. When undissolved carbides are present, both the alloying element and carbon are out of solution and this decreases the hardenability of the austenite.

3. The surface of the carbide particles can provide sites for ferrite or pearlite nucleation, resulting in a further decrease of hardenability.

4.5 TYPICAL HEAT TREATMENT PROCESSES

Typical heat treatments given to steels are described in this section. Figure 4.8 shows the heating temperatures for various treatments on the Fe-C phase diagram.

Annealing The general purpose of annealing is to *reduce the hardness, facilitate machining and to relieve internal stresses*. Different types of annealing treatments are described below.

Full annealing consists of heating the steel above the A_{c3} temperature in the case of hypoeutectoid steels and the A_{c1} temperature in the case of hypereutectoid steels, Fig. 4.8. The steel is then cooled very slowly (in the furnace) at the rate of a few tens of degrees per hour. The austenite transforms to coarse pearlite within 50°C of the eutectoid temperature. As prolonged heat treatment is involved, full annealing tends to be an expensive process. The time of annealing can be cut down by transferring the austenitized component to a constant temperature furnace kept just below the eutectoid temperature. After the transformation is completed isothermally, the steel is cooled in air. The microstructure is still coarse pearlite.

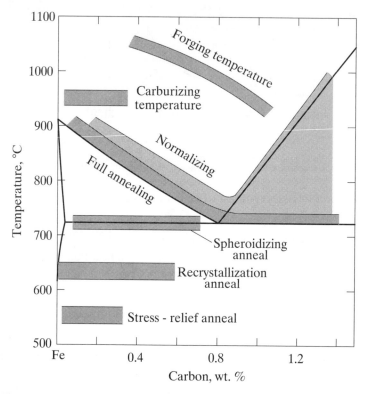

Figure 4.8 The heating temperatures for various heat treatment processes.

Spheroidizing anneal is heating to just below A_{c1} or thermal cycling in a narrow temperature interval around A_1. The cementite lamellae in pearlite colonies tend to spheroidize (become spheres) and thereby reduce their surface area. With prolonged anneal, the spheroidized particles coarsen, becoming fewer in number and more widely spaced. This corresponds to the softest state of the steel. For carbon and low-alloy structural steels, the optimum machinability corresponds to 50% spheroidized–50% lamellar carbide in the microstructure. For high alloy tool steels, the fully spheroidized condition is preferred.

Recrystallization anneal is done at subcritical temperatures in the range of 600–650°C, Fig. 4.8. The cold worked ferrite recrystallizes during this anneal. *Stress-relief anneal* is a subcritical treatment given to hypoeutectoid steels up to 0.3%C. The temperature used is up to 600°C. Recovery processes occur without recrystallization. The residual stresses due to cold working or machining are removed by this treatment. *Process anneal* is a subcritical treatment given to metals to soften them during mechanical processing. It may or may not involve full recrystallization of the cold worked metal.

Normalizing   Normalizing is done for *refining the grain structure and for improving the mechanical properties.* The hardness and strength obtained after normalizing are higher than those obtained after annealing.

Normalizing consists of heating the steel above the A_{c3} temperature for hypoeutectoid compositions and between A_{c1} and A_{cm} temperatures for hypereutectoid compositions, see Fig. 4.8. This is followed by cooling in *still air*. Fine pearlite and proeutectoid ferrite result from this treatment. In hypereutectoid compositions, heating between A_{c1} and A_{cm} helps to break down any network structure of proeutectoid cementite around the austenite grain boundaries. The subsequent aircooling is fast enough to prevent the reformation of the continuous network.

Normalizing is applied to castings and forgings. In castings, normalizing is essential to eliminate the dendritic structure. The microstructure of hot rolled products cooled in air approximates to the normalized condition.

Patenting   This is a special heat treatment process adopted for wire products of medium carbon content. The wire from the austenitizing temperature is passed through a molten lead bath maintained at 500°C. Transformation to very fine pearlite occurs at the nose of the C-curve. During subsequent wire drawing, this microstructure enables a greater reduction in area to be achieved than the annealed structure.

Quenching and tempering   Quenching of a steel is done from the austenitic range to produce martensite. The cooling rate at the centre of the cross-section should exceed the critical cooling rate for the steel to get full hardening. Hypoeutectoid steels are heated above the A_{c3} temperature to ensure full austenitization and to avoid the soft ferrite in the final microstructure. For hypereutectoid steels, this is not necessary, as the cementite that remains undissolved on heating to just above A_{c1} is itself very hard. Moreover, by heating above A_{cm}, the steel becomes susceptible to grain growth. Recall that the A_{cm} line is quite steep. In addition, the steel will crack due to the steeper temperature gradient when cooled from above A_{cm} and also due to the larger carbon content in solution in austenite.

Tempering is almost always necessary to remove the residual stresses and to reduce the brittleness of martensite. The actual tempering temperature chosen depends on the final properties desired. For example, a carbon tool for cutting is tempered only slightly to relieve the quenching stresses, so that a large part of the hardness achieved by quenching is retained. A shock-resistant tool should possess adequate toughness. So, it is tempered at a higher temperature with some loss of hardness. For structural applications, adequate ductility is required, necessitating a still higher temperature of tempering.

Temper brittleness   During tempering, certain temperature ranges may have to be avoided. Temper brittleness is an embrittling phenomenon that usually occurs during tempering in the range of 350–550°C. Brittleness also occurs during slow cooling through this critical range, after tempering at a higher temperature.

Temper brittleness is a reversible process. It disappears on heating to higher temperatures, but returns on holding in the critical range. It does not occur in plain carbon steels. Also when P, Sn, Sb, As and N are absent, temper brittleness does not occur. It is believed to be due to the interaction of common alloying elements such as Cr, Mn and Ni with the above-listed residual elements, many of which enter the steel with the scrap during steel making. The fracture path of the embrittled steel is *intergranular* (along the grain boundaries). The phenomenon appears to be associated with the *segregation of impurities at the prior austenite grain boundaries* without actual precipitation. *Molybdenum* added to steel removes temper embrittlement.

Protective atmospheres   When heated in an open furnace, steel is prone to both oxidation and decarburization. Oxidation is caused by oxygen, carbon dioxide and moisture in the air through the following reactions.

$$O_2 + Fe \rightarrow 2FeO$$

$$CO_2 + Fe \rightarrow FeO + CO$$

$$H_2O + Fe \rightarrow FeO + H_2$$

In decarburization, the carbon near the surface layers of the steel combines with oxygen, carbon dioxide or moisture in the air.

Inert atmospheres prevent oxidation and decarburization. Nitrogen can be used as an inert atmosphere, provided it is purified to remove residual oxygen and moisture. Use of gases such as argon or helium or having a vacuum are expensive methods for protection. They are used for heat treating titanium alloys and some special stainless steels, where the cost is justified. By burning producer gas partially, some industrial atmospheres are obtained. With a controlled composition, such gaseous mixtures can prevent oxidation or decarburization.

Baths used in heat treatment   Molten salt or metal baths offer protection against oxidation and decarburization. In addition, they provide for quick and uniform heating or cooling during heat treatment. *Chloride baths* consisting of mixtures of NaCl and KCl provide a working range of 700–900°C and can be used for austenitizing. Nitrate baths have a working range of 250–600°C and are used for subcritical heat treatments.

4.6   HARDENABILITY

The cooling rates during quenching vary across the cross-section of a steel. The surface cools most rapidly on quenching and hardens by forming martensite. At the centre of the cross-section, the cooling rate is slower, which can result in the formation of pearlite at the centre. If drastic cooling is done, the cooling rate at the centre will also exceed the critical cooling rate and the steel will have hardened throughout the cross-section. However, drastic quenching causes other undesirable effects such as *warping and cracking* of the steel. *The hardenability of a steel is defined as its ability to harden (by forming martensite) throughout its cross-section, without having to resort to drastic quenching.* Alloying elements play a crucial role in increasing the hardenability. If this were not so, we will be building machine components as layer structures, where each layer is thin enough to harden fully!

Grossman's critical diameter   In Grossman's experiments, a number of steel rods of different diameters, Fig. 4.9, are austenitized and quenched in the same bath. To avoid end effects, the length to the rod must be at least five times the diameter. The smallest diameter rod hardens right through. If C $\geq$ 0.6%, a hardness of ~65 R_c is obtained across the entire cross-section. As the diameter of the rod increases, the cooling rate at the centre decreases and becomes less than the critical cooling rate. Then, the hardness falls short of the full value of 65 R_c.

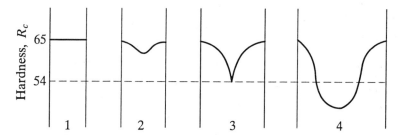

Figure 4.9   Rods of different diameters 1, 2, 3, 4 harden to different depths on quenching in the same medium. The critical diameter is that of rod 3.

The largest diameter rod 4 in Fig. 4.9 has only fine pearlite at the centre. The hardness changes most rapidly at a value of 54 R_c, corresponding to a microstructure of 50% martensite–50% pearlite. *This inflection point is taken as the transition zone between the hardened and not-hardened parts of the cross-section.* For a certain diameter (3) less than the largest, the microstructure at the centre is 50% martensite–50% pearlite with a hardness of 54 R_c. This diameter is called the *critical diameter*. Diameters more than the critical will not harden throughout, whereas smaller diameters will. The critical diameter is thus a measure of the hardenability of a steel.

Severity of quenching media   If the critical diameter is to be defined as a material property that depends only on its composition and the austenitizing treatment, the effect of the quenching medium used should be eliminated. For this purpose, Grossman defined an ideal quenching medium and an ideal critical diameter that corresponds to quenching in that medium. The severity of quenching of a medium is defined by the parameter *H*.

$$H = \frac{\text{heat transfer coefficient between steel and medium}}{\text{thermal conductivity of the steel}}$$

The ideal medium is one which brings the surface of the steel instantly to the bath temperature and maintains it at that temperature. The parameter H is infinite for such a medium. Note that the ideal medium brings only the surface of the steel instantly to the bath temperature. The heat flow from the centre to the surface of the steel still occurs *at a finite rate*, as determined by the thermal conductivity of the steel.

In real quenching media, the ideal situation described above does not exist. Usually a vapour blanket forms between the steel and the liquid. The heat transfer through this layer is slow. The viscosity of the liquid also influences the quenching efficiency. For example, oil which is more viscous than water is a less efficient quenchant. In a brine solution (e.g. 8–12% NaCl dissolved in water), the cooling rate is faster than in water. The salt particles cause little explosions to occur near the vapour blanket, thereby puncturing it. In air, of course, the cooling rate is slower than in any liquid medium.

Agitation of the quenching bath or shaking of the steel object helps to break the vapour blanket and increase the quenching efficiency. The H values for typical media are listed below.

State of the medium	Air	Oil	Water	Brine
Still	0.02	0.2	1.0	2.0
Agitated	0.04	0.4–0.8	2.0–4.0	3.0–5.0

Grossman constructed a master graph for correlating the critical diameter D_c determined in a quenching medium of known H to the ideal critical diameter D_I, Fig. 4.10.

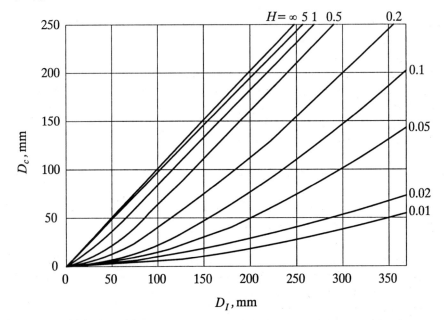

Figure 4.10 The relationship between the ideal critical diameter D_I and the critical diameter D_c for different H values.

For different values of H, we can write from the figure.

$$H \quad = \quad \infty \qquad D_I \quad = \qquad D_c$$
$$H \quad < \quad \infty \qquad D_I \quad > \qquad D_c$$
$$H \quad = \quad 0.2 \qquad D_I \quad \sim \qquad 2D_c$$
$$\text{(still oil)} \qquad\qquad (\text{at } D_c \sim 100 \text{ mm})$$

Jominy end quench test   Grossman's method of determining the hardenability is cumbersome and time-consuming, as a large number of different diameters of steel bars are to be prepared and tested. Jominy and his coworkers devised a *single-specimen test* known as the *Jominy end quench test* for determining the hardenability.

In this standardized test, a steel rod, 25.4 mm dia and 102 mm long, is austenitized and then transferred quickly to a fixture, Fig. 4.11a. A water jet is opened at the same time and the end of the rod is quenched. The variables associated with the water jet are standardized. The diameter of the water pipes is 12.7 mm. The distance of the orifice from the bottom end of the steel rod is 12.7 mm. The free jet height is 64 mm. The temperature of the water should be between 21 and 27°C.

Only the lower end of the sample is quenched directly by the water jet. The cooling rate decreases progressively, with increasing distance from that end. Near the top end, the cooling rate is approximately that of air cooling. The water jet is kept on for about 20 minutes to bring the sample to room temperature. Then, two flat surfaces are ground opposite to each other along the length of the rod. The hardness is measured at intervals of 1.6 mm from the quenched end, Fig. 4.11b. Near the end, the interval may be reduced to 0.8 mm, as the

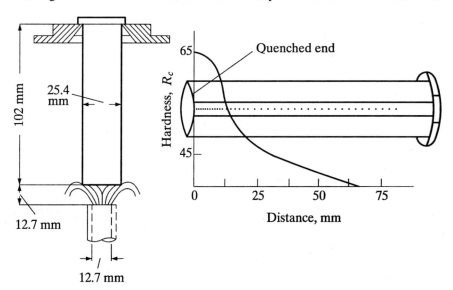

Figure 4.11   The Jominy end quench test: (a) the experimental set up, and (b) the hardness variation as a function of distance from the quenched end.

hardness impressions are smaller and the hardness may vary rapidly. The hardness changes most rapidly, at the location where the microstructure is 50% martensite. This critical distance measured from the end in units of 1.6 mm (1/16″ in the original specification) is called the *Jominy distance*. Figure 4.12 is a master plot relating the distance from the quenched end to the ideal critical diameter. For example, when the distance is 6.35 mm (4 Jominy units), the ideal critical diameter is 45 mm.

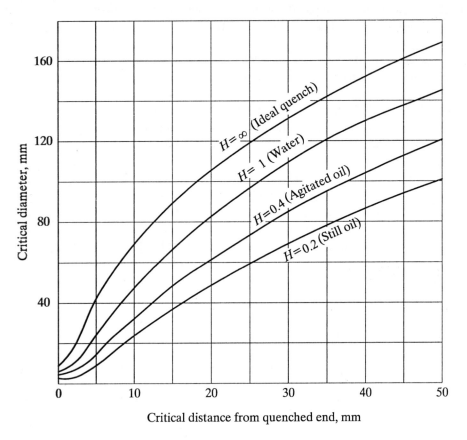

Figure 4.12 The relationship between the Jominy distance and the critical diameters for various quenching media and *H* values.

Computation of the ideal critical diameter The ideal critical diameter D_I of a steel can be computed from its composition. Figure 4.13 gives the base hardenability in terms of D_I for a carbon steel as a function of carbon content and grain size. The hardenability as measured by D_I decreases with decreasing carbon content and decreasing grain size. Recall that the nose of the C-curve shifts to the left and the hardenability decreases, as the carbon content decreases from the eutectoid value or as the grain size becomes finer. Note that the D_I values decrease when the carbon content is increased beyond 0.8%.

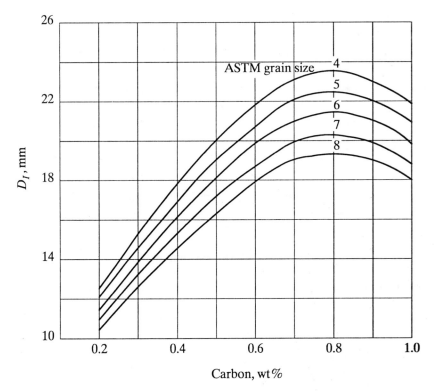

Figure 4.13 The ideal critical diameter as a function of carbon content and grain size.

The effect of alloying elements on the hardenability is shown in Fig. 4.14. Manganese, molybdenum and chromium are among the most effective. The ideal critical diameter obtained from Fig. 4.13 is multiplied by the factor given in Fig. 4.14 for each of the alloying elements present. For example, for a steel of grain size ASTM 7, with 0.4%C, 0.9%Mn and 2%Si,

$$D_I = 15.5 \text{ (from Fig. 4.13)} \times 2.05 \text{ (Mn factor from Fig. 4.14)}$$
$$\times 1.9 \text{ (Si factor from Fig. 4.14)}$$
$$= 60 \text{ mm}$$

Noting that D_c for still oil is about $0.5D_I$, 1.2″ dia rods of this spring steel is just about the size that will harden in oil through the entire cross-section. It must be pointed out here that somewhat conflicting data exist in the literature on base hardenability and multiplying factors. It should also be noted that the hardenability is not based solely on composition and grain size, as it also depends on the austenitizing treatment, which determines the extent of carbide dissolution and homogeneity of the austenite.

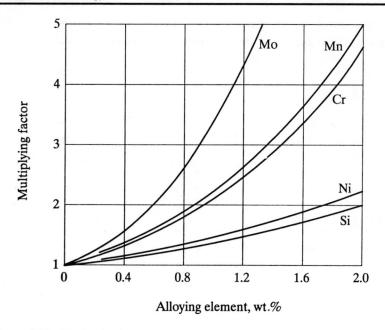

Figure 4.14 The hardenability multiplying factors for different alloying elements.

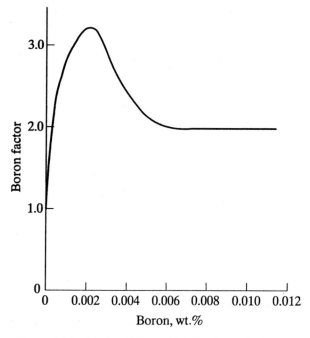

Figure 4.15 Hardenability multiplying factor for boron.

As phosphorous and sulphur (present in small concentrations in steels) have opposite effects on hardenability, their combined effect can be ignored. Boron in extremely small concentrations (0.001–0.003%) has a remarkabe effect of increasing the hardenability of steels. Boron, when in solution in austenite, is believed to segregate to the grain boundaries and strongly retard the nucleation of proeutectoid ferrite. The boron multiplying factor at the above concentration is about 3 for a 0.2%C steel (see Fig. 4.15), but decreases to 1.0 (no effect) at 0.8%C.

As steel compositions are specified over a range, the hardenability can also vary over a range. The Jominy test results for a steel are usually presented in the form of hardenability bands, corresponding to the range of composition of the steel.

4.7 QUENCH CRACKS

When thick cross-sections are quenched drastically, cracks form on the surface of the steel. Distortions of shapes of thin sections due to plastic deformation known as warping may also occur. Warping and cracking are certainly not desirable. The presence of surface cracks reduces drastically the fatigue life of machine components.

Origin of quench cracks   A steep temperature gradient is produced from the surface to the centre of the steel on quenching. Superposed on this are two effects that occur on cooling.

1. thermal contraction of the steel, and
2. volume expansion due to the transformation.

The coefficient of linear thermal expansion (or contraction) for steels is about 11×10^{-6} K^{-1}. For a change in temperature from 820 to 25°C, the total contraction is about 0.9%. The % volume expansion during the austenite-to-martensite transformation is $+ 4.64 - 0.53$ (%C). The linear expansion is about 1/3 of the volume expansion. For a 0.6%C steel, the linear expansion due to transformation is about $+1.4\%$.

When the steel is quenched from the austenitizing temperature, the surface of the steel comes more or less immediately to the bath temperature, whereas the centre is still near the austenitizing temperature. The transformation to martensite occurs at the surface layers and is accompanied by a volume increase. This produces stresses at the centre. The yield strength of austenite is low at high temperature. So, the stresses are accommodated by plastic flow of the austenite. Eventually, the centre also cools down to room temperature, undergoing the martensitic transformation. The centre now expands and produces tensile stresses at the surface. These stresses cannot be accommodated by plastic flow of the surface layers, which already contain martensite. Martensite is too brittle to flow plastically. The residual stress pattern obtained is shown in Fig. 4.16a. The outer layers are in tension and the centre is in compression. Figure 4.16b shows that the residual stress distribution is opposite, when only the surface layers are hardened.

The stress distribution due to thermal contraction is opposite in sense to that generated by the volume expansion due to the transformation. In most cases, the transformation stresses are dominant and the net residual stresses at the surface are tensile in nature. Brittle martensite, which cannot support tensile stresses, cracks. This is the origin of surface cracks in drastically quenched steels.

It should be noted that the residual stresses arise from the steep temperature gradient and the lack of simultaneous transformation throughout the cross-section. If the cooling rates are slower, the temperature gradient is less and the transformation occurs more or less simultaneously, with little residual stresses. Thus, increasing the hardenability of the steel by adding alloying elements, which permit a slower cooling rate, becomes important in reducing the stresses during quenching.

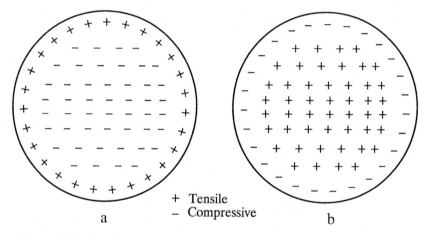

+ Tensile
− Compressive

a   b

Figure 4.16 Residual stress pattern on quenching: (a) after through hardening, and (b) after shallow hardening or surface hardening.

To remove the residual stresses, a stress relieving operation is usually done by reheating the steel to a relatively low temperature. About 85% of the stresses are estimated to be relieved on heating to 250°C. Tempering the steel at higher temperatures, of course, relieves all the stresses.

Martempering and austempering These are special heat treatment processes that are adopted for reducing residual stresses and minimizing the tendency for cracking. Figure 4.17 compares these processes with the conventional quenching and tempering process. In the conventional process, Fig. 4.17a, the surface and the centre cool at different rates and transform to martensite at different times. The residual stresses are set up due to this as discussed above. Figure 4.17b depicts *martempering* (also called marquenching). Here, the steel is quenched into a bath kept just above M_s. After allowing sufficient time for the temperature to become uniform throughout the cross-section, it is aircooled through the martensitic range. The transformation to martensite occurs more or less simultaneously across the section. Residual stresses induced are a minimum. The steel is tempered in the usual way to the desired hardness. As the cooling rate through the martensitic range is less here, more austenite tends to be retained due to thermal stabilization.

Figure 4.17c illustrates the *austempering* process. Here, the steel is quenched into the bainitic bay above M_s and kept isothermally till all the austenite is converted to lower bainite.

The pearlitic nose must be further to the right for austempering and martempering than for conventional quenching, to prevent any transformation near the nose. Also, for martempering, the time at the bainitic bay should be long enough for temperature equalization before any transformation occurs.

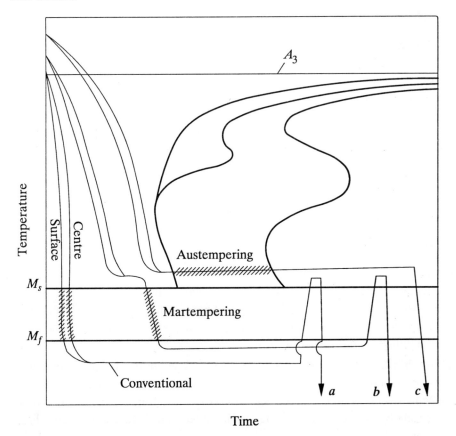

Figure 4.17 Heat treatment processes to reduce quenching stresses: (a) conventional quenching and tempering, (b) martempering, and (c) austempering.

The impact energy and elongation of a 0.95%C steel heat treated to the same final hardness by these three methods are compared as follows:

Treatment	Hardness, R_c	Izod impact, J	Elongation, %
Water quenched and tempered	53	16	0
Martempered	53	35	0
Austempered	52	56	9

Both martempered and austempered steels have better toughness. The austempered steel has the best ductility. However, austempering tends to be slow and expensive, as prolonged holding above M_s is required.

4.8 CASE HARDENING

In case hardening, the surface of the steel is made *hard and wear resistant*, but the core remains *soft and tough*. Such a combination of properties is desired in applications such as gears. A hard and wear resistant surface can be produced in two ways. In steels with more than 0.35%C, the surface can be preferentially hardened by a heat treatment. If the carbon content is lower (0.15–0.2%), the chemistry of the surface needs to be changed by adding more carbon or nitrogen to give a hard martensite after the heat treatment. Recall that the hardness of martensite is a function of its carbon content. In the first category of treatments, we have induction hardening, flame hardening and laser hardening. In the second category, we have carburizing, cyaniding, carbonitriding and nitriding.

Induction hardening   Here, an alternating current of high frequency passes through an induction coil enclosing the steel part to be heat treated. The induced emf heats the steel. The depth up to which the heat penetrates and raises the temperature above A_{c3} is inversely proportional to the square root of the ac frequency. Correspondingly, the hardened depth decreases with increasing frequency. In induction hardening, the heating time is usually a few seconds. Immediately after heating, water jets are activated to quench the surface. Martensite is produced at the surface, making it hard and wear resistant. The microstructure of the core remains unaltered. Induction hardening is suitable for mass production of articles of uniform cross-section.

Flame hardening   For large work pieces, such as mill rolls, large gears and complicated cross-sections, induction heating is not easy to apply. In such cases, flame hardening is done by means of an oxyacetylene torch. Heating should be done rapidly by the torch and the surface quenched, before appreciable heat transfer to the core occurs.

Laser hardening   A laser beam can be used for surface hardening. As laser beams are of high intensity, a lens is used to reduce the intensity by producing a defocused spot of size ranging from 0.5 to 25 mm. Proper control of energy input is necessary to avoid melting. Laser hardening has the advantage of precise control over the area to be hardened, an ability to harden reentrant surfaces, very high speed of hardening and no separate quenching step (the quench is effected by the mass of the unheated material). The disadvantage is that the hardening is shallower than in induction and flame hardening.

Carburizing   Carburizing is the most widely used method of surface hardening. Here, the surface layers of a low carbon steel (C ≤ 0.25%) is enriched with carbon up to 0.8–1.0%. The source of carbon may be a solid medium, a liquid or a gas. In all cases, the carbon enters the steel at the surface and diffuses into the steel as a function of time at an elevated temperature. Carburizing is done at 920–950°C. This fully austenitic state is essential. If carburizing is done in the ferritic region, the carbon, with very limited solubility in ferrite, tends to form massive cementite particles near the surface, making the subsequent heat treatment difficult. For this reason, *carburizing is always done in the austenitic state*, even though longer times are required due to the diffusion rate of carbon in austenite being less than that in ferrite at such temperatures.

In *pack carburizing*, the articles to be carburized are packed in a box, embedding them in a powdery mixture of 85% charcoal and 15% of energizers such as $BaCO_3$. The box is sealed with fireclay and loaded into the furnace kept at 930°C. The residual air in the box combines with carbon to produce CO. The energizer decomposes as below:

$$BaCO_3 \rightarrow BaO + CO_2$$

$$CO_2 + C \rightarrow 2CO$$

The carbon enters the steel through the following reaction.

$$2CO + Fe \rightarrow Fe\ (C) + CO_2$$

The depth of penetration increases as the square root of time, recall the diffusion equation (3.3). Typical carburizing times are 6–8 hours. The case depth obtained is 1–2 mm.

If selective carburization is to be done, copper is electroplated to a thickness of ~ 0.05 mm in regions where carburization is not desired. Alternatively, a refractory paste of fireclay mixed with asbestos can be applied. Control of temperature and penetration depth is less in pack carburizing as compared to liquid and gas carburizing. Also, direct quench from the carburizing temperature to harden the surface is not possible.

In *gas carburizing*, a mixture consisting of 5–15% methane (or propane) in a neutral carrier gas is used. The methane decomposes according to the following reaction:

$$CH_4 + Fe \rightarrow 2H_2 + Fe\ (C)$$

The carbon potential of the gas mixture increases with increasing concentration of methane. Too large a concentration or too high a gas velocity releases carbon faster than it can be absorbed and may result in soot formation on the surface. Closer control of temperature and case depth is possible in gas carburizing, as compared to pack carburizing. Also, post quenching can be done directly.

Liquid carburizing is an outgrowth of the cyaniding process discussed below. A typical bath composition is: 8% NaCN, 82% $BaCl_2$ and 10% NaCl. The following reactions take place:

$$BaCl_2 + 2NaCN \rightarrow Ba(CN)_2 + 2NaCl$$

$$Ba(CN)_2 + Fe \rightarrow Fe(C) + BaCN_2$$

Rapid heat transfer and accurate temperature control are the advantages of the liquid bath.

Post-carburizing heat treatments After carburizing at 930°C, the grain structure of the steel is usually coarse throughout the cross-section. Two separate heat treatments may be necessary to obtain the optimum properties of the core and the case. The steel is first heated above A_{c3} and cooled in air to refine the grain size in the core. The purpose of the second heat treatment is to refine and harden the case. Here, the heating is done above the A_{c1} temperature. Fine grained austenite forms and any proeutectoid cementite in the case remains undissolved. On quenching, the austenite transforms to martensite at the case. The core, rendered fine-grained by the first heat treatment, has a low hardenability and does not harden during the second heat treatment. A direct quenching from the carburizing temperature is adopted only when the steel is inherently fine-grained (e.g. aluminium-killed). A coarse grained steel, if quenched directly from the carburizing temperature, tends to harden in the core as well. These heat treatments are schematically shown in Fig. 4.18.

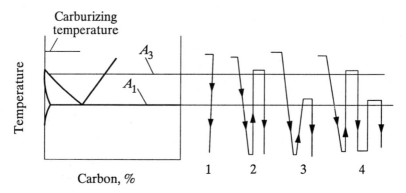

Figure 4.18 Post-carburizing heat treatments: (1) direct quenching, (2) core refining, (3) case refining, and (4) core and case refining.

The volume expansion during the martensitic transformation on the surface tends to induce compressive stresses, which are beneficial for improving the fatigue strength.

Cyaniding Cyaniding is done in a liquid bath of NaCN, with the concentration varying between 30 and 97%. Both carbon and nitrogen enter the steel via the following reactions:

$$2NaCN + O_2 \rightarrow 2NaCNO$$

$$3NaCNO \rightarrow NaCN + Na_2CO_3 + C + 2N$$

The temperature used for cyaniding is lower than that for carburizing and is in the range of 800–870°C. The time of cyaniding is 0.5–3 hour to produce a case depth of 0.25 mm or less.

Carbonitriding This process is also known as dry cyaniding or gas cyaniding. It is the gas carburizing process modified by the addition of anhydrous ammonia. The decomposition of ammonia provides the nitrogen, which enters the steel along with carbon. A typical gas mixture consists of 15% NH_3, 5% CH_4 and 80% of neutral carrier gas. The temperature used is 750–900°C. With increasing temperature, a greater proportion of carbon enters the steel.

Nitriding In contrast to the processes described before, *nitriding is carried out in the ferrite region.* Consequently, no phase change occurs after nitriding. The part to be nitrided should possess the required core properties prior to nitriding. If necessary, a prior heat treatment may be given to develop these.

Pure ammonia decomposes to yield nitrogen which enters the steel:

$$2NH_3 \rightarrow 2N + 3H_2$$

The solubility of nitrogen in ferrite is small. Most of the nitrogen that enters the steel forms hard nitrides (e.g. Fe_3N). A typical nitriding steel contains alloying elements of 1%Al, 1.5%Cr and 0.2%Mo. Aluminium, chromium and molybdenum form very hard and wear resistant nitrides.

The temperature of nitriding is 500–590°C. The time for a case depth of 0.02 mm is about 2 hour. An extremely hard case is produced with hardness in the range of 1000–2000 VPN. Compare this with the hardness of martensite which is 830 VPN (= 65 R_c). In addition to providing outstanding wear resistance, the nitride layer increases the resistance of a carbon steel to corrosion in moist atmospheres.

A common problem encountered in nitriding is the formation of γ' nitride (Fe_4N) on the outer layers of the case, known as the "white layer", as it looks white under the microscope. This layer is very brittle and tends to crack. It must be removed by a final grinding operation. Its formation can be minimized by maintaining the correct ratio of NH_3/H_2 in the gas mixture during the heat treatment.

SUGGESTED READINGS

Davis, J.R., Ed., *Surface Hardening of Steels*, ASM International, Materials Park, Ohio (2002).

Rajan, T.V., C.P. Sharma and A. Sharma, *Heat Treatment: Principles and Techniques*, Prentice-Hall of India, New Delhi (1988).

Totten, G.E. and M.A.H. Howes, Eds., *Steel Heat Treatment Handbook*, Marcel Dekker Inc., New York (1997).

QUESTIONS

1. An austenitized steel, after holding for some time at a constant temperature below the eutectoid, is quenched. The microstructure was found to be ferrite and martensite. What is the possible composition of the steel and from which phase field of the T-T-T diagram was it quenched? Explain with a sketch.

2. A continuously-cooled carbon steel shows pearlite and martensite in its microstructure. Indicate the composition of the steel and the possible cooling route on a C-C-T diagram.

3. List the three most important functions of alloying elements in steel, explaining each one briefly.

4. A high austenitizing temperature increases hardenability. Can this method be used to improve the hardenability in place of alloying elements? Explain.

5. Explain why grain refinement of a hypoeutectoid steel requires heating above A_{c3}.

6. Explain the difference between ideal critical diameter and critical diameter.

7. Calculate the ideal critical diameter of the following steel: Grain size ASTM No. 8, 0.4%C, 0.85%Mn, 0.25%Si, 0.5%Ni, 0.5%Cr, 0.2%Mo, 0.04%P (max), 0.04%S (max).

   Answer: 71 mm

8. Distinguish between austempering and martempering.

9. Explain why a 0.2% carbon steel carburizes much more easily at 875°C than armco iron.

10. In what way is the nitriding process different from the other case hardening processes? Explain.

11. Explain how quenching a carburized steel introduces residual compressive stresses at the surface.

12. Are post-carburizing heat treatments necessary? Explain.

Chapter 5

MECHANICAL PROPERTIES

Typical mechanical properties of metals and alloys are strength, ductility, creep strength, fatigue and fracture resistance. In this chapter, the details of a tensile test are first described. The role of dislocations in plastic deformation and the methods of strengthening metals against plastic yield are discussed. The mechanisms of creep and the design of creep-resistant materials are then described. At the end, the phenomena of fracture and fatigue are discussed from a fracture-toughness viewpoint.

5.1 THE TENSILE TEST

The engineering stress-strain curve Specimens used in a tensile test are prepared according to standard specifications. The test pieces can be cylindrical or flat. Figure 5.1a shows the standard dimension of a typical cylindrical specimen. It is gripped at the two ends and pulled apart in a machine by the application of a load. The stress-strain curve obtained from the tensile test of a typical ductile metal is shown in Fig. 5.1b. On the y-axis, the engineering stress, σ, defined as the load P divided by the original cross-sectional area A_o of the test piece, is plotted. The engineering strain ε, defined as the change in length ΔL divided by the initial gauge length L_o, is plotted on the x-axis. The % elongation is obtained by multiplying the engineering strain by 100.

The stress-strain curve starts with elastic deformation. The stress is proportional to strain in this region, as given by Hooke's law. At the end of the elastic region, plastic deformation starts. The engineering stress corresponding to this transition is known as the *yield strength* (YS), an important design parameter. Many metals exhibit a continuous transition from the elastic region to the plastic region. In such cases, the precise determination of the yield strength is difficult. A parameter called *proof strength* (or offset yield strength) that corresponds to a specified permanent set is used. After loading up to the proof stress level and unloading, the specimen shows a permanent elongation of 0.1 or 0.2%.

The stress-strain curve has a positive slope in the plastic region, indicating that the stress required to cause further deformation increases with increasing strain, a phenomenon known as *work hardening* or strain hardening. If the load is removed when the specimen is in the plastic region, it retraces a straight line path parallel to the initial line and reaches zero stress at a finite value of permanent elongation, see Fig. 5.1b. Thus, the elastic part of the deformation is recovered. On reloading, plastic deformation starts only on reaching the stress level prior to unloading.

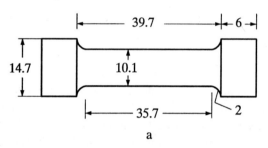

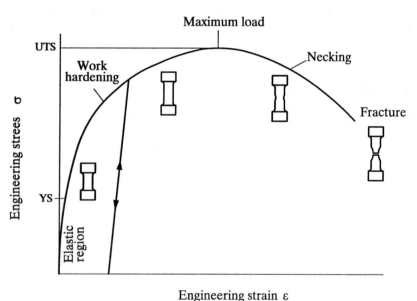

Figure 5.1   The tensile test: (a) a standard cylindrical test specimen (dimensions in mm), and (b) the engineering stress-strain curve.

The engineering stress reaches a maximum and then decreases. The maximum value is known as the *ultimate tensile strength* (UTS) or simply the tensile strength. Up to the UTS, the strain is uniformly distributed along the gauge length. Beyond UTS, somewhere near the middle of the specimen, a localized decrease in cross-section known as necking develops. Once the neck forms, further deformation is concentrated in the neck. The strain is no longer uniform along the gauge length. The cross-sectional area of the neck continuously decreases, as the % elongation increases. Voids nucleate in the necked region at the interface of *hard second-phase particles* in the material. These voids grow and coalesce, as the strain increases. The true cross-section bearing the load becomes very small, as compared to the apparent cross-section, due to the growth of these internal voids. At this stage, the specimen may fracture. Figure 5.2 shows that ductility measured in terms of the true strain at fracture (see below for definition of true strain) decreases with increasing concentration

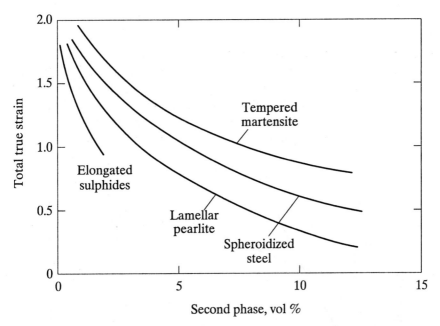

Figure 5.2 Effect of second-phase particles on the true strain at fracture. Elongated and plate-like particles reduce ductility more than spherical particles.

of second-phase particles, which are responsible for the nucleation of voids in the neck. It is seen that spherical-shaped second phase particles are less harmful than plate-like carbides or elongated sulphides. If there are no second phase particles to nucleate the voids, the specimen may neck down to a point before fracture occurs. The % elongation corresponding to the fracture point is called the *total elongation*. The % elongation corresponding to the maximum load is called the *uniform elongation*, as it corresponds to the point up to which the cross-sectional area decreases uniformly along the gauge length. The % reduction in area (% RA) is defined as the decrease in cross-sectional area of the neck at fracture, divided by the initial area A_o (expressed as a percentage). Both % elongation and % RA are used as a measure of ductility.

The maximum point on the engineering stress-strain curve is called the point of *plastic instability*. At this point, the fractional increase in stress $d\sigma/\sigma$ due to work hardening is exactly balanced by the fractional decrease in cross-section – dA/A due to elongation of the specimen:

$$\frac{d\sigma}{\sigma} = -\frac{dA}{A} \tag{5.1}$$

The true stress-true strain curve   The fall in the engineering stress beyond UTS is not due to a softening of the material. If we define the true stress σ as the load P divided by the instantaneous (minimum) cross-sectional area A and the true strain ε_t as the integral of the incremental change in length dl divided by the current value of the gauge length l, we can replot the tensile test data as a σ_t–ε_t curve. As the true stress is always larger than the engineering stress and the true strain is smaller than the engineering strain, the σ_t–ε_t curve lies above and to the left of the engineering stress-strain curve. Figure 5.3 shows the true stress-true strain curves for a number of metals and alloys. The curves have a positive slope right up to the point of fracture, showing that work hardening occurs up to fracture, even though at a decreasing rate. The decreasing rate of work hardening is called *dynamic recovery* and is attributed to the *cross-slip of screw dislocations*, which initially get piled up against obstacles.

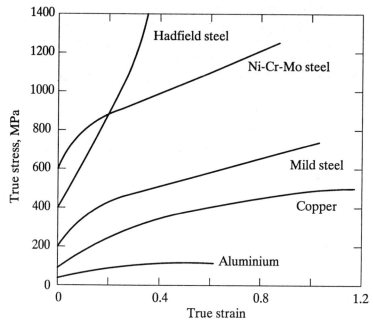

Figure 5.3   The true stress-true strain curves for a number of metals and alloys.

The rate of work hardening   The true stress-true strain curve in the plastic region is often described by the *Hollomon equation*:

$$\sigma_t = K\varepsilon_t^n \tag{5.2}$$

where K is the strength coefficient and n is the work hardening exponent. For some metals, n is constant throughout the plastic region, whereas in others n changes (generally decreases) with increasing strain. Typically, n is in the range of 0.1–0.3. A large value of n means a high work hardening rate and a high tensile strength relative to the yield strength. Combining Eqs. (5.1) and (5.2), it can be shown that the uniform true strain ε_t^u corresponding to the point of plastic instability is equal to n. So, as n increases, the uniform strain increases, Fig. 5.4, and the material exhibits more ductility.

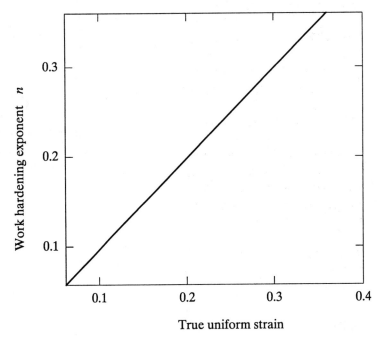

Figure 5.4   The true uniform strain is equal to the work-hardening exponent n.

In austenitic stainless steels, the work hardening rate is high. This is attributed to the low stacking fault energy (~ 0.005 J m^{-2}) and the corresponding difficulty in the cross-slip of screw dislocations. This delays the onset of dynamic recovery and increases the extent of uniform strain along the gauge length. The tensile strength of 18/8 stainless steel is more than twice its yield strength. The % elongation is also high (~ 60%). Aluminium has a high stacking fault energy (0.2 J m^{-2}), as compared to copper (0.04 J m^{-2}) and hence work hardens less, as seen in Fig. 5.3. Zinc, when added to copper, decreases the stacking fault energy. Correspondingly, alpha brass is stronger and more ductile than copper.

The flow stress Flow stress is a term used to define the stress level at which plastic deformation starts in a specimen that might have undergone a specified amount of prior plastic strain. It is easily seen that the flow stress is equal to the yield stress, if the prior plastic strain is zero; otherwise, it is greater than the yield stress, due to prior work hardening. The flow stress decreases with increasing temperature T, but increases with increasing strain rate $\dot{\varepsilon}$. The combined effect of temperature and strain rate on flow stress is denoted by the Zener-Hollomon parameter Z, which is defined as

$$Z = \dot{\varepsilon} \ \exp(-\Delta H/RT) \qquad (5.3)$$

where ΔH is the activation energy for plastic deformation. It is clear that, for the same Z, more than one combination of temperature and strain rate is possible. For example, in copper the flow stress at $\varepsilon = 0.3$ is the same (about 70 MPa) when

$$T = 600°C \quad \text{and} \quad \dot{\varepsilon} = 2 \times 10^{-3}$$
$$T = 800°C \quad \text{and} \quad \dot{\varepsilon} = 2 \times 10^{-1}$$

The stress-strain curve for mild steel Figure 5.5a shows the tensile stress-strain curve for an annealed 0.2%C steel. The end of the elastic region is marked by the upper yield point (UYP). Plastic deformation begins at this point.

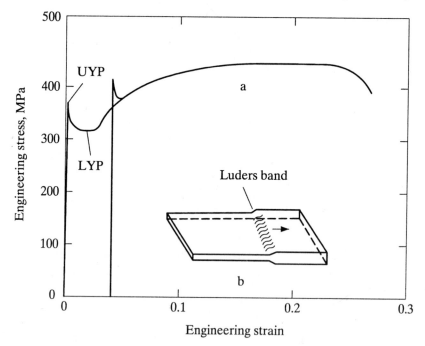

Figure 5.5 The engineering stress-strain curve for mild steel. The inset shows the passage of a Luders band during yield point elongation.

Immediately thereafter, the stress falls to a lower value known as the *lower yield point*. A horizontal part of the stress-strain curve called the *yield point elongation* ensues, where deformation bands known as *Luders bands* pass from one end to the other end of the test specimen, as illustrated in Fig. 5.5b. At the end of the horizontal region, work hardening begins.

Interstitial elements, carbon and nitrogen, are too large for the voids they occupy in ferrite. So, they tend to segregate to dislocations and lower their distortional energy in the process. They are said to form Cottrell atmospheres around the dislocations. Most of the dislocations are locked up on account of this and cannot move when a stress is applied. Very few dislocations are free to move at the onset of plastic deformation near the upper yield point. As soon as they start to move, they rapidly multiply and lower the stress required for continued plastic deformation to the level of the lower yield point.

Strain ageing   If the deformation of the steel is interrupted after the work hardening region is entered and the specimen is allowed to rest at room temperature or for a shorter time at 100–150°C, on reloading a new yield point is observed, see Fig. 5.5a. This return of the yield point is referred to as *strain ageing*. Interstitial atoms diffuse to form atmospheres and lock up the newly generated dislocations during ageing. This behaviour should be contrasted with quench ageing, discussed in Sec. 3.8, where actual precipitation (not just impurity atmosphere formation) takes place. Another point of distinction is that plastic deformation is not required to produce quench ageing, whereas it is necessary for strain ageing.

Strain ageing can cause embrittlement. For example, cold sheared mild steel plates undergo strain ageing near the sheared edge during the subsequent galvanizing treatment and may become brittle.

On increasing the temperature of test on mild steel, the single yield point is replaced by *fine serrations* all along the stress-strain curve, Fig. 5.6. These arise, because the temperature is high enough for the interstitial atoms to diffuse during deformation and form atmospheres around the newly generated dislocations. This phenomenon is called *dynamic strain ageing*, as it occurs during the test itself, as opposed to static strain ageing, which occurs on holding after deformation.

Note from Fig. 5.6 that the elongations have decreased at the higher temperatures. During dynamic strain ageing, locking of newly generated dislocations occurs more readily with increasing temperature of deformation. So, for the same deformation, the dislocation density at 200°C is found to be an order of magnitude more than that at 20°C. This high density of locked dislocations causes the decrease in ductility. This phenomenon is often referred to as *blue brittleness*, blue being the interference colour of the steel, when it gets oxidized in the temperature range of 200–300°C.

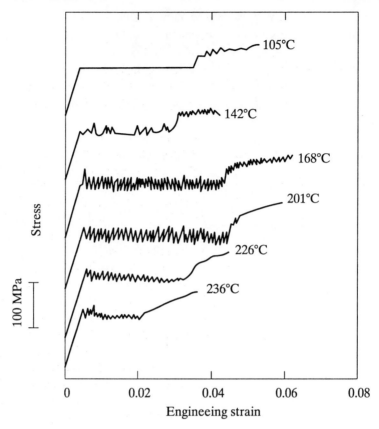

Figure 5.6 The stress-strain curves for mild steel at different temperatures, showing serrations due to dynamic strain ageing.

5.2 PLASTIC DEFORMATION MECHANISMS

Slip and twinning Plastic deformation permanently changes the shape and dimensions of a metal. X-ray analysis of a deformed metal shows that, during plastic deformation, there is no change in the crystal structure or the lattice parameters. Only the number of imperfections increases. The macroscopic change of shape and dimensions can be brought about without any change in the unit cell dimensions by two processes:

(i) slip, and
(ii) twinning.

Figure 5.7 illustrates the processes of slip and twinning. In *slip*, atoms move over a *number* of interatomic distances relative to their initial positions. The magnitude of each step in the displacement is one *full* interatomic distance. The orientation of the displaced region is *the same* as the original undeformed region.

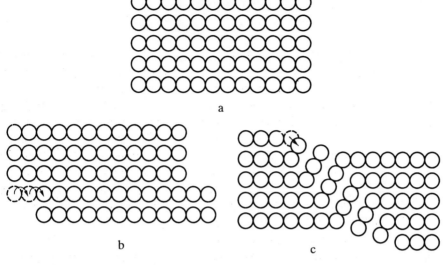

Figure 5.7 The processes of slip and twinning: (a) before deformation, (b) after slip, and (c) after twinning.

In *twinning*, each atom moves by only a *fraction* of an interatomic distance relative to its neighbours. The orientation of the twinned region is different from the untwinned region. Generally, slip is the operative mechanism of plastic deformation at higher temperatures and lower strain rates, whereas twinning is operative at lower temperatures and higher strain rates.

It is experimentally observed that slip and twinning occur on well-defined crystallographic planes along specific crystal directions. Typical slip planes, slip directions, twin planes and twin directions for common metallic crystals are listed below.

Crystal	Slip plane	Slip direction	Twin plane	Twin direction	Examples
HCP	(0001)	[11$\bar{2}$0]	(10$\bar{1}$2)	[10$\bar{1}$2]	Cd, Mg, Zn
FCC	(111)	[110]	(111)	[112]	Ag, Cu, Au
BCC	(110)	[111]	(112)	[111]	Fe, Mo, Ta

Slip produces steps on a prepolished surface which appear as parallel lines under the microscope. Figure 5.8 shows the slip lines in copper deformed at room temperature. In contrast to the straight slip lines seen in Fig. 5.8, BCC iron typically produces *wavy* slip lines, as slip occurs on (112) and (123) planes in addition to (110) planes, with a common slip direction of [111].

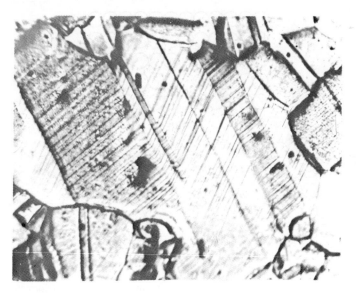

Figure 5.8   Slip lines on a prepolished surface of copper after plastic deformation.

Role of dislocations in slip   The stress required to cause slip in a perfect, ideal crystal can be estimated. It is in the range of $\mu/6$ to $\mu/30$, where μ is the shear modulus of the crystal. The experimentally determined shear stress at which plastic deformation starts in a real (imperfect) crystal is much lower, in the range of $\mu/5000$ to $\mu/100,000$. This large difference in the observed and calculated yield stresses arises from the *presence of dislocations* in real crystals.

Slip does not take place in the way visualized in Fig. 5.7. The dislocations *already* present in the crystal move in response to the externally applied stress. The dislocation configuration is moved through the crystal in a sequential fashion by *small* adjustments in the bond length, as illustrated in Fig. 5.9. The figure also shows the analogy of the motion of a caterpillar. The stress required to move a dislocation is much smaller than to shear a perfect crystal. *Whiskers* are very thin hair-like crystals, which are free of dislocations. These possess very high strengths, approaching the calculated value for perfect crystals.

Slip usually starts from sources within the crystal. A typical source is the *Frank-Read source*, which under favourable conditions of operation can produce a very large number of dislocation loops. Many of these loops are left back in the metal after deformation, as they often get piled up against obstacles in the crystal such as sessile (immobile) dislocations and grain boundaries.

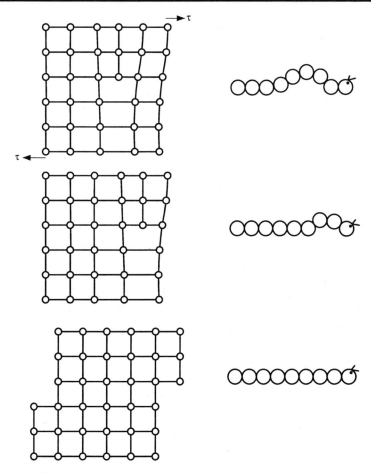

Figure 5.9 Successive positions of an edge dislocation under a shear stress τ. The analogy of a caterpillar movement is also shown.

5.3 METHODS OF STRENGTHENING METALS AGAINST YIELD

As noted above, metals are inherently weak because of the presence of dislocations. Metals of high strength can be obtained by eliminating dislocations, i.e. by making whiskers. However, this approach cannot be adopted in practice, as metal whiskers are too thin to serve as structural and machine components. Moreover, if a dislocation is introduced accidentally due to some stress concentration, the strength of the whisker falls to a much lower value. So, we have to "live" with dislocations and to adopt methods by which the *stress required to move a dislocation is increased*. Based on this approach, there are *four* main strengthening methods, which are described below.

(i) **Strain hardening:** When metals are *cold worked*, their strength and hardness increase. Annealed crystals have a typical dislocation density of

10^8 m^{-2}. This can be increased to 10^{10}–10^{12} m^{-2} by moderate cold working of the annealed metal and to 10^{14}–10^{16} m^{-2} by heavy cold working. At first sight, it appears that such striking increases in dislocation density will make the crystal more prone to slip, as many more dislocations are available, but this is not so. As the dislocation density increases, the movement of any one dislocation becomes more difficult due to the *interfering effect* of the stress fields of the surrounding dislocations. This phenomenon is the basis of work hardening. It can be described in terms of the following equation:

$$\tau = \tau_o + A\sqrt{\rho} \tag{5.4}$$

where τ is the stress to move a dislocation in a matrix of dislocation density ρ, τ_o is the stress to move the dislocation in the same matrix with zero dislocation density and A is a constant. $A \sim \mu b/2$, where μ is the shear modulus of the crystal and b is the Burgers vector of the moving dislocation.

Torsteel used as reinforcing bars for concrete is cold twisted to increase the yield strength. Under suitable conditions, very heavy cold working can increase the strength of iron to nearly the strength of a perfect crystal. The main disadvantage of cold working is the accompanying decrease in ductility, as illustrated in Fig. 5.10. Cold working is also detrimental, as it raises the ductile-brittle transition temperature of steels.

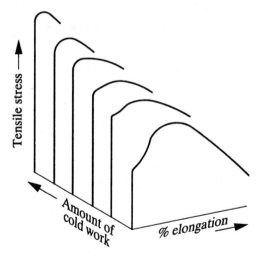

Figure 5.10   The tensile stress-strain curve as a function of prior cold work.

(ii) **Refinement of the grain size:** As the orientation changes at a grain boundary, the slip plane in a crystal does not continue in the same direction beyond the boundary. So, dislocations gliding on a slip plane are unable to cross the boundary but get piled up against it. The number of dislocations in a pile up is more for a larger grain, as the average distance from a dislocation source to the boundary is larger. The magnitude of the stress concentration produced at the leading edge of the pile up (i.e. next to the boundary) is proportional to the square root of the number of dislocations in the pile up. Thus, a greater stress concentration is produced at the boundary of a larger grain. This is able to activate more readily dislocation sources in the neighbouring grain. The propagation of the deformation from grain to grain (in the form of Luders bands in steels) occurs at a lower stress, when the grain size is larger.

This effect increases the macroscopically observed yield strength of fine grained metals and is described by the *Hall-Petch equation*:

$$\sigma_y = \sigma_i + kd^{-1/2} \tag{5.5}$$

where σ_y is the yield strength of the polycrystalline metal,
   σ_i is the yield strength at an infinite grain size,
   k is the Hall-Petch constant, and
   d is the mean grain diameter.

When d is very large, $\sigma_y \sim \sigma_i$. The additional contribution to the yield strength from the $kd^{-1/2}$ term increases, as the grain size is reduced, Fig. 5.11. It is seen from the figure that σ_i term (intercept on the y-axis) is temperature dependent, whereas k (the slope of the lines) is independent of temperature.

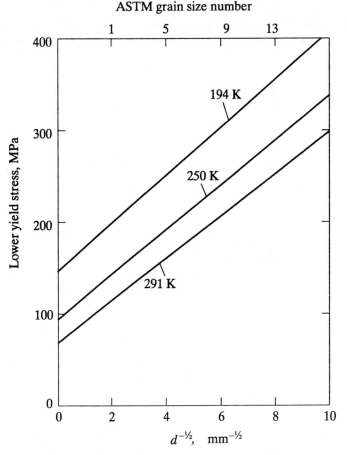

Figure 5.11   The Hall-Petch plot for mild steel at three different temperatures. The yield strength increases with decreasing grain size.

The strengthening effect for a given grain size depends on the magnitude of the constant k. In general, k tends to be larger for BCC metals, as compared to FCC or HCP metals. For example, $k = 0.71$ MN m$^{-3/2}$ for BCC iron, whereas it is 0.11 and 0.07 MN m$^{-3/2}$ for copper and aluminium (both FCC). A similar strengthening effect arises from the *subgrain boundaries* in deformed metals. Dislocation motion can be impeded by subgrain boundaries as well.

In contrast to the cold working method, grain refinement does not decrease the ductility. Further, the ductile-brittle transition temperature is lowered in steels by grain refinement, making the steel tough over a wider range of temperatures. The fatigue resistance also improves by grain refinement. Thus, grain refinement is perhaps the most desirable of the four methods of strengthening metallic materials.

The full potential of this method is being realized only in recent years. The advent of microalloyed steels, which contain small quantities of strong carbide forming elements such as Nb, V or Ti, is an example. These elements go into solution in austenite during reheating of the billet in the soaking pit. When the steel is hot rolled, solubility of the microalloying elements decreases with decreasing temperature. Strain-induced precipitation of alloy carbides takes place on a very fine scale. These precipitates effectively pin down the migrating grain boundaries during repeated recrystallization of the deformed austenite between passes at the successive stands of the rolling mill. The decreased growth rate due to pinning yields a fine grained austenite. A fine grained austenite provides more potential sites at the grain boundaries for the nucleation of ferrite, the end result being a very fine-grained ferrite in the mild steel. Thereby the yield strength increases considerably. The finest ferrite grain size is obtained by controlled rolling, wherein the nucleation of ferrite takes place from a heavily-deformed, unrecrystallized austenite. This process is sometimes called the *high temperature thermomechanical treatment* (HTMT). The excellent weldability of mild steel remains unaffected in microalloyed steels. Note that no heat treatment step (that adds to the cost) is involved in increasing the strength.

The other methods of grain refinement are the increase in the cooling rate and the use of nucleating agents during solidification. The cooling rates in rapid solidification processing are much higher than those in conventional methods, the result being a substantial grain refinement.

(iii) **Solid solution strengthening:** Solute atoms in general are either smaller or larger in size than the solvent (parent) atoms of a solid solution. Smaller atoms produce a local tensile stress field in the crystal, whereas larger atoms produce a local compressive stress field. In both cases, the stress field of a moving dislocation interacts with the stress field of the solute atom. This increases the stress required to move the dislocation. In general, therefore, solid solutions are stronger than pure metals. The yield strength of single crystals of Au-Ag alloys (showing complete solid solubility) is shown in Fig. 5.12a. The yield strength increases with increasing solute at the two pure ends, reaching a maximum at the mid-composition.

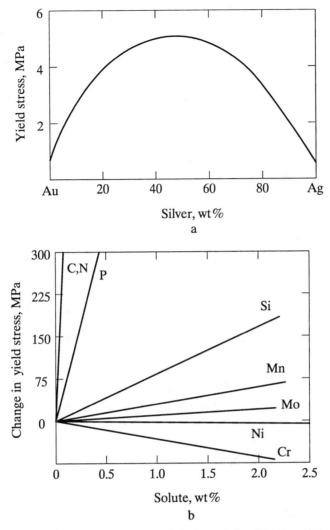

Figure 5.12 (a) The shear yield stress of single crystals of Au-Ag solid solutions.
(b) The effect of different solutes on the yield stress of iron.

The strengthening effect due to a solute atom depends on several factors:

(a) A large concentration of the solute means more frequent obstacles to dislocations moving in the matrix. The strength increases in proportion of $c^{1/2}$ where c is the concentration. For dilute solutions, a linear dependence on concentration is equally valid.

(b) As the size difference between the solute and the solvent increases, the intensity of the stress field around solute atoms and the resistance to dislocation motion increase.

(c) The nature of the distortion produced by the solute atoms is also important. Spherical distortion produced by substitutional solutes is much less effective than the non-spherical distortion produced by interstitial atoms. Figure 5.12b shows the linear increase in yield strength of ferrite with increasing concentration of different solutes. Interstitial elements (C and N) have the maximum effect per unit concentration, due to the tetragonal distortion they produce. Substitutional solutes have a much smaller effect.

In solid solutions with long-range order, the dislocations corresponding to an integral lattice translation of the superlattice possess large Burgers vectors. As the energy of a dislocation is proportional to the square of its Burgers vector, such superdislocations tend to split into two ordinary dislocations separated by an anti-phase domain boundary between them. This boundary is a surface that separates two domains of the ordered structure that do not match at the boundary. The situation is very similar to the formation of a stacking fault by the splitting of an ordinary dislocation into two Shockley partials, recall Sec. 1.4. In order not to increase the anti-phase domain boundary area, dislocations will have to move in pairs in ordered structures. This increases the strength of ordered alloys as compared to disordered alloys. In some cases, the ordered structure may even be brittle.

The strengthening effect due to solutes can be increased by forcing increased solubility by nonequilibrium methods. A supersaturated solution can be produced by quenching from a high temperature, where the solubility is more. Austenite holds 0.8% carbon in solution just above the eutectoid temperature. On quenching, it produces a supersaturated martensitic structure. The intense stress field around carbon atoms in martensite effectively hinders dislocation motion, so much so that martensite is brittle and requires tempering to restore some ductility.

(iv) **Precipitation Hardening:** Closely spaced fine precipitates obstruct the motion of dislocations moving in the matrix. A moving dislocation has two options: it can

(a) cut through the precipitates, or

(b) bend around and bypass the precipitates.

Cutting through occurs, when the precipitate particles are coherent with the matrix and less than about 50 Å in size. The increased resistance to dislocation motion in cutting through the particles is due to the creation of a step at the interface, Fig. 5.13a, and other surface imperfections like stacking faults within the particles.

When the particles are larger in size (100–500 Å), the dislocations bend around and bypass them, Fig. 5.13b. The stress to do so varies inversely as the interparticle spacing. Since finer particles are more closely spaced, a fine precipitate distribution effectively increases the stress to bend and bypass. This microstructural state corresponds approximately to the optimum aged condition of a precipitation hardening alloy. Particles of larger sizes (>1000 Å) are bypassed with ease and little hardening occurs. This state corresponds to the *overaged* or overtempered condition.

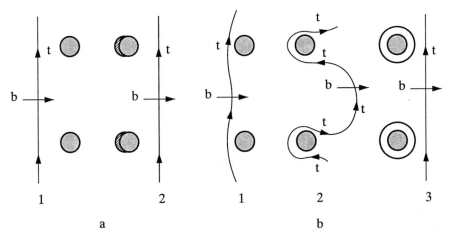

Figure 5.13 Interaction of a moving dislocation with precipitate particles:
(a) cutting-through, and (b) bending-and-bypassing mechanisms.

Large nondeforming particles are present in many two-phase alloys, e.g. pearlite in steels. As the dislocations moving in the matrix easily bypass them, the yield strength tends to be low in such two-phase materials. However, the work hardening rate can be high, as each dislocation that bypasses leaves behind a small loop around the particles, see Fig. 5.13b. The stresses from the dislocation loops tend to elastically strain the non-deforming particles to conform to the plastically deforming matrix. This results in a high tensile strength as compared to the yield strength.

5.4 CREEP RESISTANCE

At temperature above $0.4T_m$ (where T_m is the melting point of the metal in kelvin), plastic deformation of the metal occurs *as a function of time at constant load or stress*. This phenomenon is known as *creep*. Lead creeps at ambient temperature, but iron and copper do not. The fact that creep is a function of temperature and time indicates that it is a *thermally activated* process.

The creep curves Figure 5.14 shows typical creep curves, where the creep strain is plotted as a function of time at constant load and constant temperature. The curve shows *three stages*. In stage I, known as *primary creep*, the creep rate decreases with time. The work hardening due to plastic deformation is more than the recovery (softening effect) during creep. In stage II (*secondary creep*), the rate of work hardening and creep softening exactly balance each other. The slope of strain-time curve is constant and a minimum in stage II. Stage III (*tertiary creep*) is characterized by an accelerating rate of creep, where softening effects dominate. In this stage, *necking* occurs and voids form at grain junctions. These voids coalesce to cause intergranular fracture at the end of this stage. Microstructural softening effects such as recrystallization or coarsening of precipitate particles also contribute to tertiary creep. The three stages shift to shorter times, if either the stress or temperature is increased, see Fig. 5.14. At low temperatures, the creep may be transient without the three stages, the creep strain following a *logarithmic* dependence on time.

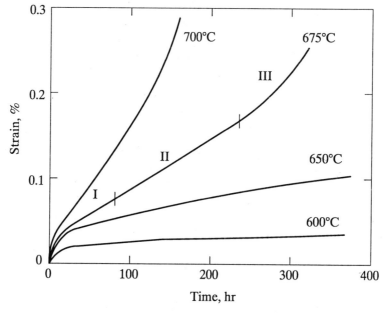

Figure 5.14 Creep curves for a low alloy steel at different temperatures at a constant tensile stress of 70 MPa.

Creep data are also presented in the form of stress-rupture curves for different temperatures of test, Fig. 5.15. Here, the time for creep rupture is plotted against the applied stress at various temperatures. The data can also be presented in the form of creep rate (% strain per 1000 hr) as a function of stress. Such data are useful in the selection of materials for high temperature use. In designs, where creep deformation can be tolerated but rupture must be prevented, the stress-rupture data are directly useful. The creep rate-stress data are useful, when the structure cannot undergo more than a specified amount of creep during the entire service life, e.g. jet engine components and steam turbine blades.

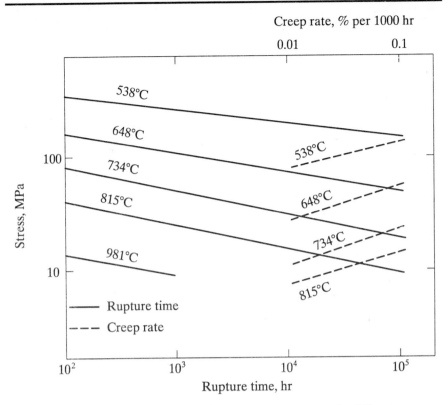

Figure 5.15 Stress-rupture and stress-creep rate curves for different temperatures for an austenitic stainless steel.

Mechanisms of creep Dislocations piled up against obstacles can bypass them during creep, with the aid of thermal energy and continue to glide and cause further deformation. Screw dislocations overcome obstacles by *cross-slip*, using thermal energy. As the screw dislocation is frequently dissociated into partial dislocations, recombination over a certain length is required before cross-slip can start and this requires thermal energy. *Recombination* is easier, if the distance of separation between the partials is less.

An edge dislocation *climbs out* of the slip plane in which it lies against the obstacle and continues gliding on another parallel slip plane. Climb requires the diffusion of atoms to or away from the dislocation. The diffusion rate increases exponentially with temperature. So, the higher is the temperature, the faster will be the diffusion and the climb. The activation energy for creep by the climb mechanism is the same as the activation energy for self-diffusion.

A jog on a screw dislocation has edge character. Non-conservative *climb motion of the jog* may be required during the glide of such a screw dislocation. If this climb motion is rate controlling during the cross-slip of the screw dislocation, the activation energy for creep will again be the same as the activation energy for self-diffusion.

Figure 5.16 compares these two activation energies for a number of metals and shows them to be equal.

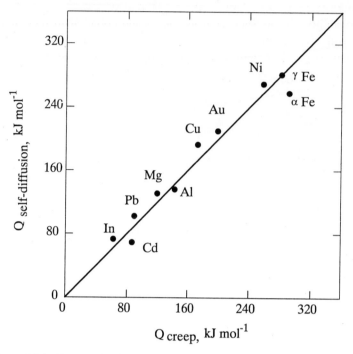

Figure 5.16 For metals, the activation energy (Q) for creep is equal to the activation energy for self-diffusion, both of these increasing with increasing melting point of the metal.

Diffusional creep occurs, when a metal crystal under a tensile stress elongates by the stress-assisted motion of vacancies. Vacancies move from faces perpendicular to the tensile axis to faces parallel to them. The flow of atoms is in the opposite direction. The activation energy for diffusional creep is the same as the activation energy for self-diffusion. In a polycrystalline metal, the vacancy flow occurs in each grain. Creep that occurs by diffusion of vacancies through the grain is called *Nabarro-Herring creep*. When the diffusion is along grain boundaries, the process is called *Coble creep*.

At a temperature called the *equicohesive temperature* (~ 0.5–$0.6T_m$), the grain boundaries reverse their role from being a source of strengthening to that of weakening the metal. Below this temperature, they act as effective obstacles to dislocation motion. Above this temperature, the boundaries undergo sliding, i.e. they behave as if they were a very viscous liquid. Creep deformation is caused by this grain boundary sliding.

Creep-resistant materials   Creep-resistant materials are required for structural and machine components used at elevated temperatures. They should be capable of withstanding these temperatures, without undergoing creep, which may cause dimensional changes not permissible in the design.

The first requirement for a material to be creep-resistant is that it should have a high melting point. Recall that creep becomes significant only at temperatures above $0.4T_m$. Consistent with the factors such as cost, availability and fabricability, metals such as iron, nickel and cobalt with moderately high melting points (around 1500°C) have been used. These metals can be made more creep-resistant by various methods. We can reexamine the strengthening methods against plastic yield described in Sec. 5.3 to determine their applicability to creep. Strain hardening cannot generally be used to improve creep resistance, as recrystallization and the associated softening can occur above $0.4T_m$. Solute strengthening is effective here in the same manner as in low temperature strengthening.

Grain refinement is not applicable for creep. In fact, the opposite is required to minimize grain boundary sliding. A fine grain size means more grain boundary area per unit volume. Coarse grained alloys, with the crystals oriented in such a way that voids are not generated at grain junctions, are adopted. In the limit, turbine blades made out of single crystals, where there are no grain boundaries, have been used.

Precipitation hardening is applicable, only when there is no risk of particle coarsening and consequent softening during service. The driving force for coarsening is the decrease in the interfacial energy per unit volume. If the interfacial energy is low, the driving force is less and the tendency for coarsening is minimized. In nickel-base and iron-nickel-base superalloys, precipitates of $Ni_3(Al,Ti)$ form a *coherent interface* with the matrix, with an interfacial energy as low as ~ 0.005 J m^{-2}. The lattice parameter of $Ni_3Ti(\gamma'$ precipitate) decreases from 3.59 Å to 3.56 Å, as titanium is completely replaced by aluminium. The optimum ratio of Ti/Al in the alloy is chosen to match the lattice parameter of the matrix with that of the precipitate for coherency.

In *dispersion hardening*, insoluble particles are embedded in a metal matrix. The components are manufactured by powder metallurgy, by mixing the metal powder and the insoluble particles (usually an oxide), compacting and then sintering it to make the metal matrix continuous. During coarsening, small particles dissolve, the solute atoms diffuse through the matrix and reprecipitate on larger particles. As oxides do not dissolve in metals, no coarsening occurs in dispersion hardening and the metal-oxide dispersion remains stable at elevated temperatures. TD nickel (thoria dispersed nickel) retains an appreciable fraction of its strength even at temperatures as high as $0.9\ T_m$.

5.5 FRACTURE

Fracture refers to the breaking of a component into two or more pieces either during service or during fabrication. Ductile fracture occurs after a considerable amount of plastic deformation. The nucleation, growth and coalescence of voids during necking, as discussed in Sec. 5.1, are responsible for ductile fracture.

Brittle fracture occurs without any apparent sign of plastic deformation. However, plastic deformation on a microscopic level at the tip of a crack frequently occurs during brittle fracture.

The Griffith criterion   Estimates show that the tensile stress required to break all the atomic bonds simultaneously across the perfect cross-section of a solid is of the order of $Y/6$, where Y is the Young's modulus of the solid. But real brittle materials fracture at a much lower stress of the order of $Y/500$ to $Y/1000$. This discrepancy is explained on the basis of the presence of cracks in real materials, which propagate at relatively low stress levels and cause fracture. Griffith proposed an energy criterion for the spontaneous propagation of a preexisting crack in a brittle solid. The critical tensile sense σ_f, at which a flat elliptical crack propagates and causes fracture, corresponds to the condition that the elastic energy released per unit area of the crack face is equal to the surface energy consumed in creating the unit area of the crack face. The Griffith condition is

$$\sigma_f = \sqrt{\frac{2\gamma Y}{\pi c}} \tag{5.6}$$

where γ is the surface energy of the crack faces per unit area, and
   c is the half-length of the crack.
Note that the fracture strength σ_f is inversely related to the square root of the crack length c.

In order for a crack to propagate after the Griffith condition is satisfied, there must exist at the crack tip sufficient stress concentration. In brittle materials such as a silicate glass, the cracks are sharp and a high stress concentration exists at the tip. Therefore, the cracks propagate, as soon as the Griffith condition is satisfied.

In less brittle (crystalline) materials, the stress concentration at the tip is relieved by *plastic deformation* and the crack becomes blunt. In such cases, the crack propagation is more difficult. Also, the Griffith energy balance should include the *plastic work*. Often, the plastic work per unit area of crack face created turns out to be much larger than the surface energy γ. The term γ_p, used in place of γ in the modified Griffith equation, includes the plastic work.

Limitations of the classical approach
1. Most structural materials are crystalline in nature and invariably undergo plastic deformation at the tip. The value of the modified surface energy γ_p at the critical condition is not easily determined.

2. The fracture strength σ_f of a material as defined by the Griffith equation is not material property like yield strength or tensile strength, as it depends on the crack length in a given component and at a given stage of the service life.

3. Structures and machine components invariably contain cracks that are introduced during solidification, fabrication or heat treatment. A material

parameter is required that will allow the design stress to be computed, if the size of the most damaging defect is known. Alternatively, the material parameter enables the computation of the maximum size of the crack that can be tolerated for a given design stress. Periodic nondestructive inspection can then be done to ensure that the most damaging defect is smaller than the tolerable size.

4. According to the Griffith criterion, a crack propagates only when the critical condition is satisfied. But in practice fracture may occur after the certain lapse of time or after a certain number of stress reversals, even though the original design stress is less than the critical stress. This is so, because slow subcritical crack growth occurs during the time interval before fracture. The crack eventually attains the critical size and fast fracture ensues. Clearly, the rate of subcritical crack growth should be known, if the life of the structural part is to be predicted. Such measurements of crack growth rates have been made both for statically loaded structures (where crack growth occurs due to the combined action of the stress and the environment) and for dynamically loaded components (where stress reversals cause slow crack growth).

Stresses at the crack tip   Figure 5.17 illustrates the three modes of loading. In the *opening mode*, known as mode I, the displacement is perpendicular to the crack faces, Fig. 5.17(I). In the *sliding mode* (mode II), the displacement is parallel to the crack faces and perpendicular to the leading edge of the crack, Fig. 5.17(II). In the *tearing mode* (mode III), Fig. 5.17(III), the displacement is parallel to the crack faces and the leading edge. In practical situations, the opening mode is the most important. The stress distribution for the opening mode at the tip of an elastic crack is considered below.

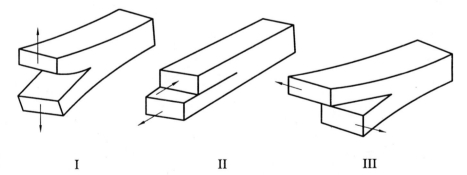

I   II   III

Figure 5.17   The three modes of loading: mode I (opening mode),
mode II (sliding mode) and mode III (tearing mode).

The normal stress σ_n on an element located at the radial coordinates $(r,\ \theta)$ (taking the crack tip as the origin) in the direction of the applied stress σ is given by

$$\sigma_n = \frac{K_I}{\sqrt{2\pi r}} f(\theta) \tag{5.7}$$

where $K_I = \sigma \sqrt{\pi c}$ and $f(\theta)$ is some function of θ. K_I is called the stress intensity factor. I stands for mode I (opening mode). K_I describes the stress field at the tip of the crack. When the crack tip stress field reaches a critical condition, fast fracture occurs. The corresponding K_I is called the *critical stress intensity factor K_{Ic}*.

Plastic zone at the crack tip   Taking $f(\theta) = 1$ (which actually corresponds to $\theta = 0$), σ_n is plotted against r in Fig. 5.18. As $r \to 0$, $\sigma_n \to \infty$. This is obviously not possible. When σ_n exceeds the yield strength σ_{ys}, plastic deformation occurs at the tip. The stress distribution at the tip is modified as shown in Fig. 5.18, the maximum value being σ_{ys}. The size of the plastic zone r_p^* can be determined by substituting $\sigma_n = \sigma_{ys}$:

$$r_p^* = \frac{K_I^2}{2\sigma_{ys}^2} = \frac{\pi \sigma^2 c}{2\sigma_{ys}^2} \tag{5.8}$$

The size of the plastic zone increases with increasing crack size c and increasing applied stress σ. But it decreases, as the yield strength of the material increases. For cases of limited plastic deformation at the crack tip, K_I can be taken to describe all stresses and strains (both elastic and plastic) around the tip.

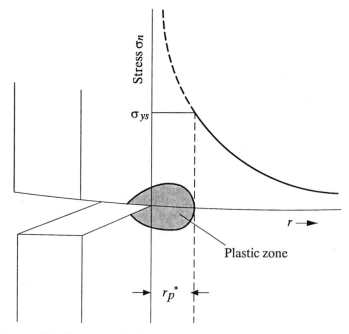

Figure 5.18   The stress distribution at the tip of a crack. When this stress exceeds the yield stress, plastic deformation occurs near the tip.

Experimental determination of K_{Ic} Test specifications have been developed for determining K_{Ic}. The test specimen contains a notch of known geometry. It is fatigue cracked, i.e. it is subjected to a limited number of stress reversals, which introduces a crack at the root of the notch. Then it is loaded statically and the load is increased until fracture occurs. The size of the initial crack can be estimated from the differences in appearance of the regions of the fracture surface. The region of slow crack growth during fatigue loading is *smooth and polished* due to the constant rubbing action of the two crack faces against each other during stress reversals. The fast crack growth region corresponding to static loading is *rough and granular*. The K_c values determined from the crack size and the stress at fracture are plotted as a function of specimen thickness in Fig. 5.19. The value of K_c reaches a limiting value at large thicknesses, corresponding to the plane strain condition. This limiting value is termed K_{Ic}, so that it becomes a reproducible material property.

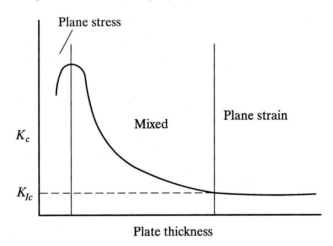

Figure 5.19 The critical stress intensity factor K_c as a function of plate thickness. The thickness must be sufficiently large for achieving the plane strain condition.

K_{Ic} values for three typical alloys are listed below:

Property	Ni-Cr-Mo Steel	Maraging Steel	Al-alloy
K_{Ic}, MN m$^{-3/2}$	46	90	32
TS, MN m^{-2}	1820	1850	560

The maraging steel, which has the largest K_{Ic}, will tolerate the longest crack for a given applied stress or with an existing crack of known length, will bear the highest stress.

Strain energy release rate G Another fracture toughness parameter is the strain energy released per unit extension of the crack known as G (named after Griffith). When the crack extends over unit area, two crack faces are created.

At the critical condition for an elastic crack, it can be shown from the Griffith equation (5.6) that

$$G_c = 2\gamma \tag{5.9}$$

When a limited amount of plastic flow occurs at the crack tip, γ can be replaced by γ_p. Then, at the critical condition,

$$G_c = 2\gamma_p \tag{5.10}$$

Both K_{Ic} and G_c are material parameters valid for high strength alloys, where plastic deformation at the crack tip is limited.

Crack opening displacement (COD)   Frequently, structural components are built out of low strength and medium strength materials. For steels, the low strength range is 250–450 MPa and the medium range is 500–800 MPa. The yield strengths being low for such steels, extensive plastic deformation occurs at the crack tip. Recall that the size of the plastic zone is inversely proportional to the square of the yield strength. For such cases, K_{Ic} and G_c are not applicable and different fracture toughness parameters called COD and J_c are used. COD stands for crack opening displacement. J_c is an energy integral fracture toughness parameter. We will discuss COD only.

Figure 5.20a compares a fully elastic crack and a crack with plastic flow at the tip. The ideally elastic crack is atomically sharp. The crack with plastic flow is blunted. Here, at the tip of the crack, the two crack faces are separated by a distance δ, which is defined as the crack opening displacement (COD). The more extensive is the plastic flow, the more will be δ. The criterion used for the fracture event is that δ attains a critical value δ_c at the time of fast fracture.

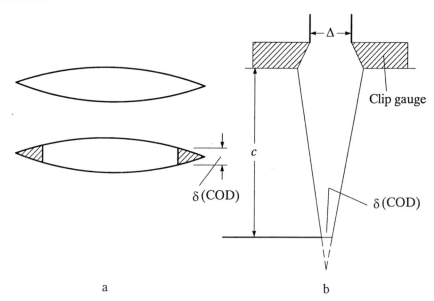

a   b

Figure 5.20   (a) A sharp crack and a blunt crack, where plastic deformation has occurred near the tip. (b) The experimental set up for determining COD.

COD can be measured experimentally, by fixing a clip gauge at the mouth of the crack as illustrated in Fig. 5.20b. In a three-point bending type of loading, as the load is increased, the displacement Δ measured by the clip gauge increases. By knowing the depth of the crack c and Δ, δ or δ_c can be calculated.

5.6 FATIGUE FAILURES

About 90% of engineering failures are attributed to fatigue of the material under cyclic loading. Machine components undergo reversals of stresses millions of time during their lifetime. Connecting rods are subjected to pull (tension) and push (compression) type of loading during each cycle. Leaf springs bend back and forth. Aircraft wings flutter in turbulent air. In a single loading, a metal withstands a stress up to its tensile strength. But under repeated loading, it may fail at a stress level much lower than the tensile strength.

Fatigue tests   Cyclic loading can be of three types:

1. tension-tension,
2. tension-zero, and
3. tension-compression.

As illustrated in Fig. 5.21, in the tension-tension type of loading, both the maximum and the minimum stresses are tensile in nature. In the tension-zero case, the minimum stress is zero. In the tension-compression loading (Fig. 5.21c and d), the minimum stress is compressive. The stress amplitude S is defined as half of the difference between the maximum and the minimum stress levels. For example, in the tension-zero cases, $S = \frac{1}{2}\sigma_{max}$.

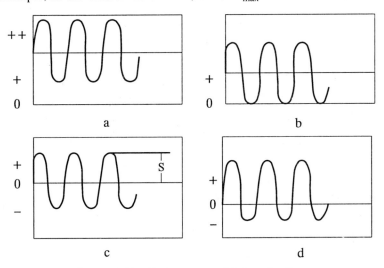

Figure 5.21   Various types of fatigue loading.
+ stands for tension and − for compression.

Figure 5.22 shows a typical experimental set up for a fatigue test. The specimen is in the form of a cantilever loaded at one end. It is rotated at the same time, by means of a high-speed motor to which it is connected. At any instant, the upper surface of the loaded specimen is in tension and the lower surface in compression, with the neutral axis at the centre. During each revolution, the surface layers pass through a full cycle of tension and compression.

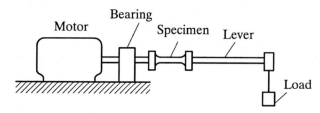

Figure 5.22   The experimental set up for a cantilever fatigue test.

The maximum stress amplitude S that the material withstands decreases with increasing frequency of stress reversals. The results of a fatigue test are reported in the form of S–N curves, where N is the number of stress cycles. Figure 5.23 shows the S–N curves for a 0.45%C steel and for an aluminium alloy. The steel exhibits a fatigue limit, i.e. if the stress amplitude is below a certain value, failure does not occur, however large is N. In the case of the aluminium alloy, there is no fatigue limit. Here, the fatigue strength can be specified only by giving the corresponding value of N.

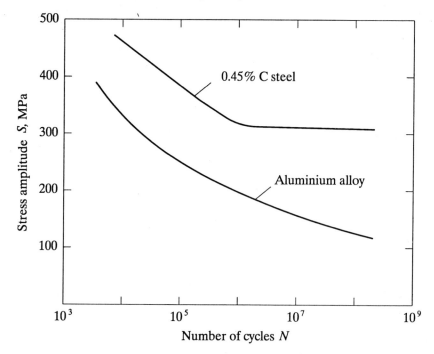

Figure 5.23 S-N curves for a carbon steel and an aluminium alloy.

The fatigue strength of a material is lower than its tensile strength and sometimes, even lower than its yield strength. Even when the cyclic stress is lower than the yield strength, microscopic plastic deformation occurs on a localized scale during stress reversals. Slip at the microscopic level may be evident, at a very early stage of the fatigue life, at about 1% of the total life. The cyclic nature of the stress causes the slip to appear as *extrusions and intrusions* on the surface, as illustrated in Fig. 5.24. During the tensile cycle, slip occurs on a plane with the maximum shear stress on it. During the compressive part of the cycle, slip may occur on a nearby parallel slip plane, with the slip displacement in the opposite direction. This results in extrusions and intrusions at the surface, Fig. 5.24. These act as sites for fatigue crack *nucleation*. Once nucleated, the crack grows inwards by a small increment during each cycle. As the critical condition is attained, the crack propagates rapidly causing fracture.

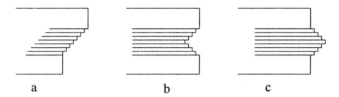

a   b   c

Figure 5.24   (a) Slip steps appear during forward loading. During reverse loading, they become either (b) intrusions or (c) extrusions.

A typical fatigue-fracture surface looks like the one shown in Fig. 5.25. The fatigue crack nucleated at the stress concentration in the keyhole of the shaft.

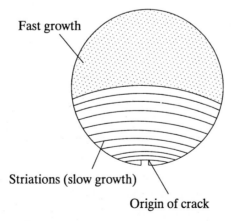

Fast growth

Striations (slow growth)

Origin of crack

Figure 5.25   The fatigue fracture surface showing various regions. The crack initiated at the root of the keyhole, a site of stress concentration.

The *rough granular* part corresponds to the stage of fast growth, after the critical condition is attained. The smooth and polished surface corresponds to the slow growth of crack, when the crack faces smoothen out by constant rubbing against each other. Concentric lines known as *ripples or striations* are often seen on this part of the fracture surface. The relatively widely spaced ripples are caused by variations in the stress amplitude during the life of the component. On a much finer level, a large number of ripples may sometimes be seen. The width of each ripple here is equal to the distance by which the crack grows during one cycle.

Low cycle fatigue The fatigue failures referred to before occur when the number of stress cycles is in excess of 10^5. In low cycle fatigue, failure occurs after a relatively small number of cycles. The stresses in low cycle fatigue are usually thermal in origin, the expansion and contraction on heating and cooling of structures such as pressure vessels and turbines. For a given range of temperature variation, the strains induced by thermal expansion or contraction are constant. Low cycle fatigue data are presented in terms of $\Delta\varepsilon_p$ (the plastic strain range) as a function of the number of cycles. The number of cycles to failure decreases with increasing $\Delta\varepsilon_p$, i.e. with larger thermal variations, Fig. 5.26.

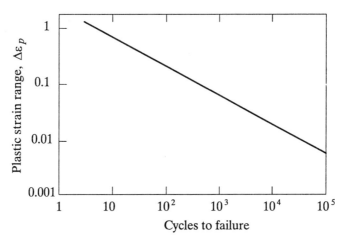

Figure 5.26 In low cycle fatigue, the number of cycles to failure decreases with increasing plastic strain range.

Slow crack growth rate The kinetics of crack growth in the subcritical stage can be experimentally determined. One of the commonly used empirical equations correlates the crack growth rate per cycle, dc/dN, to the range of the stress intensity factor, $\Delta K \ (= \Delta\sigma\sqrt{\pi c})$:

$$\frac{dc}{dN} = C(\Delta K)^n \tag{5.11}$$

Such a relationship is usually applicable when $\sigma_{min} \sim 0$. Figure 5.27 shows a plot of log (dc/dN) against log ΔK. The constants C and n in Eq. (5.11) can be

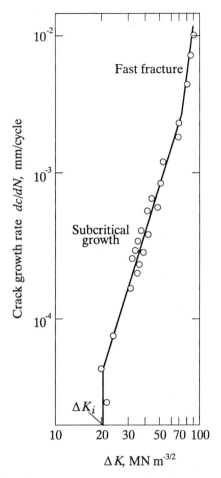

Figure 5.27 The crack growth rate during fatigue, as a function of the stress intensity range, shows a threshold stress ΔK_i, a region of subcritical growth and a region of fast fracture.

determined from the slope and intercept. It is seen that a threshold intensity range $(\Delta K)_i$ exists below which the crack does not grow. At very large values of ΔK, the crack growth rate becomes larger than predicted by Eq. (5.11). Typical experimental values are:

$$\text{Martensitic steels}: dc/dN = 0.66 \times 10^{-8} (\Delta K)^{2.25} \tag{5.12}$$

$$\text{Ferrite-pearlite steels}: dc/dN = 0.36 \times 10^{-9} (\Delta K)^{3} \tag{5.13}$$

For tension-tension type of loading, where $\sigma_{min} > 0$, the range of K as well as K_{max} influences the growth rate. For tension-compression type of loading, only K_{max} is relevant, as no crack growth occurs in compression.

Factors affecting fatigue life

1. The frequency of cyclic loading has only a small effect on the fatigue strength.
2. The form of the stress cycle such as square, triangular or sinusoidal wave has no effect on the fatigue life.
3. The environment in which the component undergoes stress reversals has a marked effect on fatigue life. The fatigue life in vacuum is some 10 times more than that in moist air. Clearly, the environment has a corrosive effect. Fatigue occurring under specific corrosive environments is called *corrosion fatigue*.
4. The thickness of the test specimen has an effect on the fatigue properties. Thinner samples show a decrease in the crack growth rate.
5. An increase in temperature around room temperature causes an increase in the crack growth rate.

Protection methods   The methods of increasing fatigue life are primarily aimed at preventing or delaying the initiation of the crack at the surface.

1. *Shot peening* introduces compressive residual stresses near the surface layers. Here, the surface is plastically deformed by repeated impingement of hard steel balls.
2. *Carburizing and nitriding* introduce compressive residual stresses at the surface, as well as increase the hardness and strength. Figure 5.28 shows

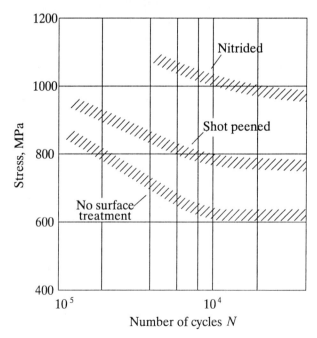

Figure 5.28   Nitriding and shot peening improve fatigue life.

the improvement in fatigue life achieved by nitriding and shot peening. Decarburization lowers the fatigue strength.

3. A *fine grain size* improves fatigue life.

4. The crack initiation invariably occurs from a site of *stress concentration*. In design, *fillets* of adequate radius of curvature should be provided at places where a sudden change of cross-section exists. Shafts are usually highly polished to reduce the chances of surface irregularities providing sites of stress concentration. Sometimes, stress concentration is introduced *accidentally*. A fatigue crack in a plane propeller was traced to the stress concentration at the root of the stamp mark, bearing the name and address of the manufacturer!

SUGGESTED READINGS

Dieter, G.E., *Mechanical Metallurgy*, 3rd Edition, McGraw-Hill, New York (1988).

Honeycombe, R.W.K., *The Plastic Deformation of Metals*, Edwin Arnold, London (1968).

QUESTIONS

1. Using Eqs. (5.1) and (5.2), prove that $n = \varepsilon_t^u$.
   Hint: Assume the volume to be constant during plastic deformation.
2. Explain the role of stacking fault energy on the deformation characteristics of FCC metals and alloys.
3. Distinguish between strain ageing and quench ageing.
4. Discuss the relative advantages and disadvantages of the four main methods of strengthening metals and alloys against plastic yield.
5. Ordered alloys are generally stronger than disordered alloys. Explain why this is so.
6. If the grain size of mild steel is changed from ASTM No. 8 to 13 by microalloying additions, estimate the increase in yield strength.
   Answer: 207 MPa
7. The presence of pearlite in the microstructure of carbon steels has little effect on the yield strength, but tends to increase the tensile strength. Explain why this is so.

8. Describe the mechanisms of creep that become important, as the temperature of deformation is progressively increased.

9. From the data of K_{Ic} values, make a plot of σ_c vs. c for the three alloys: Ni-Cr-Mo steel, maraging steel and aluminium alloy.

10. A connecting rod is made of a martensitic steel with $K_{Ic} = 46$ MN m$^{-3/2}$. It is subjected to an alternating stress of amplitude 200 MPa and has an initial crack of length 0.2 mm. Calculate the number of cycles at which the rod will fail. Assume that Eq. (5.12) is applicable.

Answer: 1.0×10^5 cycles.

Chapter 6

CORROSION AND ITS PREVENTION

Metals and alloys corrode in environments encountered during service. Rusting of iron is a common example of atmospheric corrosion. One estimate puts the loss due to corrosion at about 3% of the GDP (gross domestic product) of countries. In addition to direct losses such as replacement cost, many indirect losses can also arise from corrosion. Shut down of machinery for replacement results in loss of productivity. Leakages developed in pipelines lead to loss of the liquid product and can have a hazardous effect on the surrounding environment and populace. Deposition of the corrosion products inside a tube reduces the efficiency of heat transfer, resulting in overheating and rupture of the tube. Contamination of foodstuffs by toxic (poisonous) products can occur.

In this chapter, the electrochemical principles governing corrosion are first described. After introducing the equilibrium potentials that describe the tendency of various metals to corrode, the phenomena associated with the corrosion kinetics such as polarization and passivation are described. In the second half of the chapter, the methods of corrosion prevention are discussed. These include cathodic and anodic protection, coatings and alloying. In the end, stress corrosion cracking is briefly discussed.

6.1 THE GALVANIC CELL

The familiar galvanic cell used in calculators and transistor radios comprises two electrodes in a solution called the *electrolyte*, Fig. 6.1. Chemical reactions occur at the electrodes and the energy liberated due to these reactions is converted into electrical energy.

Anode is that electrode at which the conventional current (passage of imaginary or real positive charge carriers) flows from the electrode into the electrolyte. Cathode is that electrode at which the conventional current enters from the electrolyte to the electrode. When the cell is short circuited, electrons (negative charge carriers) flow in the external metallic circuit in a direction opposite to that of the conventional current, i.e. from the anode to the cathode. In the electrolyte, the current is carried by cations and anions flowing in opposite directions. At any instant, the total current flowing through the cell is the same in every part of the circuit.

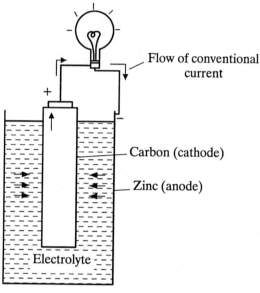

Figure 6.1 The galvanic cell comprises an anode, a cathode and an electrolyte.

The anode is defined as the electrode at which an *oxidation reaction* occurs. Removal of electrons (e^-) from neutral atoms to create positive ions is an oxidation process. Examples of anodic processes are:

$$Zn - 2e^- \rightarrow Zn^{++}$$
$$Al - 3e^- \rightarrow Al^{3+}$$

In the above reactions, the metal dissolves as ions into the electrolyte or in other words, corrodes. Oxidation reactions can also occur in the following ways.

$$Fe^{++} - 1e^- \rightarrow Fe^{3+}$$
$$2OH^- - 2e^- \rightarrow \tfrac{1}{2}O_2\uparrow + H_2O$$

Thus *oxygen evolution is an anodic reaction.*

The cathode is the electrode at which a *reduction reaction* occurs, by the addition of electrons to the reactant. Examples are:

$$Cu^{++} + 2e^- \rightarrow Cu$$
$$H^+ + 1e^- \rightarrow \tfrac{1}{2}H_2\uparrow$$

In the first example, copper is plated out on the cathode. In the second, *hydrogen evolution* occurs.

Types of corrosion cells   Two *dissimilar metals* in contact with each other form a potential galvanic cell. The atmosphere containing oxygen and moisture can act as the electrolyte. Thus a steel shaft in a bronze bearing, a bronze propeller in contact with the ship hull, or a copper tube connected to a steel pipe are combinations of dissimilar metals in contact. They form galvanic cells, in which the anode may corrode. Two phases in an alloy can form galvanic cells at the *microscopic level*. Cementite is cathodic to ferrite in steel, so that ferrite corrodes, Fig. 6.2a.

If there are variations in the state of stress within the same metal, *stress cells* may be set up. The atoms in the grain boundary region are in a distorted (stressed) state, as compared to the atoms inside the grain. Thus, the grain boundaries behave anodic to the grains. Similarly, a cold worked region is anodic to an annealed region of a metal. A bent nail may corrode at the bend, which is cold worked and anodic to the adjacent undeformed region, Fig. 6.2b.

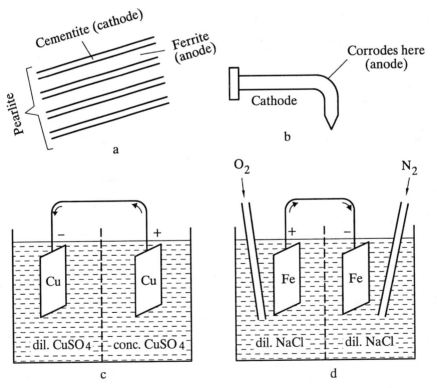

Figure 6.2   Types of corrosion: (a) microgalvanic cells between different phases, (b) a stress cell, (c) a concentration cell, and (d) a differential aeration cell. Arrows in (c) and (d) indicate the direction of the conventional current.

When the concentration of ions in the electrolyte varies from region to region, *concentration cells* may be set up. Thus, in an electrolyte containing cupric ions with two identical copper electrodes immersed in it, the region with a small concentration of cupric ions is anodic to the region that is rich in cupric ions, Fig. 6.2c.

When two electrodes of the same metal are in contact with the same electrolyte, if oxygen is bubbled through the electrolyte near one electrode and nitrogen near the other electrode, corrosion takes place at the electrode deficient in oxygen supply. This is known as a *differential aeration cell*, Fig. 6.2d. Oxygen and water take part in the cathodic reaction as follows:

$$\tfrac{1}{2}O_2 + H_2O + 2e^- \rightarrow 2OH^-$$

(Note that this reaction written in the reverse direction was introduced as an anodic reaction earlier.) Thus, oxygen deficient regions such as threaded connections, interfaces between pipes, the metal covered by rust and the part of the water tank just under the water line act as anode and corrode.

6.2   THE ELECTRODE POTENTIALS

Free energy change and emf of a cell   The tendency of a metal to combine with oxygen and water is measured by $\Delta G°$, the Gibbs free energy change under standard conditions. For the following reaction, we have

$$Mg + \tfrac{1}{2}O_2 + H_2O \rightarrow Mg(OH)_2 \qquad \Delta G° = -600 \text{ kJ mol}^{-1}$$

This large negative free energy change indicates that magnesium has a strong and spontaneous tendency to react in this manner. The above reaction can be split into two electrode reactions:

Anode reaction: $\qquad\qquad Mg - 2e^- \rightarrow Mg^{++}$
Cathode reaction: $\tfrac{1}{2}O_2 + H_2O + 2e^- \rightarrow 2(OH)^-$

The emf of a corrosion cell in which the above reactions take place is related to $\Delta G°$ as follows:

$$\Delta G° = -nF\varepsilon° \qquad\qquad (6.1)$$

where n is the number of electrons taking part in the reaction (it is 2 in the above case), F is Faraday's constant ($= 96,490$ coulomb per mole of electrons) and $\varepsilon°$ is the emf measured under standard conditions.

Standard electrode potentials   As it is useful to know the tendency of a metal to go into solution by the anode reaction, irrespective of what the cathode reaction is, we can split the emf into two *half-cell* potentials. Since the potential of a half-cell cannot be determined independently, it is measured with respect to a reference electrode known as the *hydrogen electrode*, the potential of which is taken to be zero. For convenient laboratory work, the secondary reference electrode used is the *calomel electrode*, consisting of mercurous chloride mixed in liquid Hg and in contact with a saturated KCl solution. The calomel electrode has a standard potential of $+ 0.241$ V.

In the above reaction of magnesium oxidation, $\Delta G°$ is negative and so, from Eq. (6.1), the emf $\varepsilon°$ is positive. However, the *standard potentials* have been defined as reduction potentials by international agreement. So, the standard potential $E° = -\varepsilon°$. The table of standard potentials is known as the *emf series* and is shown in Table 6.1. The potential of the Li/Li$^+$ electrode at the bottom of the series is -3.05 V (lithium is the most active metal) and that of the Au/Au^{3+} electrode at the top is $+1.50$ V (gold is the most noble metal). If, for example, zinc and copper form a galvanic cell, zinc (-0.76 V) will be anodic to copper ($+0.34$ V). The emf of this cell under standard conditions will be $+0.34 - (-0.76) = 1.10$ V.

Table 6.1 Standard Electrode Potentials of Metals

Electrode system	Standard Potential $E°$ at 25°C, volt	Electrode system	Standard Potential $E°$ at 25°C, volt
Noble end			
Au/Au^{3+}	+ 1.50	Zn/Zn^{2+}	– 0.76
Ag/Ag$^+$	+ 0.80	Mn/Mn^{2+}	– 1.18
Cu/Cu^{2+}	+ 0.34	Zr/Zr^{4+}	– 1.53
H$_2$/H$^+$	0.0	Ti/Ti^{2+}	– 1.63
Pb/Pb^{2+}	– 0.13	Al/Al^{3+}	– 1.66
Sn/Sn^{2+}	– 0.14	U/U^{3+}	– 1.80
Mo/Mo^{3+}	– 0.20	Be/Be^{2+}	– 1.85
Ni/Ni^{2+}	– 0.25	Mg/Mg^{2+}	– 2.37
Co/Co^{2+}	– 0.28	Na/Na$^+$	– 2.71
Cd/Cd^{2+}	– 0.40	Ca/Ca^{2+}	– 2.87
Fe/Fe^{2+}	– 0.44	K/K$^+$	– 2.93
Cr/Cr^{3+}	– 0.74	Li/Li$^+$	– 3.05
			Active end

The Nernst equation The Nernst equation gives the potential E under non-standard conditions, when the activity (or concentration) of the metal in the electrode or the metal ions in the electrolyte is not unity. For the zinc electrode,

$$E_{Zn} = E°_{Zn} + \frac{RT}{2.303\,nF} \log \frac{[\text{Zn}^{2+}]}{[\text{Zn}]} \qquad (6.2)$$

At room temperature, $RT/2.303\,nF = 0.059$ V. When the zinc ion concentration in the electrolyte is less than unity, $E_{Zn} < E°_{Zn}$, i.e. the zinc electrode becomes more active with a greater tendency to dissolve.

In the reference hydrogen electrode, with hydrogen gas bubbling at one atmospheric pressure, the potential as a function of hydrogen ion concentration in the electrolyte is given by

$$E_{H_2} = E°_{H_2} + 0.059 \log [\text{H}^+] \qquad (6.3)$$

By definition, $-\log [\text{H}^+] = pH$. Noting that $E°_{H_2} = 0$, we have

$$E_{H_2} = -0.059 \, pH \qquad (6.4)$$

In acidic solutions ($pH < 7$), the electrode is more noble as compared to alkaline solutions ($pH > 7$).

The Pourbaix diagrams   The emf series gives the electrode potentials under standard conditions, where the metal ion concentration in the electrolyte is unity. In aqueous solutions (most common in corrosion problems), the metal ion concentration is usually much less than unity, due to the limited solubilities of metal oxides and hydroxides. It is useful to know the equilibrium potentials between a metal, its ions and compounds as a function of pH in an aqueous solution. Pourbaix diagrams show such relationships. The diagram for iron and its hydroxides is given in Fig. 6.3. Line a, which is independent of pH, gives the equilibrium between iron and ferrous ions:

$$Fe^{2+} + 2e^- \rightarrow Fe$$

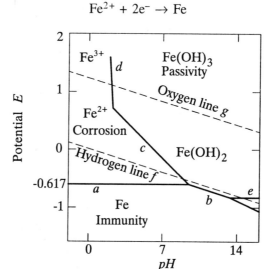

Figure 6.3   The Pourbaix diagram for iron showing the three main regions: immunity, corrosion and passivity.

This line at a potential of $E = -0.617$ V is drawn at $[Fe^{2+}]$ concentration of 10^{-6}. Lower concentrations than this can be ignored, as they correspond to negligible corrosion rates. So, below the line, we have immunity against corrosion. Above this line, corrosion can occur. Lines b, c, d and e represent the equilibrium between species on either side of a line as shown in the figure. Except for line e, the other lines involve either H^+ ions or OH^- ions in the equilibrium reaction and so are functions of pH. When $Fe(OH)_3$ is stable, protection by the passive film formation occurs. The dotted lines f and g correspond to hydrogen and oxygen evolution respectively. Below line f, hydrogen is evolved. Above line g, oxygen evolution occurs. Between f and g, water is stable.

Other such equilibrium relationships in aqueous systems are listed in the atlas of Pourbaix diagrams.

Galvanic series in sea water In view of the complex nature of engineering alloys and the difficulties in quantifying a particular environment, tables of galvanic series have been developed for commercial alloys in a given environment. These give the qualitative positions of different alloys in that environment. The galvanic series in sea water is shown in Table 6.2. Magnesium at the bottom of the list is the most active and 18/8 stainless steel (passive condition) at the top of the list is the least active. It may be noted that the order in this table is not the same as in the emf series (Table 6.1). For example, titanium and nickel which are more active in the emf series are near the noble end in the galvanic series, by virtue of their ability to form a passive film.

Table 6.2 Galvanic Series in Sea Water

Noble end	18–8 stainless steel (type 316) (passive)
	18–8 stainless steel (type 304) (passive)
	Titanium
	Nickel (passive)
	Copper
	Brass
	Tin
	Lead
	18–8 stainless steel (type 316) (active)
	18–8 stainless steel (type 304) (active)
	Pb–Sn solder
	Cast iron
	Mild steel
	Alclad
	Aluminium
	Zinc
Active end	Magnesium

6.3 POLARIZATION

The potentials given in the above section are measured under equilibrium conditions, when no current is flowing through the cell. When a net current flows, there is a shift in the potential of the electrodes; the phenomenon is known as *polarization*. The potential shift is always in a direction so as to oppose the flow of the corrosion current. The polarization of a zinc-copper galvanic cell is shown in Fig. 6.4. When no current flows, the open-circuit potential of the cell is $E^\circ_{Cu} - E^\circ_{Zn} = 1.10$ V. With increasing flow of current, the potential of the copper electrode shifts downwards to more active values, whereas the zinc potential shifts upwards to more noble values. Thus, the potential difference decreases, as the current increases. If R is the resistance of the circuit, a steady current I will flow, such that IR is the potential drop. When the cell is short circuited with negligible resistance in the circuit, the corrosion current will correspond to the point of intersection of the two polarization curves in Fig. 6.4. The corresponding potential is called E_{corr}.

Causes of polarization

1. *Concentration polarization* arises from the changes in the concentration of the reacting ions near an electrode, as soon as a current starts to flow. At the cathode, if the reaction involves the plating out of the metal ions, the metal ion concentration decreases. It is easy to see from the Nernst equation (6.2) that this decrease shifts the potential of the cathode to more active values. The metal ion concentration never drops to zero, as the ions from the surrounding electrolyte continue to replenish those lost by deposition. When the potential shifts sufficiently, some other electrode reactions such as hydrogen evolution replace the initial reaction. Similarly, with metal dissolution at the anode, there is an increase in metal ion concentration there. This build-up near the anode shifts its potential towards more noble values. If the electrolyte near the anode gets saturated with metal ions, the excess ions may form a precipitate.

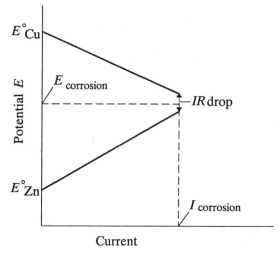

Figure 6.4   The polarization of a zinc-copper galvanic cell.

2. *Activation polarization* is due to the slowness of an electrode reaction. Metal deposition or dissolution is usually fast, but gas evolution reactions are slow. Hydrogen evolution at the cathode occurs in two steps:

$$H^+ + e^- \rightarrow H_{ads}$$

$$H_{ads} + H_{ads} \rightarrow H_2$$

The second step, where the two adsorbed atoms combine to form a molecule, is slow and requires an activation potential to keep it going at the rate required by the magnitude of the current flowing through the cell. The extra potential η known as the activation polarization (called the *hydrogen overvoltage* in this case) aids to reduce the activation barrier for the reaction, as schematically illustrated in Fig. 6.5. Metal surfaces which require a large hydrogen overvoltage retard the combination of the adsorbed hydrogen atoms into molecules. The atomic hydrogen may then diffuse into the metal and can cause hydrogen cracking.

The activation polarization follows the *Tafel relationship* over a wide range of current density i:

$$\eta = a + b \log i \qquad (6.5)$$

where a and b are constants. Note that, for a given corrosion current, a small area of the electrode means a high current density and a greater extent of polarization.

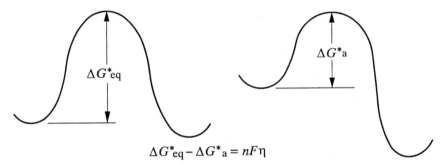

$$\Delta G^*_{eq} - \Delta G^*_a = nF\eta$$

Figure 6.5 The overpotential η lowers the activation barrier ΔG^* for an electrode reaction.

6.4 PASSIVATION

When an iron rod is immersed in dilute nitric acid, it reacts vigorously. On the other hand, if it is immersed in concentrated nitric acid, it stops reacting soon after immersion. This difference in behaviour is explained on the basis of the oxidizing capacity of the two acids. The strong acid effectively oxidizes the iron to form a thin protective film. Once it forms, the film prevents further reaction of the iron with the acid. The iron is said to become *passive*. The dilute acid is not strong enough to oxidize and produce the passive film, so the metal continues to dissolve.

A passive metal is defined as one that is active in the emf series, but nevertheless corrodes at a very low rate, behaving like a noble metal. Nickel, titanium and stainless steels are passive in the atmosphere and therefore do not rust like carbon steels. Some metals are passive only in specific electrolytes, e.g. iron is passive in conc. HNO_3 and in chromate solutions.

The potential E versus $\log I$ for iron in 1N H_2SO_4 is shown in Fig. 6.6. E_A is the open circuit potential of the metal (acting as the anode). As the current density increases, the anode becomes polarized along the line AB. At a critical current density, i_{crit}, the passive film forms and further dissolution of the metal is drastically reduced. So, the current density abruptly falls to a much lower value, $i_{passive}$. For iron, $i_{passive}$ is smaller than i_{crit} by a factor of 30,000. The corrosion rate at this current density is negligible. With further increase in the potential, the current density remains constant in the passive region of Fig. 6.6. Eventually, the *transpassive region* is reached, when the current density starts to increase again with the evolution of oxygen.

Clearly, a metal that can be passivated and retained in the passive state during service can reduce the corrosion rate to negligible values. The formation and retention of a stable passive film are promoted by the following factors:

1. A low critical current density.

2. A more active potential at which passivation occurs.

3. A high potential at which the change to the transpassive region occurs.

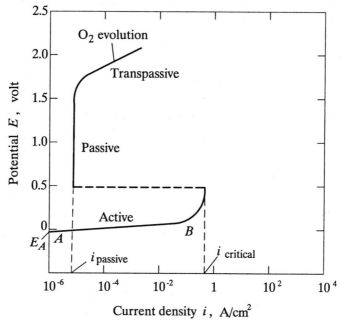

Figure 6.6 The passivation of iron in 1N H_2SO_4.

There are three main methods that use passivity as a means of corrosion protection:

1. In *anodic protection*, an external current, i_{crit}, is initially impressed on the metal so as to passivate it. Then the current density is reduced to $i_{passive}$ and maintained at that value to ensure that the passive film does not dissolve. The necessary electrical equipment is complex and expensive to install and maintain. If control is lost temporarily and the potential strays into the active region, the corrosion can be disastrously high. Because of this, anodic protection is not as widely used as the other methods.

2. *Passivators* are inorganic oxidizing anions such as chromates $(CrO_4)^{4-}$ and nitrites $(NO_2)^{2-}$. Solutions containing these anions promote the formation of the passive film.

3. Alloying is done to reduce the critical current density for passivation and also to shift the passivating potential to more active values. 12% chromium added to iron reduces i_{crit} from 200 mA/cm^2 to 2 μA/cm^2 and the passivating potential from 0.6 V to -0.2 V.

Pitting   The passive film may be destroyed in the presence of certain anions in the electrolyte. The presence of Cl$^-$ ions, e.g. in marine atmospheres, destroys the passive film on iron, chromium, nickel, aluminium and stainless steels. Titanium is the only metal that is immune to the Cl$^-$ ions. The Cl$^-$ ions act mainly by lowering the potential at which the transpassive region sets in. Figure 6.7 shows the decrease in this potential for stainless steels, with increasing concentration of NaCl in a solution of Na$_2$SO$_4$. The passive film is usually destroyed in a localized region. This region becomes anodic with respect to the surrounding passive region and corrodes at a fast rate due to the high current density over the small area. Thus a pit forms and the continued presence of the Cl$^-$ ions in the pit does not allow repassivation. The passive-active cell continues to corrode and produces a deep pit. The potential at which the current density starts to increase on entering the transpassive region is called the *critical pitting potential.*

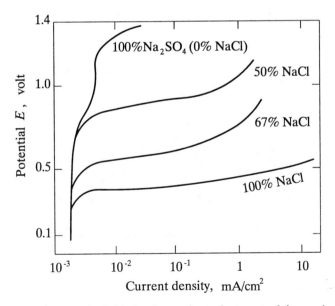

Figure 6.7   The presence of chlorine ions reduces the extent of the passive region.

6.5 GENERAL METHODS OF CORROSION PREVENTION

Some methods of corrosion prevention are understood readily. From Table 6.1, one can deduce that use of noble metals will prevent corrosion. Although this is true, the choice of a metal for an engineering application is dependent on many other factors such as cost, availability, fabricability, strength, and so on.

Avoidance of contact between dissimilar metals will prevent corrosion. Yet, we frequently come across designs such as a steel screw in brass marine equipment, a Pb-Sn solder on copper wire, a steel shaft in a bronze bearing and aluminium fins attached to copper tubes. When contact between dissimilar metals is unavoidable, the design should be such that *the metal that acts as the anode does not form a small surface area as compared to the cathode*. A small anodic area means a high current density and consequently a high rate of corrosion. A copper nut or bolt on a large steel plate is acceptable, but not a steel bolt on a copper article of large area.

In two-phase alloys, the two phases may form a galvanic couple at the microstructural level and electrical contact between them is inherent in the structure. Untempered martensite is a single phase and corrodes at a slower rate as compared to tempered martensite, where fine carbide particles and ferrite form innumerable galvanic cells. If the martensite is tempered at a relatively high temperature (e.g. 550°C), coarsening of cementite particles occurs and the number of potential galvanic cells per unit area of the exposed surface decreases. Correspondingly, the corrosion rate decreases after reaching a peak as a function of the tempering temperature, as shown in Fig. 6.8.

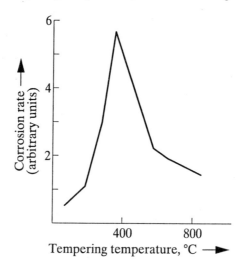

Figure 6.8 The corrosion rate as a function of tempering temperature of a quenched steel.

Unfortunately, the optimum mechanical properties of many alloys correspond to a sub-microscopic distribution of two phases. So, such alloys have a lower corrosion resistance than pure metals. For example, aluminium has a much better corrosion resistance than duralumin, in which very fine precipitates are present. In the aircraft industry, *alclad* is used as a composite sheet of duralumin covered on both sides with thin sheets of pure aluminium for corrosion protection.

Removing a cathodic reactant such as oxygen dissolved in water can reduce the corrosion rate. The feed water for boilers and cooling systems is treated with sodium sulphite to remove the dissolved oxygen, according to the reaction:

$$Na_2SO_3 + \frac{1}{2}O_2 \rightarrow Na_2SO_4$$

The dissolved oxygen can also be removed by *deaeration*, where the water is just heated to remove oxygen, by using the fact that the solubility of oxygen in water decreases with increasing temperature.

Inhibitors are additives that reduce the rate of corrosion, by slowing down or preventing an electrode reaction. Anodic inhibitors include the passivators. The oxidizing additives such as chromates and nitrites promote the formation of the passive film on the metal surface, by themselves readily undergoing reduction. The nonoxidizing anions such as silicates, phosphates and carbonates do not supply their own oxygen but catalyze the oxidation of the metal in the presence of oxygen. In the case of iron, the anodic inhibitors are effective only in neutral or alkaline solutions (recall the *pH* range of the passive region on the Pourbaix diagram in Fig. 6.3). Cathodic inhibitors slow down the cathodic reaction, e.g. hydrazine (N_2H_4) scavenges the residual oxygen in water by the following reaction:

$$N_2H_4 + O_2 \rightarrow N_2 + 2H_2O$$

This action is similar to that of sodium sulphite discussed before.

6.6 CATHODIC PROTECTION

Principle of cathodic protection   The principle of cathodic protection can be understood from the polarization diagram in Fig. 6.9. In cathodic protection, *the polarization of the cathode is done to an extent that its potential becomes equal to the open circuit potential E_A of the anode*. This can be achieved either by means of an externally impressed current or by employing a sacrificial anode. An electrolyte is needed to ensure the passage of current through the part to be protected. So, *cathodic protection is effective only in soils or aqueous media*, wherein the part to be protected is immersed. It is not effective in the atmosphere.

When the potential of the two electrodes is equal to E_A, no corrosion current passes through the cell. All the current *bc* is $I_{impressed}$, Fig. 6.9. When no current is externally supplied, the potential is E_{corr} and all current *ab* is I_{corr}. For all potentials between E_{corr} and E_A, the current passing through the cathode has two components: *ab* is the corrosion current and *bc* is the impressed current.

Under such conditions, the metal is partially protected. When the potential is E_A, the metal is fully protected. When the potential is lower than E_A, the metal is overprotected. Overprotection is usually not desirable, as it means a waste of electrical energy from the external source as well as the danger of hydrogen cracking due to excessive hydrogen liberation on the metal surface.

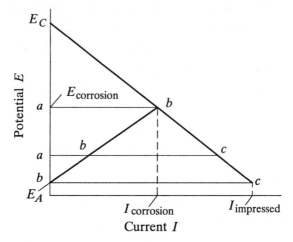

Figure 6.9 The principle of cathodic protection.

Practice of cathodic protection Cathodic protection is one of the most widely used methods of corrosion protection. It extends the service life of buried steel pipelines, offshore oil-drilling structures, ship hulls and water tanks.

In the impressed current cathodic protection (ICCP), the *externally impressed current* comes from a DC source, the positive terminal of which is connected to an auxiliary anode and the negative terminal to the part to be protected. Iron scrap can be used as the anode in some cases and it needs to be replaced periodically. The auxiliary anode in sea water for the protection of ship hulls is usually platinized Pb-2%Ag alloy. The current density required for full protection in moving sea water is about 0.01 mA/cm^2.

In the *sacrificial anode cathodic protection* (SACP), a sacrificial anode that has a much more active potential than the metal to be protected is used. For the protection of a steel hull in sea water, the potential difference for various sacrificial anodes is as follows.

Anode	Mg	Zn	Al–0.1%Sn
Potential difference	– 1.0	– 0.5	– 1.2

The aluminium alloy does not become passive in sea water. Aluminium can be used in other applications, such as protection of underground pipes, only if it is kept active by surrounding it with a solution rich in Cl$^-$ ions.

Both ICCP and SACP are used frequently in conjunction with a coating (paint) on the structure to be protected. The coating need not be pore free. The surface exposed through the pores is cathodically protected by the external current. The current requirement in the presence of a coating is much less than that for an uncoated structure. For example, an uncoated oil pipeline buried underground requires an anode every 30 m of length, whereas a coated pipeline can be protected over a distance of 30 km with one anode in SACP or 80 km in ICCP!

6.7 COATINGS

Metallic coatings   The principal methods of applying metal coatings for corrosion protection are listed below:

1. *Hot dipping:* dipping the part to be protected in a molten bath of the coat metal.
2. *Electroplating:* the part to be coated is made the cathode in a plating bath with an electrolyte containing the ions of the coat metal.
3. *Spraying:* the coat is melted into small drops of liquid and propelled by a blast of air on to the metal surface.
4. *Diffusion coating:* the coat metal is diffused into the part through the surface at an elevated temperature.

According to their electrochemical behaviour, metal coatings are classified as:

1. noble coatings, and
2. sacrificial coatings.

In *noble coatings*, the coat is noble with respect to the underlying metal. If a pore is present in the noble coating, the underlying base metal is exposed and is attacked continuously, as illustrated in Fig. 6.10a. For effective protection, such pores are to be sealed by an organic coating on top of the noble metal coating.

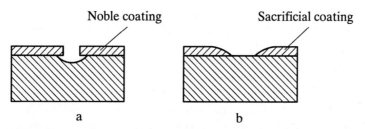

Figure 6.10   (a) A pore in a noble coating causes the underlying metal to corrode, and (b) a base coating protects by sacrificial action even in the presence of a pore.

In *sacrificial coatings*, the underlying metal is protected by the sacrificial action of the coating, which becomes the anode, Fig. 6.10b. Protection continues as long as the resistance of the electrolyte is small enough for sufficient corrosion current to flow. With a zinc coating on iron immersed in soft water, a 3 mm exposed area begins to show rust at the centre, whereas this does not happen even on a 30 mm exposed area, when the electrolyte is sea water of higher conductivity.

Nickel coatings are usually applied by electroplating. Nickel is sensitive to attack by SO_2 found in industrial atmospheres and loses lustre by the formation of $NiSO_4$. A chromium coating on nickel is given to improve the appearance in applications such as car bumpers.

Zinc coatings on iron are sacrificial. The most common method of application is by *hot dipping*, the process known as galvanizing. Low carbon steel sheets coated with zinc are called *galvanized iron* (GI). In aqueous environments with *pH* in the range of 7–12, $Zn(OH)_2$ forms as a protective layer on top of the zinc. Thus, galvanized iron is especially suitable for use in aqueous environments.

Tin coatings are applied by electroplating, which produces a uniform layer. To save tin, which is expensive, coatings may be as thin as 0.002 mm. Tin with standard potential of -0.136 V is cathodic to iron ($E^0 = -0.440$ V). This situation prevails on the outer surface of a tin can. On the inside, the stannous ions form complexes with the juices in foodstuffs and their activity is drastically lowered, so much so that tin becomes anodic to iron! In the absence of a readily occurring cathodic reaction, the corrosion rate is negligible. The stannous ions are nontoxic.

Aluminium coatings are obtained by hot dipping or spraying. Passive aluminium is cathodic to iron and a coating needs sealing of pores with an organic lacquer. Active aluminium (e.g. in sea water) protects by sacrificial action.

Nonmetallic coatings *Enamel and porcelain* are inorganic nonmetallic coatings. They act by simply excluding contact of the metal with water and air and also by providing a high resistance path. They are essentially alkali borosilicate ($Na_2O.B_2O_3.SiO_2$) glasses. The composition is adjusted to give a matching thermal expansion coefficient with the metal. Brittleness and poor thermal shock resistance are the main disadvantages of such coatings. *Portland cement* coatings used on underground water pipes have similar characteristics and they are cheaper.

Organic coatings refer mainly to *paints* applied to metals. Here also, protection arises from the exclusion of air and water and from the high electrical resistance of the paint layer. Paints are a mixture of particles of a *pigment* in a continuous organic medium. The common pigments are *red lead* (Pb_3O_4) and *zinc chromate* ($ZnCrO_4$). The PbO_4^{4-} and CrO_4^{4-} ions are passivators and promote the formation of a passive film on iron. The medium is either linseed oil or other drying oils, which polymerize by oxidation with air and solidify. Paints are applied in several coats, as this helps in sealing up pores and reduces the tendency to crack. The number of coats given increases with the severity of the exposure.

A good surface preparation is a must for the application of paint. Chemical solvents can be used to clean out dirt, oil and grease from the surface. Scales (oxide layers) are removed by dissolving them with dilute sulphuric acid or hydrochloric acid. A final dip in phosphoric acid is desirable to remove ions like Cl^- which prevent passivation. Oxide layers can also be removed by blasting the surface with sand, steel balls or silicon carbide particles.

6.8   CORROSION PREVENTION BY ALLOYING

Stainless steels   Alloying is an important method of corrosion prevention. As a typical example, *stainless steels* are discussed here. As already pointed out under passivation, chromium, when alloyed with iron, changes the passivating potential of iron to more active values and drastically lowers the critical current density required for passivation. At very small i_{crit} values, *self passivation* occurs, i.e. the corrosion current during atmospheric exposure is sufficient for the formation of the passive film. Steels with more than 10–12%Cr are self-passivating and are known as stainless steels.

The passive film on stainless steels is attacked under reducing conditions. In addition, Cl^- ions are destructive to the passive film. Nickel and molybdenum improve the corrosion resistance imparted by chromium. The 304 type austenitic stainless steel with 18%Cr, 8%Ni and 0.08%C is resistant to neutral chloride solutions. Molybdenum improves resistance to pitting as well as to sulphuric acid. Type 316 stainless steel, which contains in addition 2%Mo, is widely used in the chemical industry.

Intergranular corrosion   Stainless steels are prone to intergranular corrosion (corrosion along grain boundaries) under certain conditions. The pseudobinary phase diagram for 18/8 stainless steel as a function of carbon content is shown in Fig. 6.11. With about 0.08%C, the steel is in the fully austenitic state only when quenched from above 800°C. If cooled slowly from this temperature, chromium carbide particles precipitate preferentially along the austenitic grain boundaries. With a thin carbide film at the grain boundaries, the steel is said to be in the *sensitized condition*.

The composition profile near a grain boundary in the sensitized state is schematically shown in Fig. 6.12. At the boundary, where the chromium carbide is present, the chromium content may exceed 70%. In regions immediately surrounding the carbide on either side of the boundary, a thin region is depleted of chromium, as it has diffused to the boundary to form the carbide. If the chromium content in this thin region falls below 12%, they lose their self-passivating property and become anodic to the grain interiors, which contain 18%Cr and are passive. The galvanic cell thus set up attacks the thin region selectively, resulting in intergranular corrosion. Under extreme conditions, the steel crumbles into a fine powder, with each particle in the powder corresponding to one or more grains of the steel before the attack!

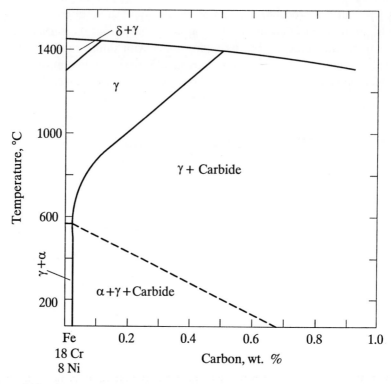

Figure 6.11 The pseudo-binary phase diagram for an 18/8 stainless steel as a function of carbon content. The precipitation of the α phase below the dotted line rarely occurs.

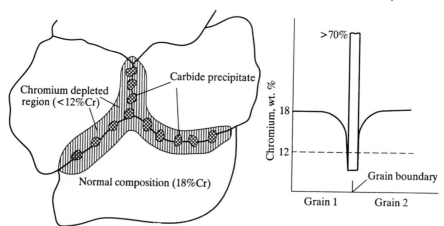

Figure 6.12 Chromium carbide precipitation at a grain boundary and the composition profile near the boundary.

A sensitized steel can be restored to its original state of excellent corrosion resistance in the following ways.

1. The steel is reheated into the single austenitic region, Fig. 6.11, and then *quenched*. The carbides go into solution during austenitizing and have no time to reprecipitate during quenching. This procedure cannot be adopted, if the steel is to be used in service at temperatures between 500 and 800°C, as grain boundary precipitation will again occur during service.

2. A *low carbon grade* of stainless steel such as 304L or 316L can be used. In these grades, the carbon content is limited to a maximum of 0.03%. So, there is no precipitation of carbides, note the solubility of carbon in austenite in the phase diagram in Fig. 6.11.

3. The *stabilized grades* 321 and 347 can be used. In type 321, titanium greater than 5 times the wt%C is added. In type 347, niobium greater than 10 times the wt%C is present. Both titanium and niobium form more stable carbides than chromium, recall the carbide stability scale given on p. 107. So, carbon combines preferentially with titanium or niobium. Chromium remains in solution and sensitization does not occur.

The above description is valid for austenitic stainless steels. Because of the low solubility of carbon in ferrite, ferritic stainless steels sensitize much more rapidly and at lower temperatures. Here, the intergranular corrosion cannot be prevented, by a solutionizing treatment and water quenching. They must be annealed at about 800°C to replenish the Cr-depleted regions near the grain boundaries by diffusion of Cr from the interior of the grains. Reducing C to 0.03% is also not applicable here. *Duplex stainless steels*, which contain metastable ferrite within the austenite grains, are known to be remarkably resistant to intergranular corrosion.

6.9   STRESS CORROSION CRACKING

Stress corrosion cracking (SCC) refers to the cracking of a material under static load by the combined action of a stress and a corrosive environment. The related phenomenon of hydrogen cracking or hydrogen embrittlement is due to the absorption of atomic hydrogen into the metal.

General characteristics   The experimentally known characteristics of stress corrosion cracking are summarized below.

1. Stress corrosion cracking is found in *alloys* and not in pure metals. However, there is some uncertainty as to what level of purity can be classified as "pure"!

2. SCC occurs only in a *specific environment* for a given alloy. Some examples of environments and the corresponding alloys are given below.

Alloy	Environment
Mild steel	Conc. NO_3^-, OH^-
High strength steel (T.S. > 1200 MPa)	H_2O
Stainless steel	Cl^-
α-brass	Traces of NH_3 or NH_4^+
Aluminium alloys	H_2O, NaCl solutions

3. The presence of a *tensile component* of stress is necessary. The stress may be externally applied. Or it can be residual stresses in the alloy. Early examples of SCC were due to residual stresses: the *season cracking* of brass and the *caustic embrittlement* of boilers. When cold drawn cartridge cases of α-brass are exposed to traces of ammonia in the atmosphere, they crack spontaneously. When the cold worked brass is given a stress-relieving anneal at 250–300°C, the susceptibility to SCC disappears. Boiler water is treated with NaOH to control *pH*. In the crevices between bolts and the boiler plates, evaporation results in a concentration of OH^- ions, leading to SCC of the bolts having residual stresses induced by plastic deformation during tightening. Welded boilers are also prone to SCC, in the presence of residual welding stresses.

4. The cracks in SCC move on a very narrow front. In hydrogen cracking, the cracks are known as *hairline cracks* often difficult to identify. If cracking is due to anodic dissolution at the crack tip, extremely localized corrosion must be taking place.

5. The crack path is often *intergranular* in SCC, Fig. 6.13. Transgranular crack propagation, i.e. propagation across the grains, has also been found in some cases.

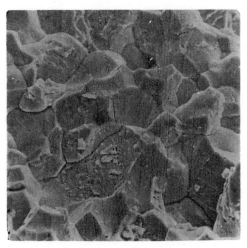

Figure 6.13 Intergranular fracture in stress corrosion cracking.

6. Many of the alloys which are susceptible to SCC form passive films. Examples are aluminium alloys and stainless steels. However, this is not always the case.

7. Cracking consists of two stages: (i) *initiation* and (ii) *propagation*. Titanium alloys are immune to crack initiation in chloride solutions. But when the alloys are precracked, crack propagation is found to occur.

Mechanisms of crack growth In the electrochemical mechanism, corrosion by anodic dissolution is believed to occur at the crack tip. In alloys that form a passive film, the crack tip is not covered by the film, because the plastic deformation at the tip exposes fresh metal or the stress concentration at the tip is sufficient to break the brittle oxide film. An active-passive cell is set up between the tip and the crack faces that are covered with the film. Only a very small area of the tip is exposed, resulting in a high current density at the tip.

Intergranular corrosion is due to the galvanic cells set up at the grain boundaries by segregation or precipitation. In this mechanism, cathodic protection should be effective in preventing SCC, as is found in some cases.

In hydrogen cracking, the adsorption of atomic hydrogen at the crack tip faces can lower the surface energy γ in the Griffith equation (5.6). This explanation is probably valid for the time-dependent cracking observed in non-metallic materials, where an electrochemical mechanism is not possible. In ductile alloys, γ_p is much larger than γ and an adsorption mechanism is unlikely. Hydrogen atoms presumably diffuse into the metal near the crack tip and *lock up the mobile dislocations* thus preventing plastic flow. The yield strength increases locally and the lack of plastic flow at the tip causes embrittlement.

Alternatively, supersaturated hydrogen atoms can precipitate as H_2 molecules at a crack nucleus or interface. The stresses from the build-up of hydrogen pressure can induce the nucleation and/or growth of cracks. At room temperature, hydrogen being a small interstitial atom can diffuse over a number of interatomic distances in a matter of seconds. A high hydrogen overvoltage slows down the combination of hydrogen atoms into molecular hydrogen, thus facilitating their inward diffusion. Sulphur containing oil increases the hydrogen overvoltage and thereby causes embrittlement of oil pipelines.

The stress intensity factor K_{Iscc} The time dependent fracture under a corrosive environment has been studied experimentally by measuring the stress intensity factor K_I. After precracking, a cantilever specimen that is surrounded by the corrosive environment is subjected to a constant load. The measured time for fracture is plotted in Fig. 6.14 as a function of K_I. If the applied stress corresponds to K_{Ic}, fast fracture occurs instantly. When $K_I < K_{Ic}$, fracture occurs after a delay period, during which the crack grows slowly. When the stress intensity factor is below a critical value known as K_{Iscc}, no fracture occurs even after prolonged holding, see Fig. 6.14.

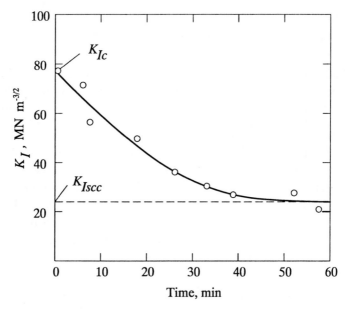

Figure 6.14 The critical stress intensity factor decreases with increasing time in a corrosive environment, reaching a constant value of K_{Iscc}, below which no cracking occurs.

Figure 6.15 shows the measured rates of crack growth as a function of K_I. Below K_{Iscc}, the crack growth rate is zero. Above K_{Iscc}, in region II, the crack grows at a constant rate independent of K_I. The growth rate is probably controlled by an electrochemical process in this region. Region III corresponds to fast growth that culminates in fracture.

The energy balance for crack growth in the Griffith equation (5.6) needs to be modified to take into account the electrochemical energy released at the crack tip due to anodic dissolution. For unit extension of the crack, we can write the condition for spontaneous growth as:

surface energy + plastic work = elastic energy + electrochemical
  of the crack   at the tip   released   energy released

$$\underbrace{2\gamma_p} \qquad = \pi\sigma^2 c/Y \quad + \quad (nF\rho\delta/M)\varepsilon$$

where σ is the tensile stress,
        c is half-length of the crack,
        Y is Young's modulus of the alloy,
        n is the number of electrons taking part in the anodic reaction,
        F is Faraday's constant,
        ρ is the density of the alloy,
        δ is the opening at the crack tip,
        M is the atomic weight, and
        ε is the oxidation potential $(= - E)$.

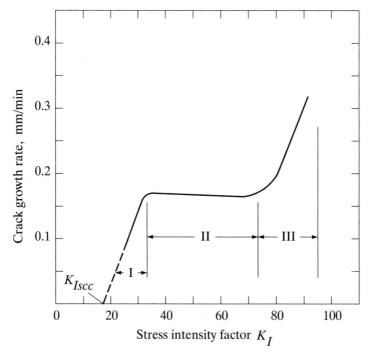

Figure 6.15 The crack growth rate in a Ni-Cr-Mo steel in a NaCl environment as a function of the stress intensity factor, depicting the three stages.

Rewriting the critical condition in terms of K_{Iscc}, we have

$$K_{Iscc} = [2\gamma_p Y - (nF\rho\delta/M)\varepsilon]^{1/2} \tag{6.6}$$

Equation (6.6) shows that K_{Iscc} decreases with an increase in yield strength (which decreases γ_p) and with an increase in the corrosion tendency as given by ε.

SUGGESTED READINGS

Jones, D.A., *Principles and Prevention of Corrosion*, Prentice Hall, New Jersey (1996).

Uhlig, H.H., *Corrosion and Corrosion Control*, John Wiley, New York (1971).

QUESTIONS

1. Calculate the amount of zinc (anode) that corrodes, when a current of 100 mA passes for 5 hr through a galvanic cell.

2. Calculate the corrosion rate in mm per year, when iron dissolves as ferrous ions at a current density of 0.15 mA/cm^2.

   Answer: 1.75 mm.

3. Calculate the stannous ion concentration required to shift the standard potential of tin to that of iron inside a tin can.

   Answer: 5×10^{-11}.

4. Ordinary brown rust is ferric hydroxide, $Fe(OH)_3$. Write down the chemical reaction which converts iron to $Fe(OH)_3$, splitting it into an anode and a cathode reaction.

5. Explain the similarities and differences between the table of standard electrode potentials and the table of galvanic series.

6. Is a steep polarization curve an advantage or a disadvantage in corrosion control? Explain.

7. Explain the significance of the terms: i_{crit}, $i_{passive}$, $E_{passive}$, and $E_{transpassive}$.

8. A pit in a 18/8 stainless steel exposed to sea water grows to a depth of 50 mm in a year. To what average current density does this correspond?

   Answer: 4.3 mA/cm^2.

9. Explain why aluminium used as a sacrificial anode needs to be kept in a solution of Cl^- ions.

10. Explain the differences in the electrochemical mechanism of protection offered by (i) zinc, and (ii) tin, applied as a coating.

11. A high strength bolt of a low alloy steel is heat treated to a hardness of 42 R_c, instead of the specified hardness of 35 R_c. The bolt fails after some time in a moist atmosphere. Explain the reason for this behaviour.

Chapter 7

ENGINEERING ALLOYS

In this concluding chapter, the structure, treatment, properties and uses of individual engineering alloys are considered. The first part deals with tonnage steels such as low carbon steels and mild steels and their more recent modifications. This is followed by a brief discussion of high strength steels and spring steels. Tool steels are then described in some detail. Different types of cast irons are considered. Among the light alloys, emphasis is on aluminium. We close the chapter with a discussion of copper and its alloys and bearing metals.

7.1   STEEL SPECIFICATIONS

To select the right steel for a particular application, some familiarity with standard specifications and the associated notation is necessary. Specifications vary from country to country and can be based on differing criteria. The majority of specifications are in terms of the *chemical composition* of the steel. For an experienced engineer, the composition indicates the probable treatment given to the steel and the corresponding mechanical properties obtainable. Alternative criteria based on mechanical properties or hardenability are also used to specify steels.

Indian standard specifications   The Indian standard specifications for steels are based mainly on chemical composition. For example, *IS*: C07 is a carbon steel with 0.07%C. Similarly, C15 stands for 0.15%C. The concentrations of the other alloying elements may be expressly stated. For example, 55Mn1stands for 0.55%C, 1%Mn. 15Mn75 refers to 0.15%C, 0.75%Mn. The underlining of 75

185

indicates that the manganese content is 0.75% and not 75%. Even if the underlining is missing, it is to be understood this way, as there is no steel with 75% Mn! For low alloy steels, the same notation is applicable. The student should write down the compositions of the following steels: 25Mn1S14, 55Si2Mn90, 50Cr1V23, 40Ni2Cr1Mo25.

For tool steels, the letter T is used at the start of the notation. For example, T118 stands for 1.18%C tool steel. Examples of alloy tool steels are T105Cr1Mn60 and T75W18Cr4V1, the latter being the 18-4-1 high speed tool steel.

AISI-SAE classification   As an engineer may come across imported steels or may have to order a steel from abroad, some familiarity with foreign specifications is useful.

The US designations for steels are those of the American Iron and Steel Institute (AISI) and the Society of Automotive Engineers (SAE). In both of them, the composition is denoted by a four digit number. The last two digits stand for the carbon content. For example, xx45 stands for 0.45%C. The first two digits denote the other alloying elements. The table below gives the meaning of these digits for some typical cases. For example, 1040 stands for a 0.4%C steel. AISI 4340 means a Ni-Cr-Mo steel, with 1.8%Ni, 0.8%Cr, 0.25%Mo, and 0.4%C. 9260 is a spring steel with 2%Si, 0.9%Mn, and 0.6%C. 52100 is a ball bearing steel with 1.45%Cr and 1.0%C.

AISI-SAE Classification	Type of steel
10xx	Plain carbon steels
11xx	Resulphurized grades
13xx	Manganese steels (1.6–1.9%Mn)
40xx	Mo steels
41xx	Cr-Mo steels
43xx	Ni-Cr-Mo steels
51xx	0.8%Cr steels
52xx	1.45%Cr steels
61xx	Cr-V steels
92xx	Si-Mn steels
50B60	boron treated steel (0.5%Cr, 0.6%C)

British specifications   The older British specifications for steels have the letters En followed by a number. For example, En 2 stands for a carbon steel with 0.15%C. En 8 is a 0.4%C steel. En 8A is the resulphrized grade of En 8. En 24 is a Ni-Cr-Mo low alloy steel. In the later British specification BS970, the first three digits stand for the alloy content. The middle letter A, M or H stands for analysis (A), mechanical properties (M) or hardenability (H) based specifications. The last two digits give the carbon content. The following table gives some examples of nearest equivalents of different specifications.

Indian	British (old)	British (new)	AISI-SAE
55Cr 70	En 11	526 M 60	5155
40Ni2Cr1Mo25	En 24	817 M 40	4340
C100	En 44	060 A 96	1095
55Si2Mn90	En 45	250 A 53	9260
50Cr1V23	En 47	735 A 50	6150

The German specification starts with the letters DIN, the Japanese with JIS and the Russian with GOST. Details of these can be found in reference books. Classifications of stainless steels and tool steels are described under those sections in this chapter.

Unified numbering system (UNS)   The Unified Numbering System for metals and alloys provides a means of correlating many internationally used numbering systems currently administered by societies and trade associations. A UNS designation is not, in itself, a specification, because it establishes no requirements for form, condition, property or quality. It is a unified identifier of a metal or an alloy for which controlling limits have been established in specifications published elsewhere. The UNS designation consists of a single letter followed by 5 digits. The letter is suggestive of the family of metals: G for carbon and low alloy steels, S for stainless steels, T for tool steels, A for aluminium alloys and P for precious metals. For example, UNS G10200 = AISI-SAE 1020 and T11301 = AISI T1.

Common residual elements in steels   The four common impurities or residual elements in a steel are the following: sulphur, phosphorous, manganese and silicon. In addition, the steels may contain residual aluminium or nitrogen.

Normally, *sulphur* should not exceed 0.04–0.05%. However, much lower sulphur contents are obtained nowadays by special processing techniques, as removal of residual sulphur appreciably enhances the properties. If no manganese is present, the sulphur forms FeS, which is present in the form of a *thin film* along the grain boundaries. This compound has a low melting point and may melt, when the steel is heated to high temperatures, resulting in *hot shortness*, i.e. brittleness at high temperatures. In the presence of manganese, sulphur combines preferentially with manganese to form *globules* of MnS. The steel is free of hot shortness in this form. It is necessary to have manganese at least five times the weight of sulphur to ensure globule formation.

Normally, the *phosphorus* content of a steel does not exceed 0.04%. Even though phosphorus is an effective strengthener of ferrite (see Fig. 5.12b), it drastically lowers the ductility. Phosphorus is said to induce *cold shortness*, in contrast to the hot shortness effect of sulphur.

The beneficial action of *manganese* on sulphur has already been referred to. In addition, the solute strengthening effect of manganese is appreciable. It also lowers the critical temperatures and promotes the formation of finer pearlite. The ductile-brittle transition temperature of a steel decreases in the presence of manganese. As manganese increases the hardenability markedly (see Fig. 4.14), its presence in excess of 2% may result in the formation of martensite, when it is not desired.

Silicon is a good strengthener of ferrite. It retards softening during tempering (see Fig. 3.21) and thus aids in the removal of quenching stresses without appreciable decrease in hardness.

Figure 7.1 shows the general variation in mechanical properties of ferrite-pearlite steels as a function of carbon content. The detailed description of steels of specific carbon ranges is given in several sections below.

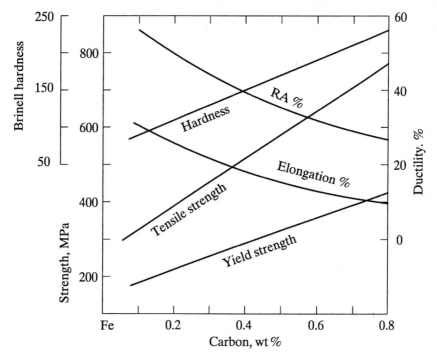

Figure 7.1   The variation in typical mechanical properties as a function of carbon content in ferrite-pearlite steels.

7.2   LOW CARBON STEELS

Conventional low carbon steels   Low carbon steels contain about 0.1% carbon. They are not heat treated, as the hardenability is too low to produce martensite. They are used in the form of cold rolled sheets. The microstructure consists essentially of ferrite, with a small amount of pearlite. Typical mechanical properties are:

Y.S., MPa	T.S., MPa	% Elongation
200–300	300–370	28–40

The excellent formability of these steels makes them suitable for cold-formed applications such as stampings of automobile and refrigerator bodies, tin cans and corrugated sheets.

In the tensile test, low carbon steels show a pronounced yield point, followed by plastic deformation at constant load (yield point elongation), recall Fig. 5.5. This plastic deformation is inhomogeneous and occurs by the passage of Luders bands. This produces a rough surface, called the *orange peel effect*. Surface roughness mars the appearance of the final product, and hence is not desirable. The effect can be minimized by having a *fine ferrite grain size*, in the range of ASTM 7–9. Also, *temper rolling* eliminates surface roughness. Here, the sheets are given a skin pass, i.e. a small reduction of about 1% by passing through rolls. The steel is thereby deformed beyond the yield point, prior to the stamping operation.

Low carbon steels are susceptible to strain ageing. Even though strain ageing can serve as a method of strengthening, it can lead to a dramatic increase in the impact transition temperature and consequent embrittlement at ambient temperatures.

Cold forming characteristics Low carbon steels are ideally suited for cold forming operations such as deep drawing and stretch forming. The deep drawing quality of a steel is primarily controlled by the *plastic anisotropy parameter R* which is defined as

$$R = \frac{\varepsilon_w}{\varepsilon_t} \tag{7.1}$$

where ε_w is the true strain in the width direction and ε_t is the true strain in the thickness direction of a strip tensile specimen. A large value of R is indicative of good resistance to thinning of the walls of a sheet during deep drawing. A proper recrystallized texture must be developed for increasing R. Figure 7.2 shows that R increases with increasing grain size and is more for Al-killed and Ti-added steels than for rimmed steels.

Stretch forming, where the ends of a sheet are firmly gripped during stretching, is primarily influenced by the *work hardening exponent n*. The larger is n, the more is the uniform elongation and this helps in delaying localized necking during forming.

Dual phase steels In recent years, a good deal of effort has been put in the development of higher strengths in low carbon steels, without an appreciable loss of formability. Dual phase steels are characterized by:

1. The absence of a discontinuous yield point,
2. A low ratio of yield strength to tensile strength,

3. A high work hardening rate,

4. A high tensile strength, and

5. A large uniform elongation.

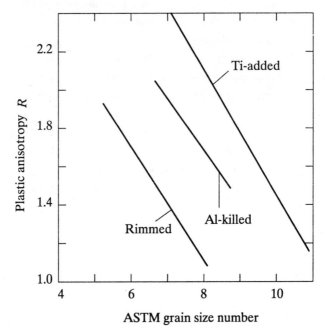

Figure 7.2 The effect of grain size and Al/Ti additions on the plastic anisotropy parameter *R*.

Low carbon sheets are annealed in the inter critical ($\alpha + \gamma$) region of the Fe-C phase diagram and then cooled rapidly enough to convert the austenite part to lath martensite. The final microstructure consists of 15–20% of *martensite islands in a fine-grained ferrite matrix*, Fig. 7.3. Typical mechanical properties attained are:

Y.S., MPa	T.S., MPa	% Elongation
350	650	30

The formability of dual phase steels is only slightly inferior to the conventional low carbon steels, but they have the advantage that no Luders bands form during deformation. Due to the high work hardening rate, the strength increases to 550 MPa after only 3% of plastic strain.

The dual phase steels are used in various stamped automobile components such as bumpers, wheel discs and door panels. Weight saving by as much as 10% is possible. A 45 kg reduction in weight saves about 2% of fuel in city driving. Besides automobiles, the energy savings can be significant in other modes of *ground transportation*.

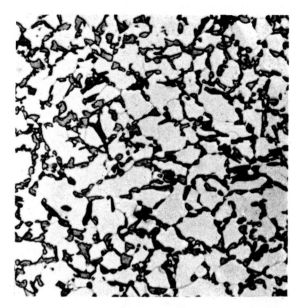

Figure 7.3 The microstructure of a dual phase steel consists of 15–20% of lath martensite dispersed in a matrix of ferrite.

7.3 MILD STEELS

Conventional mild steels Mild steel used in large tonnages for structural purposes contains 0.15–0.25% carbon. It is not heat treated, but used in the as-rolled and air-cooled condition. The microstructure is about 25% of fine pearlite interspersed in a ferrite matrix. Typical mechanical properties are:

Y.S., MPa	T.S., MPa	% Elongation
300–350	400–450	26–30

Due to higher carbon contents, the strengths are higher here, as compared to the low carbon steels, but the ductility is lower.

Both mild steels and low carbon steels possess *excellent weldability*. The heat affected zone (HAZ) near the weld attains a temperature above A_3 and becomes austenite. When the welding is complete, this region cools more rapidly than in air cooling, due to the quenching effect of the surrounding cold metal. If the carbon content does not exceed 0.25%, the hardenability (taking into account the residual manganese) is sufficiently low for non-martensitic products to form in the HAZ. Even if martensite is to form, its hardness is about 45 R_c and so, it is not brittle. *Structural components* (that are often welded *in situ*) such as plates for ship hulls, boilers, oil pipelines, I beams, H beams, angles, channels and girders are some of the numerous applications of mild steel.

Banding, frequently encountered in mild steel, refers to the microstructural condition that consists of alternate layers of ferrite and pearlite, Fig. 7.4. It is caused by the *interdendritic segregation* of manganese during solidification. Manganese reduces the activity of carbon in austenite and so, carbon also segregates with manganese. At such concentrated regions, pearlite forms during cooling after rolling. For many applications, banding is not harmful. Since it is easier for a crack to propagate parallel to a band than normal to it, banded steels are to be avoided in applications where *lamellar tearing* is possible. Figure 7.5 illustrates lamellar tearing (crack propagation parallel to the band) in members constrained due to heavy welding, as in very large ships and off-shore platforms.

Figure 7.4 Banding in mild steel.

The anisotropic properties of hot-rolled steels are not so much due to banding as due to *nonmetallic inclusions*. These inclusions get elongated during rolling and give rise to anisotropy. The ductility and toughness are lower in directions *normal* to the rolling direction. To obtain uniform mechanical properties in all directions, the sulphur and oxygen content of the steel should be reduced as much as possible to prevent the formation of sulphides and oxides. Any inclusion present must be small and equiaxed or globular. To obtain this condition, it is necessary to precipitate equiaxed particles that resist deformation during subsequent rolling. This is done by adding elements such as Ca, Zr or Ce (or mixed rare earths). Calcium additions globurize the alumina-type oxides by forming calcium aluminates. Zirconium dissolves in manganese sulphide and decreases its plasticity. Rare earths form a non-deformable sulphide or oxysulphide. The major effect of these additions is to increase the transverse ductility and toughness to levels comparable to those obtained in the longitudinal direction.

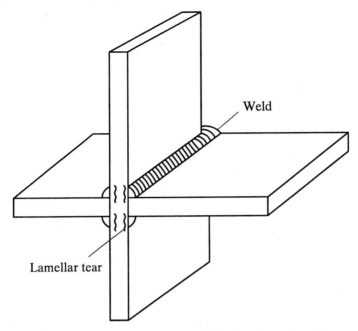

Figure 7.5 Lamellar tearing (parallel to banding) occurs in members constrained by welding.

Microalloyed steels Attempts have been made to improve the strength of mild steel, without impairing its excellent weldability. This has led to a new class of steels known as *microalloyed steels*. To the basic composition of mild steel, *small amounts of strong carbide forming elements such as niobium, vanadium and/or titanium are added*. The total concentration of the microalloying elements is less than 0.2%.

As discussed under Sec. 5.3, the microalloyed steels have a very fine ferrite grain size, in the range of ASTM 12–14. The yield strength increases with decreasing grain size, recall the Hall-Petch equation (5.5). In addition, the fine dispersion of alloy carbides results in *precipitation hardening*. Typical contributions from various strengthening mechanisms to the total yield strength are as follows:

Strengthening mechanism	Contribution, MPa
Iron lattice	35
Solid solution	135
Precipitation	45
Dislocations	50
Grain size	260
Total	525

It is evident that the major contribution comes from grain refinement. It has the additional advantage in that the *impact transition temperature (ITT) decreases with decreasing grain size,* whereas it increases with other strengthening methods. For example, the increase in the transition temperature per unit increase in yield strength is compared below for precipitation hardening and grain refinement. The factor is negative for grain refinement.

Strengthening mechanism	$\Delta ITT/\Delta\sigma$, °C/MPa
Precipitation hardening	+ 0.3
Grain refinement	− 0.8

Typical mechanical properties of microalloyed steels are:

MPa Y.S.	MPa T.S.	% Elongation
400–500	600–650	20–22

It may be noted that the increase in the strength of microalloyed steels results in lower elongation values. Unlike dual phase steels, which have good formability in spite of an increase in the tensile strength, microalloyed steels have poorer formability than the conventional low carbon steel. The stress-strain curves of a low carbon steel, a dual phase steel and a microalloyed steel are compared in Fig. 7.6.

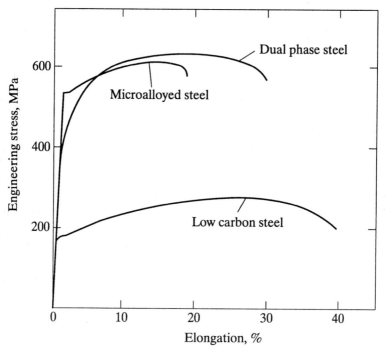

Figure 7.6 Comparison of the engineering stress-strain curves of three steels.

Weathering steels If copper and phosphorus are added to mild steel, the resistance to atmospheric corrosion is vastly improved. These are known as *weathering steels*. Cu^{2+} and PO_4^{3-} ions promote the formation of a cohesive crack-free layer of FeOOH ($Fe_2O_3.H_2O$), thereby limiting the access of oxygen and water to the metal surface. Copper in conjunction with chromium is also used for improving the corrosion resistance of mild steels. The life of many paint systems is doubled on weathering steel surfaces.

Free cutting steels When machinability is the main criterion for selection, free cutting grades are specified. These steels generally contain intentionally added sulphur and are known as *resulphurized* grades. Sufficient amount of manganese (5–8 times the weight of sulphur) is also added to form globular MnS particles in the ferritic matrix.

A very hard material such as high carbon martensite is difficult to machine. At the other extreme, a very soft steel is also difficult to machine, because during turning on the lathe a soft phase like ferrite forms continuous curls, which produce a rough surface and also heats the tool. If the curls were to break into *chips*, the tearing and heating can be avoided. In the resulphurized grades, the presence of an adequate number of *globular* MnS particles breaks the continuity of the matrix and promotes the tendency for *chip formation*. The machinability index of resulphurized grades is about twice that of a medium carbon steel.

Machinability can also be improved by adding insoluble metals like lead and copper to the ferrite matrix. Addition of phosphorus up to 0.12% results in the formation of Fe_3P particles, which serve a function similar to that of MnS particles.

7.4 MEDIUM CARBON STEELS

Forged components such as agricultural implements have carbon contents in the range of 0.3–0.5%. After hot forging, the components are air cooled. The microstructure is fine ferrite-pearlite mixture.

Rail structurals Structural parts used by the railways such as rails, wheels, wheel tyres and axles are either forged or hot rolled and have a carbon content of 0.5–0.65%. The higher level of carbon combined with about 1% Mn shifts the eutectoid composition sufficiently to yield a mostly-pearlitic structure. The lowering of the transformation temperature by Mn results in a finer pearlite. Figure 7.7 shows the weight loss due to wear as a function of hardness and interlamellar spacing in pearlite.

For service conditions with exceptionally high rates of wear in rails, an alloy steel (sometimes called Hadfield steel) with 0.75–0.9%C and 12–14%Mn is used. The steel is austenitic in structure and has a high rate of work hardening associated with the formation of stacking faults in the austenite.

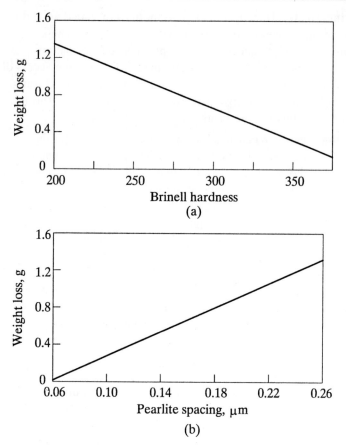

Figure 7.7 The weight loss due to wear of rail steels decreases with increasing hardness of the steel and decreasing interlamellar spacing of pearlite.

Spring steels Spring steels have carbon contents in the range of 0.5–0.65%. They are *quenched and tempered* to a high level of yield strength. A spring must possess a *high resilience*. It must be capable of storing a large amount of elastic energy, so that it can spring back without permanently deforming. The quantity σ_y/Y should be maximized for this purpose. The Young's modulus Y being a structure-insensitive property, a *large increase in the yield strength* is the key to achieve a high resilience. Tempering is done to give a yield strength of about 1500 MPa.

The alloying elements in a spring steel have several functions. They increase the hardenability so that martensite is obtained without resorting to drastic quenching. The presence of silicon in the 55Si2Mn90 spring steel serves the additional purpose of retarding softening during tempering, so that residual stresses are relieved without much loss in hardness and strength. Vanadium in the 50Cr1V23 steel prevents grain coarsening during austenitizing and improves the toughness of the steel. A fine grain size and prevention of decarburization during heat treatment ensure a good *fatigue strength*.

7.5 HIGH STRENGTH STRUCTURAL STEELS

High strength steels have often tensile strengths in excess of 600 MPa. Those with strengths up to 1000 MPa are called *high strength steels*. Those with strengths greater than 1000 MPa are called *ultra high strength steels*.

High strength low alloy (HSLA) steels   These steels contain carbon in the same range as mild steels (0.15–0.25%), but in addition have small quantities of alloying elements. The microalloyed steels discussed earlier are sometimes called HSLA steels. In many HSLA steels, the alloying elements serve the purpose of increasing the hardenability to some extent. The microstructure may consist of ferrite and bainite or ferrite and tempered martensite. Typical mechanical properties are:

Y.S., MPa	T.S., MPa	% Elongation
400–700	500–800	18–25

These steels have satisfactory weldability, as the carbon content of martensite (if present) is low.

Ni-Cr-Mo low alloy steels   Among the common alloying elements, *nickel* is the only one which *increases the toughness of ferrite*. Chromium, in addition to increasing the hardenability, increases the strength and wear resistance, but at the expense of toughness. For structural alloys, the Ni/Cr ratio should be about 2.5. To counter the temper brittleness inherent in Ni-Cr steels (recall Sec. 4.5), about 0.25%Mo is added. One of the well-known low alloy structural steels is the Ni-Cr-Mo steel corresponding to AISI 4340.

A 0.4%C steel, when quenched and tempered at 450°C, has the following properties:

Y.S., MPa	T.S., MPa	% Elongation	Izod impact, J
650	800	15	30

A 4340 steel, when quenched and tempered for the same elongation and impact value, has the following strength properties:

Y.S., MPa	T.S., MPa	% Elongation	Izod impact, J
1200	1350	15	32

It is clear that, for the same ductility and toughness, the low alloy steel possesses *superior strength*. Conversely, for the same strength, the low alloy steel would have larger ductility and toughness. This superiority arises from the presence of nickel among the alloying elements, as also from the increased hardenability, which enables slower quenching rates with less residual stresses in the steel. The ideal critical diameter for the 4340 steel is 65 mm, as compared to 15 mm for a 1040 steel. The high hardenability, however, makes welding difficult in the case of 4340 steel.

Ausformed steels   Thermomechanical treatments (TMT) refer to a combination of thermal treatment and mechanical deformation of steels. Controlled rolling of microalloyed steels discussed under Sec. 5.3 is TMT carried out on stable austenite. TMT of metastable austenite is called *ausforming*, as discussed below.

In ausforming, the steel after austenitizing is cooled to a temperature that lies in the bainitic bay (the temperature interval between the bainitic nose and the M_s temperature) and plastically deformed. It is then quickly oil quenched to room temperature before any non-martensitic products form. The martensitic units that form in the deformed austenite are smaller and finely dispersed. The dislocation substructure of the deformed austenite is inherited by martensite. The properties after tempering at 100°C are:

Y.S., MPa	T.S., MPa	% Elongation
2300	2700	8

This is a remarkable combination of strength and ductility. A plain carbon steel tempered to the same hardness level will be brittle with poor tensile strength.

Maraging steels   Another group of ultra high strength steels are the maraging (martensite plus ageing) steels. A typical composition is 0.03%C, 18%Ni, 3–8% each of Co and Mo, a fraction of a percent each of Ti and Al. The steel transforms on cooling to martensite, which is soft due to the low carbon content. The steel is then cold worked as desired and aged around 500°C. During ageing, *strain induced precipitation* of intermetallic compounds such as $Ni_3(Ti,Al)$ and Ni_3Mo form, resulting in precipitation hardening. A very high yield strength of ~1800 MPa is combined with an excellent fracture toughness $K_{Ic} = 120$ MN m$^{-3/2}$. Full weldability is another advantage, due to the softness of martensite. By virtue of their high cost, maraging steels are used mainly in special applications such as rocket casing and other aerospace applications.

Trip steels   TRIP stands for Transformation Induced Plasticity. A typical composition of trip steels is 0.25%C, 2%Mn, 2%Si, 8%Ni, 9%Cr, and 4%Mo. The composition is so adjusted that the M_s is below room temperature and M_d is above room temperature (M_d is the highest temperature up to which deformation of austenite can induce martensite). The steel is first heavily deformed above M_d, where no transformation occurs. The deformation produces the right degree of metastability so that a small plastic strain at the tip of the crack is sufficient to induce the austenite to transform to martensite. The plastic zone size at the crack tip is thus enlarged, so that more work is done during crack growth. The result is a high yield strength 1400 MN m^{-2}, combined with a high fracture toughness $K_{Ic} = 100$ MN m$^{-3/2}$. Like maraging steels, TRIP steels are expensive and used for specialized applications.

7.6 TOOL MATERIALS

Classification and property requirements The production of almost every object in industry requires tools. In addition to the familiar *hand tools*, there is a wide variety of *machine tools* used by industry. Tools play a vital role in industrial advancement. Most tools have been developed on the basis of shop floor experience. Nevertheless, the structure-property relationships in tool steels are better understood today, due to increasing availability of new data on phase relationships and T-T-T diagrams.

Tools can be classified into the following types:

1. *Cutting tools* such as those used on a lathe,
2. *Shearing tools:* shears and blanking dies,
3. *Battering tools:* chisels, rail track tools and punches, and
4. *Forming tools:* forging dies, piercing tools, extrusion dies, die-casting dies and cold forming dies.

The general properties required of a tool are:

1. *Wear and abrasion resistance*, a property that is met by the presence of hard alloy carbides,
2. *Toughness* that is obtained with lower carbon contents,
3. *Red hardness* is the ability to retain hardness at elevated temperatures, a property that is imparted by secondary hardening during tempering,
4. *Nondeforming property* is the resistance to distortion or dimensional changes during heat treatment, a property that is achieved by a high hardenability that permits air cooling during hardening, and
5. *Minimum cost*, the steel should be no more expensive than is needed to meet the particular requirements.

Heat treatment of high speed steel The general principles involved in the heat treatment of a tool steel can be illustrated with the example of a tungsten-based high speed steel: 0.7%C, 18%W, 4%Cr, and 1%V. A pseudo-binary phase diagram for this steel is shown in Fig. 7.8. The left end corresponds to Fe-18W-4Cr-1V and percent carbon is plotted along the x-axis. The eutectoid temperature is 840°C. The maximum solubility of carbon in austenite is only 0.7% and this occurs at the eutectic temperature of 1330°C. In the early stages of development of high speed steel, these phase relationships were not well understood. An austenitizing treatment of 850°C followed by quenching produced a hardness of 45 R_c, that is characteristic of martensite with 0.22%C. Clearly, higher austenitizing temperatures are required to put more carbon in solution in austenite. Chromium carbide ($Cr_{23}C_6$ or Cr_7C_3) begins to dissolve above 900°C and is fully in solution at 1100°C. The M_6C-type carbides ($Fe_3(Mo,W)_3C$) begin dissolving above 1100°C. Vanadium carbide (VC) is the last to dissolve. To put most of the carbon in solution, heating close to the eutectic temperature is required. This introduces additional problems in heat treatment such as large temperature gradients, oxidation, decarburization and austenitic grain growth. To minimize these, the heating is done in two stages: first to about 850°C, followed by rapid heating for only a few minutes at 1250–1300°C before quenching. The short time at this high temperature minimizes oxidation and decarburization. Much of vanadium carbide is still undissolved after a few minutes of soaking and aids in restraining the austenitic grain growth.

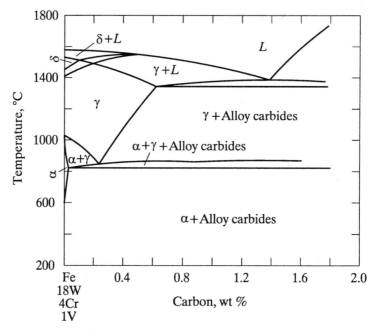

Figure 7.8 The pseudo-binary phase diagram for Fe18W4Cr1V tool steel as a function of the carbon content.

The T-T-T diagram for the same composition and austenitizing treatment is shown in Fig. 7.9. The steel is quenched in two stages to reduce thermal stresses: first to 500°C, where the time for transformation is very large. After equalization of temperature across the cross-section, it is quenched to room temperature. As M_s is below room temperature, the steel is further cooled to −80°C (subzero treatment) to convert the retained austenite to martensite. It is then tempered at 550°C, corresponding to the peak of secondary hardening. Very fine precipitates of tungsten and chromium carbides form. Retained austenite that is still left over does not transform, but gets conditioned by probably losing carbon to the surroundings and transforms to martensite on cooling. A second tempering treatment is necessary to temper the newly formed martensite. Sometimes, as many as four tempering treatments are given.

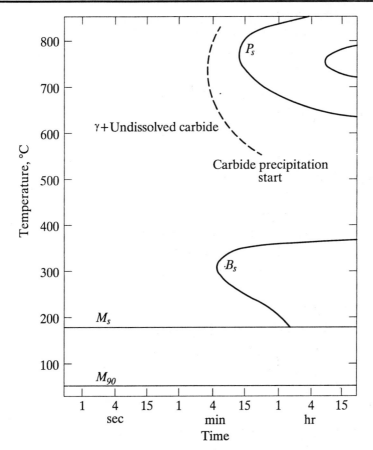

Figure 7.9 T-T-T diagram for a 18W4Cr1V0.75C tool steel.

Medium duty tools   The cheapest tool steel is the *water hardening* type denoted by W in the AISI classification. It is a plain carbon tool steel, with carbon in the range of 0.6–1.4%. A small quantity of vanadium is present in some cases to keep the austenite grain size small. The austenitizing temperature is above A_{c3} for hypoeutectoid steels and above A_{c1} for hypereutectoid compositions. Tempering is done in the range of 150–300°C and the tempered hardness ranges from 40–55 R_c. These steels are used for general purpose medium duty applications such as woodworking tools, files, taps, reamers and most drill bits.

The *shock resisting* tool steels denoted by S contain lower carbon, ~0.5%. Small quantities of chromium, tungsten and molybdenum are present to increase hardenability. These are oil quenched to reduce quenching stresses and to impart shock resistance. Typical uses include chisels, hammers and punches.

Tool for cold and hot forming   *Cold work tools* fall under three categories, depending on the severity of duty. The oil hardening type denoted by O has typically 0.9%C, with small quantities of alloying elements. They are tempered at a relatively low temperature to obtain a high hardness, that will withstand without deforming the higher loads involved in cold forming operations. The O type is used for light duty applications such as moulding plastics. Medium duty applications are met by the air hardening type denoted by A. The concentration of alloying elements is higher to ensure adequate hardenability for air hardening. For heavy duty applications, such as coining dies and cold forging dies, the high-chromium, high-carbon type denoted by D is used. It contains 1.5–2.25%C and 12%Cr. To put sufficient quantity of chromium in solution, a higher austenitizing temperature is used. Still an appreciable quantity of undissolved chromium carbide persists, which adds to the final hardness.

Hot work tools used in hot forming and hot extrusion dies are of two types. The chromium-based ones denoted by the numbers H1 to H19 contain 5–7%Cr and 0.35–0.55%C. A high austenitizing temperature is used to put almost all carbon in solution during austenitizing. The tempering temperatures are also high, in the range of 500–650°C. Hot forming service temperature can be up to 400°C. Note that the service temperature is at least 100°C lower than the tempering temperature, for the properties of the steel to remain stable during service. The higher tempering temperature means a lower hardness. This is usually adequate, as loads in hot forming are less as compared to cold forming. Hot shears, aluminium and magnesium extrusion dies and die-casting dies are some of the applications.

The *tungsten-based* hot forming steels are denoted by H20 to H39 and contain 9–18%W and 0.35–0.5%C. The austenitizing and tempering temperatures are higher than those for chromium-based hot work tools. Hot extrusion dies for brass, nickel or steel are made out of these steels.

Tools for high speed cutting   *High speed steels* have the characteristic property of *red hardness*. They cut at twenty times the speed of a plain carbon tool without losing their sharpness even when they are hot enough to glow with a dull red colour in a dark room! The *tungsten-based* ones denoted by T contain typically 0.75%C, 18%W, 4%Cr, and 1%V (this composition is designated T1). Tungsten provides for toughness, wear resistance and cutting ability, chromium serves to increase the hardenability and vanadium is for grain refinement. The heat treatment steps for this steel have already been discussed.

In the *molybdenum-based* high speed steel denoted by M, part or all of the tungsten is replaced by molybdenum. To provide the same atom ratio for carbide formation, the wt% of molybdenum required is less, as the atomic weight of molybdenum is only half of that of tungsten. M2 with 0.85%C, 6%W, 5%Mo, 4%Cr and 2%V is very common high speed steel, ranking higher than T1 in popularity.

In *sintered carbide* tools, tungsten carbide particles are embedded in a matrix of 5–20% cobalt. The carbide and metal powders are mixed, compacted and sintered close to the melting point of cobalt. Cobalt undergoes incipient fusion during sintering and forms a continuous matrix with interspersed WC particles. The hardness of this tool material is extremely high, about 1500 on the Vickers scale (note that 65 R_c = 830 VPN). This tool is used for very heavy duty applications such as cutting cast iron and drilling rocks. It can cut at five times the speed of high-speed steel.

Other tool materials (which are not steels) are *stellites*, cermets and ceramic tools. Stellites are Co-Cr-W-C alloys with excellent red hardness. Cermets are generally titanium and chromium carbide particles embedded in a nickel-base matrix. Ceramic tools are made primarily from Al_2O_3.

7.7   STAINLESS STEELS

Stainless steels are generally chosen for service conditions where *corrosion and oxidation resistance* is important. In addition, they often have good creep strength, as cross-slip of screw dislocations is difficult due to the low stacking fault energy. They contain not less than 10–12%Cr and often Ni in addition. Chromium forms a protective passive film on the steel surface. Referring to the Fe-Cr phase diagram, Fig. 2.13, we note that, for Cr > 12.7%, the ferrite phase becomes stable over the entire temperature range up to the melting point. In the presence of carbon, to produce an all-ferrite microstructure, we need (Cr – 17 × %C) > 12.7. If this is less than 12.7%, we have the martensitic stainless steel, as martensite forms on cooling the high temperature austenite to room temperature. In austenitic stainless steels, the gamma stabilizers such as Ni and Mn are present in sufficient amounts to make austenite stable at room temperature.

The effect of other elements present in Cr-Ni steels can be expressed as nickel equivalent if they stabilize the austenite and as chromium equivalent if they stabilize ferrite:

Ni equivalent = Ni + Co + 0.5Mn + 0.3Cu + 30C + 25N

Cr equivalent = Cr + 2Si + 1.5Mo + 5V + 5.5Al + 1.75Nb + 1.5Ti + 0.75W

The *Schaeffler diagram* (Fig. 7.10) depicts the phases present in an alloy as a function of nickel and chromium equivalents. More recent thermodynamic calculations by this author indicate that the Ni and Cr equivalents are also a function of the annealing temperature.

In discussing the various stainless steels, we can follow the AISI classification, as it is widely understood. Three digits are used in this classification. The AISI 500 series steels contain 4–6%Cr and so are not true stainless steels. However, they are 5–10 times more resistant to sulphide corrosion than a carbon steel and 3 times more oxidation resistant. Typical uses are in the petroleum refining industry for valve bodies and cracking still tubes.

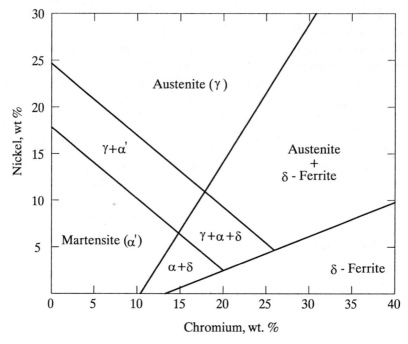

Figure 7.10 The Schaeffler diagram depicting the phases present as a function of the nickel and chromium equivalents.

Ferritic stainless steels When (%Cr − 17 × %C) > 12.7, the stainless steel is in the ferrite state and cannot be heat treated, as austenite does not form at any temperature. The strength can be increased only by cold working. Grain refinement is done by recrystallization following cold work. AISI 430 with 16%Cr and 0.12%C max. and AISI 446 with 25%Cr and 0.20%C max. are typical examples. By virtue of the high chromium content, these steels possess excellent corrosion and oxidation resistance. Typical mechanical properties of 430 in the annealed condition are:

Y.S., MPa	T.S., MPa	% Elongation	Izod impact, J
350	550	30	75

The formability of ferritic stainless steels is poorer than that of the austenitic steels. In recent years, the formability has been improved considerably, by *lowering the level of the interstitial carbon and nitrogen* to 100 ppm (0.01%) by special processing techniques. Addition of 2%Mo to the basic compositions of 18%Cr and 25%Cr improves the resistance to pitting corrosion. By virtue of their lower cost (expensive nickel is not present!), the ferritic stainless steels with improved properties are competing with austenitic stainless steels in household and transportation uses.

Martensitic stainless steels AISI 410 and 416 are typical of the low carbon martensitic varieties, with 12–14%Cr and 0.15%C max. Here, (%Cr − 17 ×

%C) < 12.7. They respond to heat treatment, but due to the low carbon, the martensite is not brittle. Typical as-quenched properties are:

Hardness, R_c	Y.S., MPa	T.S., MPa	% Elongation
42	1200	1300	5

The *cutlery grade* AISI 440B is typical of high carbon martensitic stainless steels, with 17%Cr and 0.75%C. The as-quenched hardness is 60 R_c. This grade is used for cutlery items, surgical instruments and high quality ball bearings.

Austenitic stainless steels Austenitic stainless steels of the 300 series contain nickel as the austenite stabilizing element. When nickel is partly or fully replaced by the cheaper manganese, we have the 200 series.

In the 300 series, the most commonly used type is 304, with 18%Cr, 8%Ni, and 0.08%C max. The significance of the carbon content in relation to intergranular corrosion was discussed in Sec. 6.8. The low carbon variety with 0.03%C max. is much less susceptible to intergranular corrosion. Addition of 2%Mo gives the 316 variety, which has better resistance to pitting and sulphuric acid.

The formability of the 18/8 austenitic stainless steels is excellent. The work hardening rate is high and is attributed to the very low stacking fault energy of 0.002 J m^{-2}. The uniform elongation is also large. Typical tensile properties of 304 stainless steel are:

Y.S., MPa	T.S., MPa	% Elongation
240	600	65

By moderate working, the yield strength can be increased up to 1000 MPa. It is used in a very wide variety of applications in the chemical industry and for household and sanitary fittings.

Precipitation-hardened or controlled-transformation stainless steels contain, in addition to the basic composition, Mo, Nb, Ti or Al. Precipitates such as Ni_3Ti form on ageing and increase the strength. 17-7PH grade, for example, contains 1.15%Al in addition to 17%Cr and 7%Ni.

7.8 HIGH TEMPERATURE ALLOYS

The properties required in a high temperature alloy are:

1. Good oxidation resistance.
2. Adequate creep strength.
3. Microstructural stability, i.e. no deterioration of microstructure and properties with time at the service temperature.
4. Depending on the application, other properties such as corrosion resistance, fatigue strength and impact toughness may be required. For

example, turbine blades undergo stress reversals and must have sufficient fatigue strength at the operating temperature.

5. The alloy must be capable of easy fabrication and should not undergo large property changes on heating and cooling. (Jet engine parts repeatedly cool down and heat up, as the engine is shut off and restarted.)

A number of alloys which can serve at high temperatures have already been introduced in earlier sections and chapters. Here, only a short summary (including such alloys as are not discussed up to now) is given.

In low alloy steel, molybdenum and vanadium are the two alloying elements which significantly improve the creep resistance. 0.5%Mo steel is used for *pressure vessels and superheater tubes* for use up to 450°C. The service temperature can be increased by about 100°C by the addition of 1–2%Cr, which improves the resistance to graphitization.

Stainless steels possess many of the properties required of high temperature alloys. Martensitic stainless steels have adequate creep strength and good corrosion and oxidation resistance up to 650°C. For higher temperatures, the excellent oxidation resistance of ferritic stainless steels such as 430 and 446 can be used. The creep strength and corrosion resistance of austenitic stainless steels are the best. They are used up to 900°C in applications such as furnace linings and exhaust systems.

Superalloys For superior creep strength in sophisticated aircraft applications, *superalloys* are used. There are three main types; iron-nickel-base, nickel-base and cobalt-base superalloys. In the first two, the major creep strengthening constituent is the intermetallic compound $Ni_3(Ti,Al)$, recall Sec. 5.4. An additional strengthening effect arises from the precipitation of carbides, e.g. $Cr_{23}C_6$. In the iron-nickel superalloys, some typical names are *discaloy* and *incoloy*, the compositions being 15%Cr, 20–40%Ni, and smaller concentrations of molybdenum, titanium and aluminium and balance iron. These are the least expensive among superalloys. Nickel-base superalloys have the best creep strength and some of the names are *nimonics*, *inconel*, and *waspalloy*. A typical composition of a nimonic alloy is 0.2%C, 10%Cr, 20%Co, 5%Mo, 5%Al, 1.3%Ti and balance nickel. The creep resistance of cobalt-base superalloys lies between the above two types. A typical composition is 25%Cr, 10%Ni, 8%W, 2%Fe, 0.5%C and balance cobalt. Here, the major strengthening comes from tungsten and chromium carbide precipitates. *Vitallium* is a precision cast cobalt-base superalloy. Figure 7.11 compares the creep strength of a number of high temperature alloys discussed above.

Superalloys rapidly lose their strength above 1000°C. Special alloys for use at higher temperatures based on the refractory metals of molybdenum, niobium, tantalum and tungsten are being developed. Ceramic materials such as silicon nitride have a very high melting point and are being explored for high temperature use. They have no problem of oxidation but their brittleness is the major obstacle in development. Cermets are refractory ceramics such as Al_2O_3 and TiC embedded in a Ni-Cr metal matrix and have good high temperature properties. Recall that cermets are also used as cutting tools as discussed in Sec. 7.6.

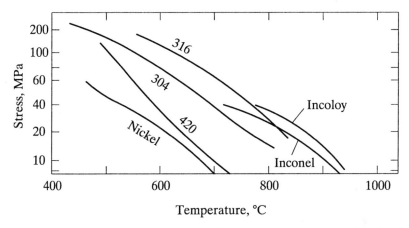

Figure 7.11   The creep strength as a function of temperature for 0.01% creep strain per 1000 hr for a number of alloys.

7.9   CAST IRONS

White versus gray cast irons   Alloys of iron and carbon with more than 2.11%C are called cast irons. Referring to the Fe-C phase diagram in Fig. 2.10, we note that iron-carbon alloys with more than 2.11%C undergo the eutectic reaction at 1146°C, whereas compositions with less carbon (steels) do not. The eutectic mixture is known as *ledeburite*. Compositions to the left of the eutectic composition (4.3%C) contain proeutectic austenite in addition to ledeburite just below the eutectic temperature. The solubility of carbon in austenite decreases from 2.1% at 1146°C to 0.77% at 727°C. The excess carbon precipitates as cementite both from the proeutectic and the eutectic austenite. On cooling through the eutectoid temperature (727°C), the austenite decomposes to pearlite. The microstructure of a hypoeutectic cast iron shown in Fig. 7.12 consists of cementite (white regions) and pearlite (dark regions). In the above description, the carbon is present in the combined form and the alloy is called *white cast iron*, as the fracture surface of such irons looks white. White cast iron has excellent wear resistance, but it is very brittle. It finds uses as balls for grinding mills, liners for cement mixers and rolls for paper manufacture.

In the Fe-C phase diagram (Fig. 2.10), in addition to the cementite equilibrium, some important graphite lines are also shown as dotted lines. The graphite eutectic line is at 1152°C, six degrees above the cementite line. When carbon is present in the free form as graphite, the fracture looks gray (also spelt as grey) and the alloy is called *gray cast iron*. Graphite has a lower free energy than cementite. Yet, cementite often forms, because only 6.67%C has to segregate to form cementite, whereas 100% segregation is required to nucleate graphite.

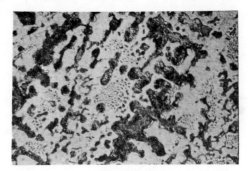

Figure 7.12 The microstructure of white cast iron.

Factors that promote the formation of graphite are:

1. *Slow cooling:* thick cross-sections or castings in sand moulds tend to have graphite, as the cooling rate is slow. Chill castings (in metal moulds) and thin cross-sections tend to have cementite. This effect can also be seen in the fracture appearance across the cross-section varying from white at the surface to gray inside. The transition region has the *"mottled"* appearance.

2. Among the alloying elements which influence graphitization most is *silicon*. Silicon shifts the graphite eutectic line upwards, so that the temperature interval between the graphite line and the cementite line increases from 6°C at 0%Si to 35°C at 2%Si. So, during cooling from the liquid state, a larger degree of undercooling is possible with a greater chance to form graphite, before cementite formation becomes feasible.

3. *Increasing carbon* in the melt tends to promote graphite formation.

4. The effect of alloying elements other than silicon on graphitization is described in terms of the silicon equivalent:

$$\text{Si equivalent} = \% \text{ Si} + 3(\%\text{C}) + \%\text{P} + 0.3(\%\text{Ni}) + 0.3(\%\text{Cu})$$
$$+ 0.5(\%\text{Al}) - 0.25(\%\text{Mn}) - 0.35(\% \text{ Mo}) - 1.2(\%\text{Cr})$$

Noncarbide forming elements Cu, Ni and Al have positive factors, i.e. they promote the formation of graphite. Carbide forming elements Mn, Cr and Mo have negative factors.

Gray cast iron—microstructure If all the carbon is in the form of graphite, we have *ferritic gray iron*, where the *graphite flakes* are embedded in a matrix of ferrite, Fig. 7.13. Flakes are in fact *curved plates* often interconnected in three dimensions. If only a part of the carbon is in the form of graphite, we have the pearlitic gray iron, with pearlite as the matrix. Graphite flakes are sharp at their tips and act like internal cracks or stress raisers. For this reason, gray iron is brittle and shows only about 0.5% elongation in tension. As the cracks do not propagate under compressive loads, the strength of gray iron is more in compression than in tension.

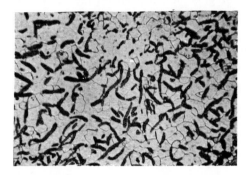

Figure 7.13   The microstructure of gray cast iron consists of graphite
flakes in a matrix of ferrite (or pearlite).

The standards set up by AFA-ASTM (American Foundrymen's Association
and the American Society for Testing and Materials) describe different morphologies of graphite. Type *A* refers to the random orientation of uniformly
sized flakes. Type *B* is rosette groupings (flakes arranged radially like petals of
a rose). Type *C* is flakes of mixed sizes with a random orientation. *D* is
interdendritic flakes randomly oriented and *E* is the same preferentially oriented. Figure 7.14 shows schematically the graphite flake sizes from 1 to 6.

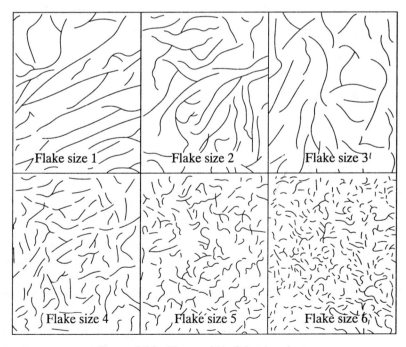

Figure 7.14   The graphite flake-size chart.

The properties of gray iron depend on the morphology and size of the graphite flakes and the matrix. The most desirable microstructure is fine and randomly oriented flakes. Large flakes act as long internal cracks and hence lower the strength. A pearlitic matrix has a greater strength than a ferritic matrix. According to strength, class of gray iron is specified as 20, 30, 40, 60, etc. For example, class 40 stands for a tensile strength of 40,000 psi (280 MPa). Figure 7.15 shows the stress-strain curves for class 20 and class 40 gray irons in tension and in compression.

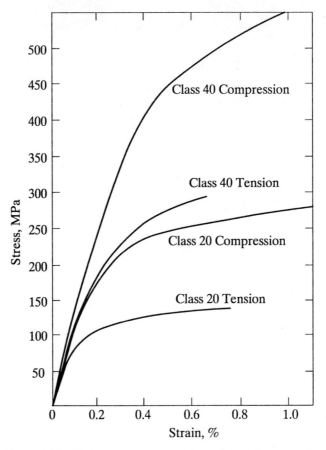

Figure 7.15   The stress-strain curves in tension and compression for Class 20 an Class 40 cast irons.

Gray cast iron—properties and uses   Gray cast iron has certain unique properties:

1. Cast iron is *cheaper* than steel, as the temperature to be attained for making it is several hundred degrees lower than that for casting steel. Also, control of impurities is not critical here, as in steel making.

2. It has excellent *fluidity* and takes mould impressions quite well.

3. The *wear resistance* of gray iron is very good, as graphite flakes act as lubricant. (White cast iron has also good wear resistance but for an entirely different reason that cementite is very hard.)

4. Gray iron is *easy to machine*, as chip formation is promoted by the graphite flakes. In addition, the flakes serve as a lubricant for the cutting tool. (White cast iron cannot be machined.)

5. The *damping capacity* (ability to damp vibrations) of gray iron is superior to that of steel.

Gray iron has manifold uses. The good damping capacity and the high compressive strength make it suitable as a base for erection of machinery. Ease of machining, good wear resistance and damping capacity are utilized in applications such as locomotive and internal combustion engine cylinder blocks and heads. Ease of casting and low cost make it suitable for flywheels and counterweights for lifts.

Alloying elements added to gray iron improve the properties, but the cost tends to increase. *Nihard iron* with 4%Ni and 1.5%Cr has excellent wear resistance due to the presence of martensite and alloy carbide. *Niresist*, with 20%Ni and 2%Cr has graphite and alloy carbide particles embedded in an *austenitic* matrix. It has excellent corrosion resistance and heat resisting properties and is used for handling alkalis at high temperatures.

The poor tensile ductility of gray iron results from the flaky form of graphite. If the graphite particles are more *spherical* in shape, the stress concentration is reduced and the tensile ductility improves. Two such modifications of gray iron with spheroidal shaped graphite particles are described below.

Malleable cast iron   White cast iron, where the carbon is in the form of cementite, is heat treated to produce malleable cast iron. A typical composition of the white iron used is 2.5%C and 1%Si. The silicon equivalent is low enough to prevent the formation of graphite flakes during casting, but adequate to keep the time of subsequent annealing for graphite precipitation within reasonable limits. The castings are packed in boxes with sand used as a filler to exclude air. The sealed boxes are given a prolonged annealing for several days at 900–950°C and then cooled very slowly, the cooling time down to 600°C also being a few days. Cementite decomposes during this heat treatment to the more stable form (graphite). The free carbon precipitates in the form of *spheroidal particles called temper carbon*, Fig. 7.16. Some carbon is lost by combination with the residual oxygen in the box. In white heart malleable iron, most of the carbon is lost by oxidation, leaving behind an essentially ferrite matrix. In black heart malleable, temper carbon is present.

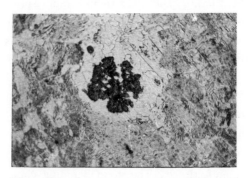

Figure 7.16 Temper carbon is present in the form of approximately spherical aggregates in a malleable cast iron.

Malleable cast iron has tensile strengths up to 700 MPa, with an elongation of 10–15%. They are more expensive than gray irons because of the heat treatment involved. They are used in applications such as automobile crankshafts, chain links and brackets.

Spheroidal graphite (SG) iron   Spheroidal graphite iron also known as *nodular iron or ductile iron* is produced by adding small quantities of a modifier such as magnesium or cerium to the melt. Good control of the melt charge is essential to keep residual and impurity elements within specified limits. The basic composition of the melt is 3–4%C and 2.5%Si. This fairly-high silicon equivalent promotes graphitization during solidification. The modifier has the effect of making the growth rate of graphite to be approximately the same in all directions, so that a spherical shape results, Fig. 7.17. Note that the graphite nodules here are truly spherical, in contrast to the irregular aggregate of temper carbon in Fig. 7.16. Magnesium is almost universally used as the modifier. Due to its lightness, it is added in the form of Ni-Mg alloy (note that nickel is a graphitizer). In the pressure ladle method, the alloy is added in a capsule and the ladle is sealed with a cover to prevent the magnesium vapour from escaping. The residual magnesium in the casting is about 0.05%.

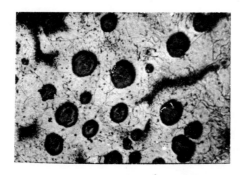

Figure 7.17 Spherical nodules of graphite in SG iron.

Nodular iron is a major engineering material, as it combines the engineering advantages of steel with the processing economics of cast iron. The tensile strength of nodular iron ranges from 400 to 700 MPa, with elongation between 10–18%. Agricultural implements, industrial fan hubs, coke oven doors, crankshafts and gears are some of the applications of nodular iron.

Cast iron exposed to elevated temperatures may deteriorate through a process called *growth*. Oxidation of iron occurs through gases penetrating into the graphite cavities. Any cementite present decomposes into graphite. Volume expansion due to these produces fine surface cracks called *crazes* on the cast iron, which eventually fails. Among alloying elements, chromium is particularly effective in reducing growth.

7.10   THE LIGHT ALLOYS

Introduction   The light metals are Be, Mg, Al and Ti. Their specific gravities and Young's moduli Y are compared with those of other common metals below:

Metal	Be	Mg	Al	Ti	Fe	Cu	Pb	W
Specific gravity	1.86	1.74	2.71	4.5	7.86	8.9	11.3	19.3
Y, GN m^{-2}	289	44	71	106	210	124	15.7	396

In the properly treated condition, the light alloys possess favourable strength-to-weight and stiffness-to-weight ratios as shown below:

Alloy	T.S./specific gravity, MN m^{-2}	Y/specific gravity, GN m^{-2}
High strength steel	170	26.5
Duralumin	200	25.9
Mg alloy	190	24.9
Ti alloy	280	26.5
Beryllium	170	102.0

In the following table, the mass of metal required for the same stiffness of beams of equal length is compared using steel as reference:

Metal	Steel	Ti	Al	Mg	Be
Comparative mass	1	0.81	0.59	0.48	0.20

In addition to weight saving seen in the above table, with a smaller mass, the inertial forces are less in reciprocating parts such as connecting rods and pistons. Also, the elastic buckling of slender columns or wrinkling of thin sheets bearing loads is less of a problem with light metals and their alloys, as they have a larger volume (and thickness) for the same stiffness.

The other desirable properties of the light metals are listed below:

Aluminium	High corrosion resistance
	High electrical conductivity
	High thermal conductivity
Magnesium	Outstanding machinability
Titanium	Outstanding corrosion resistance

The major disadvantage of the light metals is the large energy requirement for production. For aluminium, the energy required is 75,000 kWh per tonne from ore to primary metal, which is five times that for steel. The energy requirements for magnesium and titanium are even larger. However, aluminium scrap requires only 5% of the energy required for the production of the primary metal from the ore. So, recycling is an important process.

Classification of aluminium alloys The AAA (Aluminium Association of America) classification for wrought aluminium alloys has been adopted by the International Alloy Development System (IADS) and is now accepted by most countries. The classification is based on a four-digit system.

1xxx	Commercial purity and high purity aluminium
2xxx	Al-Cu alloys
3xxx	Al-Mn alloys
4xxx	Al-Si alloys
5xxx	Al-Mg alloys
6xxx	Al-Mg-Si alloys
7xxx	Al-Zn alloys

In addition to the four digits, specific letters are added to denote the thermal/mechanical treatment given:

O	annealed
H	work hardened only
H12	quarter-hard; H14 half-hard; H18 full-hard; H19 > 80% reduction
H2 and H3	work hardened and recovery annealed
T	age hardened
T1	naturally aged after hot working
T4	solution treated, quenched and naturally aged
T6	solution treated, quenched and artificially aged
T8	same as T6, except cold worked before ageing

Non heat-treatable aluminium alloys Starting with aluminium metal, we note that pure aluminium (1350H16 in Table 7.1) is used in the *electrical industry*. Even though the electrical conductivity of aluminium is only 60% of that of copper, for equal weight, the conductivity is 200% of copper, as aluminium of the same weight has more than three times the volume of copper. After the electrical industry, the largest use for aluminium is in the *packaging industry*. Aluminium is attractive for this purpose, due to its good corrosion resistance, high thermal conductivity, and impenetrability to oxygen, moisture and micro-organisms. In addition, unalloyed aluminium of the 1xxx series is used in chemical process equipment and for architectural purposes.

In the 3xxx series, Al-Mn and Al-Mn-Mg alloys have moderate strength and are used for beverage cans, cooking utensils, buildings and roofing sheets. The composition and properties of 3003H18 are listed in Table 7.1.

4xxx Al-Si alloys are used only as welding and brazing electrodes.

The 5xxx series Al-Mg alloys are widely used in welded applications as transportation structural plate for truck bodies and large tanks carrying petrol, milk or grain, and for pressure vessels at cryogenic temperatures. Their high corrosion resistance makes them suitable for boat hulls and superstructures of ocean-going vessels. As an example, the properties of 5052H38 are listed in Table 7.1.

Heat-treatable aluminium alloys The following aluminium alloys can be given an age hardening treatment.

In the 2xxx series of Al-Cu alloys, $CuAl_2$ and the associated transition phases form the precipitates, recall Sec. 3.8. Referring to Table 7.1, 2219T62 (Al-6.3Cu) is produced as sheets, plates and extrusions for structural purposes. 2024T6 is used as sheets, plates and forgings for aircraft structures. To improve the corrosion resistance, Al-Cu alloys (and also Al-Zn-Mg alloys) are sandwiched between two pure aluminium sheets and rolled to produce the composite *Alclad*.

Nickel improves the creep resistance needed for supersonic aircraft. In 2618T61 alloy (Rolls Royce designation RR58), copper and magnesium contribute to strengthening by age hardening, whereas nickel and iron form the intermetallic compound $FeNiAl_9$, which causes dispersion hardening.

6xxx series Al-Mg-Si alloys are used as medium strength structural alloys having the advantage of good weldability, corrosion resistance and immunity to stress corrosion cracking. 6063T6 in Table 7.1 is a commonly used alloy of this series. It responds well to colour anodizing and is used in decorative and architectural applications.

7xxx series offers the greatest potential for age hardening. Note the rapid decrease in the solubility of zinc with decreasing temperature in the Al-Zn equilibrium diagram, Fig. 7.18. In addition to the base composition of Al-Zn-Mg, many of the alloys contain copper, which reduces the susceptibility to SCC. The best known is 7075T76 (see Table 7.1 for composition and properties), which is a major aircraft structural material, the British equivalent being DTD 683.

Table 7.1 Aluminium Alloys

Alloy Designation	Composition									Temper	0.2% P.S. MPa	T.S. MPa	%E	Applications
	Si	Fe	Cu	Mn	Mg	Zn	Cr	Ti	Others					
I. Non heat-treatable Alloys														
1100	1.00	Si+Fe	0.1	0.05	—	0.1	—	—	—	H18	152	165	5	Sheets, plates, tubes
1199	0.006	0.006	0.006	0.002	0.006	0.006	—	0.002	—	O	10	45	50	Capacitor foils
1350	0.1	0.4	0.05	0.01	—	0.05	0.01	—	—	H16	110	124	4	Conductors, ACSR cables, bus bars
3003	0.6	0.7	0.15	1.2	—	0.1	—	—	—	H18	185	200	7	Rigid containers, cooking utensils
5052	0.25	0.4	0.1	0.1	2.5	0.1	0.25	—	—	H38	255	290	7	Marine fittings, aircraft fuel tanks
II. Age Hardenable Alloys														
2024	0.05	0.5	4.4	0.6	1.5	0.25	0.1	0.15	—	T6	395	475	10	Aircraft structures, truck wheels
2219	0.2	0.3	6.3	0.3	0.02	0.1	—	0.05	0.1V	T62	290	415	10	Welded aircraft parts
2618	0.15	1.1	2.4	—	1.5	0.1	—	0.07	1.1Ni	T61	310	400	4	Forgings, aircraft pistons
6063	0.4	0.35	0.1	0.1	0.7	0.1	0.1	0.1	—	T6	215	240	12	Furniture, pipes, extrusions
7075	0.4	0.5	1.6	0.3	2.5	5.6	0.23	0.2	—	T76	470	540	12	High strength aircraft structures

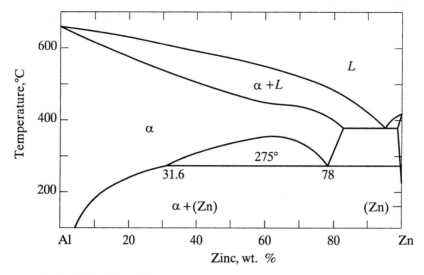

Figure 7.18 The Al-Zn phase diagram shows the rapid decrease of the solubility of zinc in aluminium with decreasing temperature.

Cast aluminium alloys Aluminium is a common foundry metal. Apart from light weight, the low melting temperature is an advantage. Al-12%Si alloy (AAA 413) is among the most important cast alloys. The advantage is the high fluidity imparted by silicon. The Al-Si phase diagram is a simple eutectic system, with the eutectic temperature at 577°C and the eutectic composition at 12.6%Si. Other advantages of Al-Si castings are good weldability, corrosion resistance and wear resistance. The lower thermal expansion coefficient of Al-Si alloys makes them more suitable than Al for use as pistons and cylinder heads in cast iron engine cylinders.

Rapid cooling of the Al-Si alloy refines the eutectic structure, probably by a transition from the plate-like to the rod-like form of silicon in the eutectic mixture. Rod-like units are smaller in size compared to plates. The refinement can also be achieved by the process known as *modification*, in which small quantities of metallic *sodium* or sodium salts are added to the melt before casting. Sodium either depresses the eutectic temperature or slows down the growth rate of silicon by poisoning, causing the transition in morphology and the refinement.

Excessive sodium is known to cause the condition known as *overmodification*, where the coarser eutectic structure tends to reappear. More recently, strontium has been used in place of sodium, as it does not vaporize or oxidize as sodium does. Overmodification is less of a problem with strontium.

Magnesium and its alloys The production of magnesium is an energy intensive process. Electrolytic reduction of $MgCl_2$ is the standard method. More than 50% of magnesium produced is used to alloy with aluminium and as an additive for making SG iron. Oxidation and fire hazard are problems with magnesium melts. The metal melts at 650°C. The rate of oxidation increases rapidly with temperature and, at 850°C, the melt spontaneously bursts into flames.

A well-known example of a magnesium alloy is AZ81, with 8%Al and 1%Zn. This alloy gives tough, leak-tight castings and is used for light-weight crank cases in some cars. With a small quantity of beryllium added, the alloy is used for pressure die castings.

Titanium and its alloys   The density of titanium is midway between that of aluminium and steel. The critical need for new materials with high strength-to-weight ratio in aerospace industries provided the stimulus for the development of titanium alloys. Titanium with a melting point of 1678°C has adequate creep strength to resist aerodynamic heating. Over 80% of titanium produced is used in the aerospace industry.

Titanium is a highly reactive metal, but due to the formation of a stable, self-healing passive film, it exhibits *outstanding corrosion resistance* in a wide variety of environments. The film resists attack by chloride ions. Its resistance to sea water is the best among structural alloys. Uncracked titanium is immune to SCC. The outstanding corrosion resistance of titanium is increasingly utilized in the chemical industries and in the medical profession (as body implants).

At 882°C, titanium changes its crystal structure from HCP (α) to BCC (β) on heating. Alloying elements with electron/atom ratio of less than 4 stabilize the α phase, whereas elements with ratio more than 4 stabilize the β phase. Zirconium, tin and silicon with the ratio of 4 are neutral. Most two-phase ($\alpha + \beta$) alloys contain alloying elements to stabilize and strengthen the α phase, together with 4 to 6% of β stabilizing elements, which allow substantial amounts of β phase to be retained on quenching. Strength is enhanced by ageing the quenched alloy. Tensile strengths in the range of 1400 MPa can be realized. Ti-6% Al-4%V is the most important commercial alloy. Aluminium, with three valence eletrons per atom, stabilizes the α phase and vanadium with 5 electrons stabilizes β. The principal use of this alloy is as forged fan blades in aircraft jet engines. It is also used for airframe structural components in supersonic aircraft requiring strength up to 300°C.

7.11   COPPER AND ITS ALLOYS

Among the common metals, copper is the *best conductor* of heat and electricity, next only to the noble metals silver and gold.

The common impurity in copper, oxygen, is virtually insoluble and forms a eutectic mixture of Cu-Cu_2O. It helps in removing the dissolved impurities from copper and in indirectly increasing the conductivity. The conductivity of tough pitch copper with 0.02–0.05% oxygen is 101% of IACS (International Annealed Copper Standard). In contrast, OFHC (oxygen free high conductivity) copper has a conductivity of 95% of IACS. Phosphorus is often used to deoxidize copper, which leaves some residual phosphorus in solution. As little as 0.04%P lowers the electrical conductivity of copper by 15%. Among the solutes, cadmium is the least harmful and can be used for solid solution strengthening, without impairing the conductivity much.

The *high thermal conductivity* of copper makes it useful in radiators and for circulating the coolant fluid in refrigerators and airconditioners. The good corrosion resistance of copper and the nontoxic nature of copper ions make it suitable for pipes to carry foodstuffs and beverages.

The brasses   Brasses are alloys of copper and zinc. The Cu-Zn phase diagram is discussed under Sec. 2.7 and should be recalled. The copper rich end of the diagram is reproduced in Fig. 7.19. The Cu-Zn alloys are classified as α-brasses and (α + β) brasses. α-brasses containing up to 20%Zn are reddish in colour.

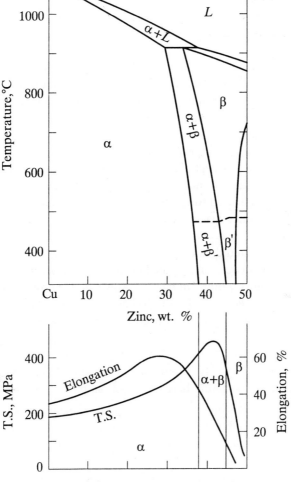

Figure 7.19   The strength and ductility of brasses as a function of the zinc content.

Above 20%Zn, the brass is yellow in colour. Yellow α-brasses have zinc content between 20 and 36%. (α + β) brasses, also yellow in colour, have compositions between 36 and 46%Zn.

The improvement in mechanical properties of copper with the addition of zinc is illustrated in Fig. 7.19, both the tensile strength and the elongation increase with increasing zinc content almost up to the limit of α stability. This is attributed to a lowering of the stacking fault energy of copper by zinc and the consequent increase in work hardening rate and uniform elongation. Beyond 36%Zn, in the (α + β) region, the tensile strength continues to increase, but the ductility decreases. As the β phase content exceeds 50%, the strength also decreases.

α-brass has *excellent* cold formability. The 70/30 brass containing 70%Cu is a single α solid solution, known as *cartridge brass*. It has excellent deep drawing property and is used for making cartridge cases, radiator fins and lamp fixtures. Cold worked α-brass is susceptible to season cracking as discussed under Sec. 6.9. This susceptibility is removed by a stress-relief anneal at about 250°C.

Admirality brass with 29%Zn and 1%Sn has good corrosion resistance and is used for condenser tubes and heat exchangers in steam power plants. However, it is susceptible to *dezincification* in marine environments, where the zinc corrodes preferentially leaving behind a porous mass of copper. *Aluminium brass* with 22%Zn and 2%Al and a trace of arsenic (0.04%) is not susceptible to dezincification and has largely replaced admirality brass for marine uses.

Red brasses are not susceptible to season cracking or dezincification. Gilding metal with 5%Zn is used in making coins, medals and emblems. "Commercial bronze" with 10%Zn is used for costume jewellery. Leaded brasses contain 0.5–3% lead and have better machinability.

The 60/40 (α + β) brass known as *muntz metal* is cheaper and stronger than α-brass, but with limited ductility. In contrast to the excellent cold formability of α-brass, (α + β) brasses can only be hot worked. The ordered β phase present at room temperature is brittle. On heating, however, the order-disorder reaction occurs above 465°C, see Fig. 7.19, the β phase becomes ductile and hot working can be done readily. (α + β) alloys become a single phase β solid solution at elevated temperatures.

With the addition of 1%Sn to (α + β) brass, the corrosion resistance to marine environments is vastly improved. Brass with 39%Zn and 1%Sn, called *naval brass*, is used in marine hardware such as properller shafts.

The bronzes   The name bronze was originally used to denote copper-tin alloys. When copper is alloyed with other metals such as Al, Si and Be, the term bronze is still used. For example, Cu-Al alloys are called aluminium bronzes and Cu-Si alloys are known as silicon bronzes. The Cu-Sn bronzes are commercially known as *phosphor bronzes*, as some residual phosphorus used in deoxidation is always present. As in brasses, both the tensile strength and elongation of the solid solutions formed by different solutes increase with the increasing concentration of the solute in the single phase region. In the annealed condition, the tensile strength is about 400 MPa and the elongation is over 60% at 10%Sn, or 3%Si or 5%Al as the solute in copper.

The copper rich end of the Cu-Sn equilibrium diagram is shown in Fig. 7.20. At 798°C, a peritectic reaction occurs and the β phase forms. At 586°C, the β phase undergoes a eutectoid reaction to form a mixture $(\alpha + \gamma)$. At a still

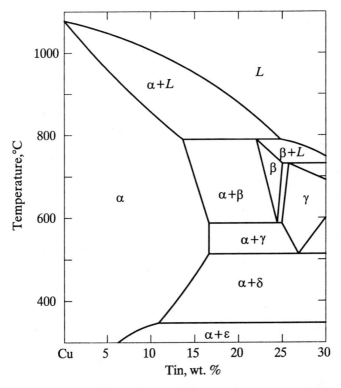

Figure 7.20 The copper-rich end of the Cu-Sn phase diagram.

lower temperature of 520°C, the γ phase undergoes another eutectoid reaction to form $(\alpha + \delta)$ phase. The δ phase decomposes to $(\alpha + \varepsilon)$ phases by a third eutectoid reaction at 350°C. However, this reaction is so sluggish that the ε phase is never seen in the microstructure. The solubility of tin in copper is about 17% at 520°C and decreases considerably on cooling to room temperature. Here again, at normal cooling rates, the precipitation of δ is not complete, so that phosphor bronzes with less than 10%Sn are usually single phase solid solutions at room temperature.

In the Cu-Si system, the solubility of silicon in copper is 5.3% at 852°C and decreases with decreasing temperature. Here also, the precipitation of the excess silicon does not occur at normal cooling rates so that the single α phase is found in compositions up to 5%Si.

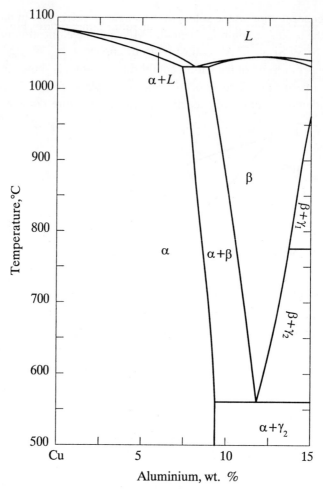

Figure 7.21 The copper-rich end of the Cu-Al phase diagram.

The copper rich end of the Cu-Al equilibrium diagram is shown in Fig. 7.21. At 500°C, copper dissolves up to 9.5%Al. The Cu-11.5%Al alloy undergoes an eutectoid reaction at 566°C:

Reaction :	β	$\longleftrightarrow$	α	+	γ_2
Structure :	BCC		FCC		complex cubic
Al% :	11.8		9.4		15.6

On furnace cooling this composition, a lamellar structure resembling pearlite forms. On quenching, the β phase transforms *martensitically* to β' without a change in composition. The phase can be tempered in the same manner as in a steel. In this way, tensile strengths up to 700 MPa can be obtained. Heat treated aluminium bronzes are used as gears, dies, bearings and pump parts.

In the Cu-Be system, the solubility of beryllium in copper is 2.3% at 800°C and decreases to less than 0.2% at room temperature, Fig. 7.22. This makes the Cu-Be alloys *age hardenable*. The precipitation process involves several transition phases shown in Fig. 7.22 and is quite similar to that in an Al-Cu alloy discussed in Sec. 3.8. A high yield strength of 1300 MPa can be obtained by optimum ageing. This high strength combined with the lower stiffness of copper as compared to steel results in a large σ_y/Y ratio and a high resilience. Cu-Be age hardened alloys are used for nonmagnetic springs and nonsparking tools.

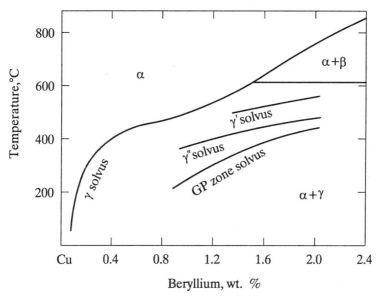

Figure 7.22 The copper-rich end of the Cu-Be phase diagram.

7.12 BEARING ALLOYS

Despite the development of ball and roller bearings, the conventional stationary bearing is still in use. The properties that are required of such a bearing are:

1. The friction between the bearing and the rotating part should be as small as possible.
2. The wear of the contacting metals should be as low as possible.
3. The bearing must be capable of withstanding pressures that arise from small misalignments.
4. It must contain a relatively low melting component, which will soften or melt and prevent seizures.

Usually a thin film of lubricating oil separates the bearing and the rotating part. This ensures that requirements 1 and 2 above are satisfied. The pressures that a bearing can withstand depend on the strength and the melting point of the bearing alloy. Soft and low-melting alloys can withstand comparatively low pressures only. Bimetal bearings use a strong bearing back (e.g. steel) to which a softer, relatively thin layer of a bearing alloy is metallurgically bonded. By this combination, the excellent surface and corrosion-resistant properties of a weak bearing alloy are combined with the high load-bearing capacity of the back-up material.

The microstructure of a bearing alloy usually consists of a soft matrix in which hard particles are embedded. After some use, the soft matrix wears off more rapidly and the hard particles stand out in relief. The lubricating oil is retained in the channels between the hard particles. Soft pockets embedded in a strong matrix are obtained in some bearing alloys like leaded bronze.

The alloys known as *babbits or white metals* are either lead-based or tin-based. A typical lead-based white metal consists of 80%Pb, 10%Sb and 10%Sn. The microstructure contains hard cube-shaped particles (cuboids) of SbSn in a soft lead-rich matrix. The pressure and speed that the bearing will withstand increases with the addition of a few percent of arsenic. A typical composition of a tin-base babbit is 90%Sn, 5%Sb and 5%Cu. In addition of SbSn, needle-shaped CuSn (or Cu_6Sn_5) particles are also present in the microstructure. Tin-base babbits are more expensive but have better corrosion and wear resistance.

For high bearing loads, *bronze bearings* are specified. In the widely used 10%Sn phosphor bronze, the hard ($\alpha + \delta$) eutectoid mixture is embedded in the softer α matrix. Leaded bronzes contain in addition 5–10% lead for better lubricating action. The low-melting lead particles also prevent seizure. Aluminium and silver based bearings are also known.

SUGGESTED READINGS

Hoyle, G., *High Speed Steels*, Butterworths, London (1988).

Lllewellyn D.T. and R.C. Hudd, *Steels: Metallurgy and Applications*, Butterworth-Heinemann, Oxford (1998)

Metals and Alloys in the Unified Numbering System, 8th Edition, ASTM-SAE Joint Publication, Warrendale, PA (1999).

Properties and Selection: Irons, Steels and High Performance Alloys, Metals Handbook, 10th Edition, Vol. 1 (1990); *Properties and Selection: Nonferrous Alloys and Special Purpose Materials*, Vol. 2 (1990).

Worldwide Guide to Equivalent Irons and Steels, American Society for Metals, Metals Park, Ohio (1979).

QUESTIONS

1. Write down the compositions corresponding to the following specifications of steels: T105, AISI1118, SAE8640, En23, En19, AISI 321.

2. What are the advantages of the residual manganese in a carbon steel?

3. Compare in tabular form the properties and uses of conventional low carbon steel, mild steel, dual phase steel and microalloyed steel.

4. Distinguish between ausforming and austempering in terms of processes, microstructures and properties of the product.

5. What are the special problems encountered in heat treating high speed steel and how are these solved?

6. Discuss the significance of the compositions of the melt used for making malleable cast iron and nodular cast iron.

7. What is the difference in the heat treatment schedule for production of pearlitic malleable and ferritic malleable cast iron?

8. For the same weight, calculate the relative stiffness of steel, titanium, aluminium and magnesium, taking the stiffness of steel to be unity.
   Answer: 1:1.53:2.85:4.29.

9. Comment on the relative weldability of age hardened aluminium alloys and aluminium alloys that are not heat treated.

10. Describe the composition and heat treatment of $(\alpha + \beta)$ titanium alloys for optimum mechanical properties.

11. Distinguish between season cracking and dezincification.

12. Describe the role of hard particles, soft matrix and insoluble metals in the functioning of a bearing alloy.

Chapter 8

NANOMATERIALS

The famous lecture of Richard Feynman in 1959 at the American Physical Society titled *There's Plenty of Room at the Bottom* gave birth to the vast field of nanoscience and nanotechnology. Feynman talked about the staggeringly small world out there and gave the example of how all the 24 volumes of *Encyclopaedia Britannica* can be written on the head of a pin, by demagnifying 25,000 times! It took several decades for the concept to develop into a full-fledged interdisciplinary field covering physical metallurgy, materials science, physics, chemistry, biology, mechanical and electrical engineering and medicine. In this chapter, we discuss briefly how and why phase relationships and mechanical properties in conventional alloys described in earlier chapters get modified in the nanosize range. A brief discussion of other properties of nanostructured alloys is also included.

8.1   CHARACTERISTICS OF THE NANORANGE

The prefix *nano* stands for nanometre (10^{-9} m or 10 Å). Typical microstructural size ranges that were discussed in the previous chapters like ultra fine grain size have the lower limit of ~0.1 μm (1000 Å or 100 nm), whereas the atomic dimensions like a lattice parameter lie in the range of 3–10 Å (0.3–1.0 nm). The nanorange lies between these two ranges (1–100 nm or 10–1000 Å).

The study of microstructure of materials and its correlation with properties in the nanorange is a relatively new subject. It has assumed importance, following the experimental advances in the development of materials with size parameters lying in this range and their technological applications. It must be pointed out, however, that the nature of the experimental techniques required to synthesize nanomaterials does not easily allow the scaling up of production to a level known for industrial products such as rolled steel or aluminium alloys manufactured in millions of tonnes.

The most important parameter that influences the properties of nanostructured materials is the large surface area to volume ratio of nanosized particles. The ratio of the surface area to volume of a spherical particle varies inversely as the radius r of the particle: $4\pi r^2/(4/3)\pi r^3 = 3/r$. For very small spheres, therefore, this ratio is very large. This feature is mainly responsible for the modification of properties at the nanostructural level. As in grain boundaries (see Fig. 1.15a), the distorted nature of atomic arrangement at the external surface extends one or two atomic diameters into the solid. In Fig. 8.1, the fraction of surface atoms expressed as a percentage of total atoms is plotted as a function of particle size. When the dimension is less than 1 nm, virtually all atoms in the material are in the distorted state and the above parameter reaches 100%.

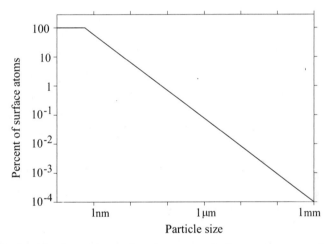

Figure 8.1 Particle size versus surface atoms expressed as a percentage of total atoms.

Depending on the number of dimensions in the nanorange, materials are classified as follows:

(i) *Zero-dimensional* (called a nanoparticle), where all three dimensions of the particle are in the nanorange. Note that the term 'zero-dimensional' is applied to a particle, which has all the three dimensions in the nanorange and none in the larger-than-nanorange. The submicroscopic particles of $CuAl_2$ that precipitate during ageing of a duralumin alloy (Section 3.8, Chapter 3) fall in the nanorange, as also the carbide particles that form during the early stages of tempering of martensite in steels. These examples refer to nanoparticles embedded in a bulk material.

(ii) *One-dimensional,* where two dimensions are in the nanorange and the third dimension is much larger, e.g., nanorods, nanowires and nanotubes.

(iii) *Two-dimensional,* where one dimension is in the nanorange and the other two are much larger, e.g., nanofilms, nanosheets and nanocoatings. Two-dimensional crystalline nanosheets have thickness in the nanoscale. In addition, the internal structure of the sheet can be nanosized grains.

(iv) *Three-dimensional,* where all three dimensions of a particle are much larger than the nanorange. This category forms part of this classification, as the bulk solid itself may be composed of nanoparticles, e.g., nanosized crystals in a bulk polycrystalline material.

Figure 8.2 illustrates the geometry of the above types of nanomaterials.

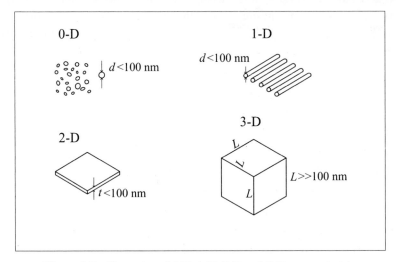

Figure 8.2   Geometry of 0-D, 1-D, 2-D and 3-D nanomaterials.

8.2   PROCESSING OF NANOMATERIALS

There are two basic approaches for the synthesising or processing of nanostructural materials. The "top-down" approach involves breaking down the bulk material into nanosized particles. The second approach is the "bottom-up" approach, where individual atoms or molecules are put together to form the desired nanoparticle. In the top-down category, we have high-energy ball milling, sliding wear and high pressure torsion. The bottom-up category includes inert-gas condensation, physical/chemical vapour deposition, sputtering, electrodeposition, high temperature evaporation, flame synthesis and plasma synthesis.

Among the "top-down" methods, *ball milling* of powders of conventional grain sizes into nanocrystalline grains has been popular. Milling of elemental or compound powder is termed *mechanical milling.* Milling of different powders together is called *mechanical alloying,* as the powders react to form alloys during the process. In this method, small hard balls made of hardened steel are placed along with the material to be crushed in a rotating drum. During rotation, the collision with the balls breaks up the material into fine particles and also causes heavy plastic deformation. A continuous refinement of the internal structure occurs. The average grain size can be reduced to a few nm after extended milling. Retaining the nanograin sizes during the subsequent process of compaction remains a challenge, as recovery processes tend to occur allowing the grains to grow.

Not only ductile metals can be deformed as above, but the normally-brittle ceramic materials can also yield a refined microstructure after extended milling. Metal powders of Ti, V, Zr, Fe, etc. are transformed to a nanocrystalline nitride by high energy ball milling under nitrogen gas flow. New surfaces of the fragmented starting powder react with nitrogen to form the nitride. Extensive milling can convert the entire metal particle into nitride. Partial milling produces nanocomposite particles which have a metal core and a nitride surface.

Electrodeposition is a "bottom-up" method. It is a single-step method, as no separate consolidation step is involved. In recent years, a large number of metals, alloys, ceramics, conducting polymers and composite materials with nanocrystalline structures have been made by this method. Good control is essential over the process variables such as the bath composition, bath additives, *pH*, temperature and overpotential. *Overpotential* refers to the height of the activation barrier (recall Fig. 6.5) for the electrode reaction. A high overpotential tends to delay the electrode reaction, thus allowing time for more nucleation to occur. High nucleation rates combined with low growth rates will produce finer grain sizes. One method to slow down the growth rate is to add organic additives, which slow down the surface diffusion of adsorbed ions on the electrode surface, which is a preliminary step for the electrode reaction to occur. The disadvantage of organic additives is that they tend to get entrapped at grain boundaries and may adversely affect the ductility of the product.

An example of a structural bulk material prepared by chemical reactions is tungsten carbide tools, consisting of WC particles embedded in a ductile matrix of cobalt (Section 7.6, page 203). For making tools with a nanocrystalline structure, precursor powders of W and Co are first obtained by spray-drying of aqueous solutions of soluble salts of W and Co. They are then reduced in hydrogen and reacted with CO to yield the right mixture of WC-Co nanopowder, with a grain size of ~200 nm. Finally, compacting is done of the powder mixture into the desired shape of the tool, which is followed by sintering. The nanosized particles in the tool provide superior hardness and toughness, as compared to the larger grains in the conventional WC-Co tool.

8.3 PHASE DIAGRAMS FOR NANOSIZED ALLOY PARTICLES

The melting point of a pure substance is a fundamental reference point on the temperature scale. This is a valid statement for bulk materials which have a low surface area-to-volume ratio. In nanostructured materials, this ratio becomes very large. Surfaces possessing extra energy contribute to the breaking of bonds between atoms during melting and hence *lower* the melting point. Figure 8.3 shows the melting point of gold as a function of particle radius in the nanorange. The bulk melting point drops significantly with decreasing particle size, from 1063°C for bulk samples to ~900°C at a particle radius of 5 nm.

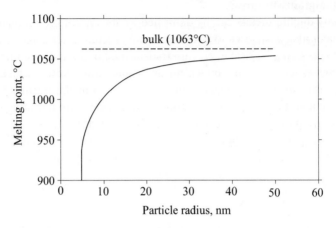

Figure 8.3   Effect of particle radius on the melting point of gold.

Figure 8.4 shows the Cu-Ni phase diagram for nanosized alloy particles. For comparison, the conventional Cu-Ni phase diagram is redrawn from Fig. 2.1. During heating, the start of the melting at the solidus and the completion of

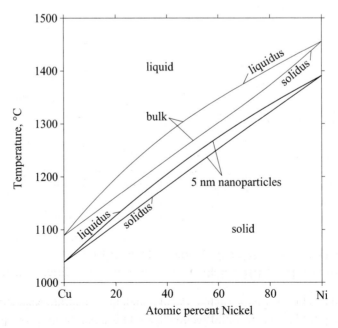

Figure 8.4   Cu-Ni phase diagram for nanosized alloy particles.

melting at the liquidus are both depressed in the nanosized particles. Similar phase diagrams are known for other isomorphous systems such as Ag-Au and Ge-Si. In simple eutectic systems (see Fig. 2.2), the liquidus and solidus lines shift downwards with a corresponding lowering of the eutectic horizontal. The eutectic point may also shift to the left or right of the eutectic composition of the bulk samples.

Experimental data on phase diagrams of bulk materials have been catalogued in the form of numerous handbooks. Clearly, it is necessary to do a similar collection of phase equilibria in nanomaterials. However, such data for nanostructured alloys are scarce. Production of nanopowders and their characterization with respect to particle shape and size distribution remain a challenge. In addition, for the phase equilibrium studies of nanostructured alloys, the standard techniques for phase diagram determination have to be supplemented with other sophisticated techniques.

8.4 MECHANICAL PROPERTIES OF NANOMATERIALS

One of the areas of research and development on nanomaterials is the mechanical properties of materials with internal features in the nanorange. We have noted in Section 5.3 that microstructural refinement of grain size is the key for increasing the strength of crystalline materials without loss of ductility. Grain boundaries do not allow dislocations to cross into the next grain, due to the abrupt change in orientation at the boundary. The finer is the grain size, the more effective is the impediment to dislocation motion. Currently used industrial production processes refine the grain size to a level that still lies above the upper limit of the nanorange. Recall from Section 5.3 that repeated recrystallization due to deformation between passes in a hot rolling mill, combined with the pinning action of precipitate particles on migrating grain boundaries, reduces the grain-size in microalloyed steels down to ~2 μm (2000 nm).

New developments have been successful in reducing the grain size of metals well into the nanorange. Early studies showed that much higher hardness and strength levels can be achieved in nanocrystalline pure metals. At a grain size of ~10 nm, the hardness can be higher by a factor of 2 to 10, when compared with conventional fine grain sizes of a few μm. In some results, however, a decrease in elastic modulus was observed, but later studies attributed this effect for processing-artifacts like porosity in nanomaterials. Nanocrystalline powders produced by inert gas condensation or by ball milling undergo a subsequent step of consolidation into bulk materials. These compacted bulk materials tend to show porosity.

As a typical example of the beneficial effect of the nanocrystalline state, the true stress-true strain curves of copper produced by three different methods are shown in Figure 8.5. Coarse-grain copper produced by conventional methods is soft, showing a low strength but combined with a high ductility. Nanocrystalline copper made by a two-step process of inert gas condensation and subsequent consolidation shows high strength but limited ductility. *In situ consolidated*

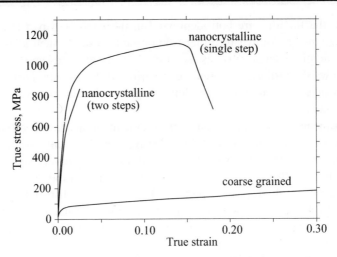

Figure 8.5 True stress-true strain curves for coarse grained copper and nanocrystalline copper made by two-step or single-step process.

copper during ball milling with a grain size of 23 nm shows high strength combined with good ductility. For the *in situ* ball-milled copper, the yield strength and UTS reach the values of 971 MPa respectively and 1120 MPa with 15% elongation. This yield strength is an order of magnitude higher than that of coarse-grained copper. *In situ* consolidated copper is free of pores and inclusions. Experiments with *in situ* consolidation during ball milling of an Al-5% Mg alloy gave a grain size of 26 nm with a narrow grain size distribution. This nanoalloy had a yield strength of 620 MPa, which is four times larger than that of the alloy with the conventional grain size.

   Conventional methods of refining grain size in bulk materials by plastic deformation and subsequent annealing have been modified to produce nanograin sizes with dramatic results. Copper heavily rolled to create a high dislocation density at *liquid-nitrogen temperature* (–196°C or 77 K) showed a remarkable increase in strength and ductility. Recall the phenomenon of *dynamic recovery* discussed under Section 5.1. The thermal energy kT available at liquid-nitrogen temperature is just about one-fourth of the room temperature value, so that no dynamic recovery occurs during rolling at 77 K. The dislocation processes associated with recovery such as mutual annihilation and rearrangement into lower energy configurations do not occur, recall the discussion on recovery in Section 3.9. Subsequent annealing is done at 200°C (<0.4 T_m for copper) for just a few minutes. The microstructure after annealing showed that the majority of grains present fall into the nanorange; about 25% of the volume fraction consisted of much larger grains in the 1–3 μm range (apparently due to partial grain growth). This mixed grain size somewhat decreases the strength, but increases the ductility. The yield strength obtained is 7 times larger than for conventional grain sizes and the total elongation of ~65% is comparable to that of conventional copper.

Aluminium alloys were cryomilled (i.e., ball milled at the cryogenic temperature of liquid nitrogen), followed by powder compaction, hot isostatic pressing and extrusion. Here, the grain size obtained was ~35 nm. Submicrospic precipitate particles like Mg_2Si and Al_3Mg_2 form during pressing and extrusion, which contribute to strength by pinning the grain boundaries and restricting grain growth. The yield strength was four times larger than that of the conventional Al alloy. As in the copper example discussed above, here also a mixed grain size was noted, with some grains being much larger. This microstructural feature resulted in a moderate increase in strength combined with good ductility.

Recall the Hall-Petch equation (Section 5.3, page 139) that relates the yield strength of a material σ_y to its grain size (mean grain diameter) d through the equation: $\sigma_y = \sigma_i + kd^{-\frac{1}{2}}$, where σ_i and k are constants. A log-log plot of σ_y versus d should yield a straight line with a slope of -0.5. Figure 8.6 shows such a plot for FCC metals including the nanograin size range. At grain sizes larger than 10 nm, the plot is a straight line with a slope of -0.5, in agreement with the Hall-Petch equation. At grain sizes around 10 nm and below, the straight line in Fig. 8.6 flattens out. This flattening effect has been attributed to the increasing presence of grain boundaries. Grain boundary sliding or viscous flow becomes important, as the grain boundary volume in relation to the good part of the crystal increases. Recall that we defined creep (Section 5.4, page 143) as plastic flow of the material as a function of time at temperatures above $0.4\ T_m$. Grain boundary sliding is one of the mechanisms of creep. Apparently, this effect in nanomaterials occurs even at temperatures less than $0.4\ T_m$. At grain sizes of 1 nm and less, the grain boundary region dominates, so that the entire volume of the material is like a noncrystalline solid. Here, viscous flow of a glassy substance will be a more apt description of the deformation mechanism.

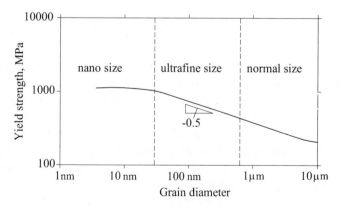

Figure 8.6   Yield strength versus grain size plot for FCC metals covering the nanorange.

For high temperature strength as in creep, the general principles of strengthening crystalline solids are valid, except that the fine microstructural features tend to become unstable at high temperatures. Grain size increases due to grain growth. Fine nanosized precipitate particles coarsen by coalescence, which results in loss of strength. Hence, for high temperature applications, nanograined materials are generally not suitable.

Nanolaminates consist of alternating layers of two different materials, with the thickness of each layer lying in the nanorange. Thousands of such layers are deposited one over the other by sequential evaporation of the elements from different sources. Figure 8.7 shows the tensile strength of Cu-Ni multilayers as a function of the layer thickness. The strength increases by more than a factor of three, when the layer thickness is decreased in the nanorange. When the layer thickness is only a few nanometers, the material strength approaches that of the ideal crystal within a factor of 2 or 3; recall from Section 5.2 that the strength of an ideal crystal is typically about 1/6 of the shear modulus. As with the increase in strength in the nanograin size range of polycrystalline materials, the boundaries between nanosized layers offer effective obstacle to dislocation motion and thereby the strength improvement occurs.

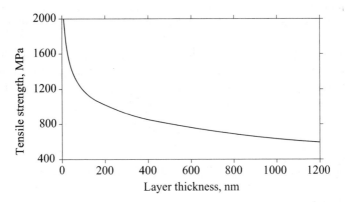

Figure 8.7 Tensile strength of Cu–Ni multilayered composite as a function of layer thickness.

Till now, we have discussed bulk 3-D nanomaterials. An interesting example of a 1-D nanomaterial is the carbon nanotube (CNT). A single-walled CNT is a one-atom thick sheet of graphite (called *graphene*) rolled into a seamless hollow cylinder with diameter of ~1–2 nm. The length of the cylinder is much larger. Figure 8.8 is a model of a single-walled CNT. Each carbon atom is bonded to three neighbours by primary covalent bonds, with an interbond angle of ~120°. Along the length of the tube, the nanotube exhibits a very high elastic modulus and extraordinary strength. Young's modulus of ~1000 GPa and tensile strength of ~30 GPa have been estimated using the Atomic Force Microscope. (This microscope was invented in the early nineties and provided an impetus to nanoresearch.) The above numbers are unique values, larger by one or two orders of magnitude as compared to currently-known values of the best engineering materials.

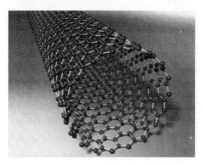

Figure 8.8 Model of a single-walled carbon nanotube.

Full exploitation of the mechanical properties of CNTs in building large scale engineering structures will revolutionize technology on an unprecedented scale. However, many problems are yet to be solved. Currently, the production figures of nanotubes are very low (of the order of a few kg per day), the cost is very high, impurity-free products and nanotubes of constant diameter are difficult to achieve.

The nanoscale materials have been used successfully for reinforcement of a matrix of low modulus and strength. Nanocomposites can have 0-D, 1-D or 2-D reinforcing nanomaterial embedded in a metal, ceramic or polymer matrix. By virtue of the vastly superior properties of the nanoscale materials, remarkable enhancement of properties can occur, even at small concentrations of reinforcement of 2–5 vol %, as compared to 30–40 vol % used in conventional composites. In addition to the enhancement of mechanical properties, improvements have also been obtained in electrical, thermal and optical properties. The use of CNTs for reinforcement has received wide attention. Here, several critical factors need to be controlled: (i) uniform dispersion of the CNTs within the matrix; (ii) alignment of CNTs in the direction of stress application; and (iii) good interfacial bonding between CNTs and the matrix. CNTs have smooth surfaces, not ideal for good bonding with the matrix. The weak van der Waals attraction between neighbouring CNTs can result in agglomeration and consequent deterioration of mechanical properties.

8.5 OTHER PROPERTIES AND APPLICATIONS

Physical metallurgy plays a significant role in the control of other properties not covered in the earlier chapters. A brief discussion on the electrical, magnetic and chemical properties is included below.

Nb-Ti alloys and intermetallic compound Nb_3Sn are typical examples of materials used for making superconductors. *Type II hard superconductors* are of great practical interest, because of the high current density that they can carry, before reverting back to the normal state from the superconducting state. Microstructural features such as heavy cold working, precipitation hardening and fine grain size are the key to enhance the critical current density J_c of hard superconductors. By heavy cold working and precipitation hardening, J_c of Ni-Ti based alloys can be increased by two to three orders of magnitude. Reduction of grain size into the nanorange also raises the critical current density. J_c in Nb_3Sn was found to increase by an order of magnitude, when the grain size was reduced to 50 nm.

Permanent magnets are made from hard magnetic materials. An important parameter that determines the stability of a permanent magnet is the coercive field H_c. This is defined as the value of the reverse field that must be applied to a magnet for it to lose all its magnetization. The larger is H_c, the higher is the strength of the permanent magnet. In the normal grain size range, H_c increases inversely with grain size d ($H_c \propto 1/d$). Hence, a fine grain size increases the strength of a permanent magnet. However, in the nanograin size range, H_c falls precipitously: $H_c \propto d^6$, as illustrated in Fig. 8.9 for Si steels. Note that in the log-log plot shown, H_c decreases by more than three orders of magnitude in the nanorange from the peak value. So, nanograin sizes are detetrimental to permanent magnets. However, the negligible value of H_c in the nanograined alloy is useful for soft magnets, where easy reversal of the magnetic field direction is a desirable property. Easy reversals minimize the hysteresis loss, i.e., the loss of magnetic energy during each cycle of field reversal. An example of the consequence of this effect is amorphous Fe-Ni-Co alloys partially crystallized to a grain size of about 10 nm, which show practically no hysteresis loss.

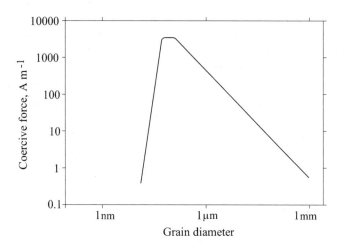

Figure 8.9 Coercive force H_c as a function of grain size in Si steels.

Magnetic tapes and floppy discs have been developed from nanocomposites, obtained by embedding needle-shaped single-domain nanoparticles in a nonmagnetic polymer matrix. Separation by the nonmagnetic polymer prevents magnetic coupling between the nanoparticles. Magnetic hard disc media are made of a CoCrPt alloy film with an average grain size of ~8 nm. Here, a suitable heat treatment results in the formation of single-domain nanosized grains of the magnetic phase separated from one another by a nonmagnetic matrix. A high density of information (~20 Gbits/cm^2) can be stored in this alloy film.

The thermal and electrical conductivities of carbon nanotubes in the longitudinal direction are very high, well exceeding those of copper. Thermal conductivity is of the order of 5000 W m^{-1} K^{-1}. The ability to carry high current densities of 10^9 A cm^{-2} without much I^2R heating makes CNT a candidate material to replace copper in integrated circuits, where I^2R heating is a problem. The ease with which the free electrons are transported along the tube (called *ballistic transport*) and the high mobility of phonons in the longitudinal direction are the reasons for these outstanding properties.

Fuel cells are energy conversion devices, where chemical energy is directly converted to electrical energy. In contrast to the batteries and capacitors, where the energy is stored, fuel cells produce electricity continuously. The efficiency of the generation process in fuel cells is about 50%, as compared to 25% in combustion engines. At present, the cost of production from fuel cells is 7–8 times more than that from conventional engines. The fuel cell consists of an anode, where typically hydrogen gas is bubbled. Using a catalytic agent such as platinum (Pt), hydrogen is oxidized, that is, stripped of its electron. At the cathode, oxygen (or air) is made available to reduce it to OH⁻ ions. This reaction is also promoted by a catalytic agent. The electrolyte is either a polymer membrane or a ceramic such as Y_2O_3-stabilzed ZrO_2. Use of Pt nanoparticles increases the effective surface area of the electrodes, as well as enhances the catalytic activity.

Gaseous hydrogen occupies large volumes. Liquid hydrogen (boiling point –253°C) requires heavy cryogenic equipment for storage. For transportation applications, the most promising route for *hydrogen storage* is in solid crystals like Mg in the form of a hydride MgH_2. The compound forms reversibly from the elements. Hydrogen can be recovered at a moderately high temperature of ~300°C. The absorption and desorption rates are low and require a catalyst to speed up the reaction. Nanocrystalline Mg produced by ball milling shows a marked improvement in the adsorption/desorption rates. Carbon and boron nitride (BN) nanotubes are also promising materials for hydrogen storage.

Gold nanoshells are new composite nanoparticles and are promising materials for medical applications. They consist of a dielectric core (gold sulphide), with a metal (gold) outer shell. The shell has the same surface properties as colloidal gold and can bind to a variety of biomolecules. By varying the relative thickness of the core and the shell, the optical resonance of gold nanoshell can be shifted from the visible range to the infrared range, which is the range of highest physiological transmissivity.

SUGGESTED READINGS

Ashby, M.F., P.J. Ferreira and D.L. Schodek, *Nanomaterials, Nanotechnologies and Design,* Elsevier, Amsterdam (2009).

Gleiter, H., *Nanostructured Materials: Basic Concepts and Microstructure,* Acta Materialia, Vol. 48, pages 1–29 (2000).

Koch, C.C., "Nanostructured Materials: An Overview", *Bulk Nanostructured Materials*, M.J. Zehetbauer and Y.T. Zhu (Eds.), Wiley-VCH, Weinheim (2009).

QUESTIONS

1. How is the nanosize range defined?
2. Which is the most important factor that influences the mechanical properties of nanocrystalline materials?
3. Explain why heavy deformation at cryogenic temperatures and short time annealing just above room temperature are beneficial for achieving nanograin sizes.
4. Estimate the diameter of the single-walled carbon nanotube shown in Fig. 8.8. (*Hint:* The length of a C-C bond in graphite is 1.42 Å)

   Answer: ~1.5 nm.

INDEX